Assistive Technology

This book is printed on recycled paper. ♻

Assistive Technology

A Resource for School, Work, and Community

edited by

Karen F. Flippo, M.R.A.

Katherine J. Inge, Ph.D., O.T.R.

and

J. Michael Barcus, M.Ed.

**Rehabilitation Research and Training
Center on Supported Employment
Virginia Commonwealth University
Richmond, Virginia**

·P A U L·H·
BROOKES
PUBLISHING C°

Baltimore • London • Toronto • Sydney

Paul H. Brookes Publishing Co.
Post Office Box 10624
Baltimore, Maryland 21285-0624

Typeset by Brushwood Graphics, Inc., Baltimore, Maryland.
Manufactured in the United States of America by
BookCrafters, Chelsea, Michigan.

Library of Congress Cataloging-in-Publication Data

Assistive technology: a resource for school, work, and community /
   edited by Karen F. Flippo, Katherine J. Inge, and J. Michael Barcus.
     p.   cm.
   Includes bibliographical references and index.
   ISBN 1-55766-189-8
   1. Self-help devices for the disabled.   2. Physically handicapped—
Services for. I. Flippo, Karen F., 1947– . II. Inge, Katherine J.,
1953– . III. Barcus, J. Michael, 1952– .
RM698.A85   1995
617′.03—dc20   94-47585
                                                                CIP

British Library Cataloguing-in-Publication data are available from the British Library.

Contents

Contributors

Joseph Ashley, Ph.D.
Project P.E.R.T.
Woodrow Wilson Rehabilitation Center
Fishersville, VA 22939

J. Michael Barcus, M.Ed.
Director of Training
Rehabilitation Research and Training Center
  on Supported Employment
Virginia Commonwealth University
Post Office Box 842011
Richmond, VA 23284-2011

Chris Barrett
300 West Franklin Street
Apartment 103-W
Richmond, VA 23220

Michael M. Behrmann, Ed.D.
Director
Center for Human Disabilities—1F2
Fairfax, VA 22030-4444

Ann Cutshall
2313 Wright Avenue
Richmond, VA 23224

Jane M. Everson, Ph.D.
Project Director
Helen Keller National Center
Technical Assistance Center
c/o Louisiana State University Medical Center—
  Human Development Center
1100 Florida Avenue
Building 119
New Orleans, LA 70119

Karen F. Flippo, M.R.A.
Training Associate
Rehabilitation Research and Training Center
  on Supported Employment
Virginia Commonwealth University
Post Office Box 842011
Richmond, VA 23284-2011

Robin Friedlander, M.Ed.
Community Recreation Liaison
Project REC
Children's Hospital
Institute for Community Inclusion
University Affiliated Program
Boston, MA 02115

Beth Bader Gilson, M.S.W.
Rehabilitation Research and Training Center
  on Supported Employment
Virginia Commonwealth University
Post Office Box 842011
Richmond, VA 23284-2011

Debra Hart, M.Ed.
Special Projects Coordinator
Children's Hospital
Institute for Community Inclusion
University Affiliated Program
Boston, MA 02115

Becky Hayward, Ph.D.
Research Triangle Institute
Post Office Box 12194
Research Triangle Park, NC 27709

Diane S. Huss, R.P.T.
Director of Physical Therapy
Woodrow Wilson Rehabilitation Center
Fishersville, VA 22939

Katherine J. Inge, Ph.D., O.T.R.
Training Associate
Rehabilitation Research and Training Center
  on Supported Employment
Virginia Commonwealth University
Post Office Box 842011
Richmond, VA 23284-2011

Jean Keiningham
217 North Boulevard
Apartment 1
Richmond, VA 23220

Kenneth Knorr
Virginia Assistive Technology System
8004 Franklin Farms Drive
Box K-300
Richmond, VA 23288-0300

Cheska Komissar
Community Recreation Liaison
Project REC
Children's Hospital
Institute for Community Inclusion
University Affiliated Program
Boston, MA 02115

Bryan K. Lacy
1532 Americana Drive
Richmond, VA 23228

M. Sherril Moon, Ed.D
Department of Special Education
University of Maryland
1308 Benjamin
College Park, MD 20742

Sarah Oliver
Virginia Assistive Technology System
8004 Franklin Farms Drive
Box K-300
Richmond, VA 23288-0300

Cindy L. Richardson
531 Cameo Terrace
Chesapeake, VA 23322

Rustie Rothstein, M.A.
Helen Keller National Center
Southwest Regional Office
6851 Lennox Avenue
Van Nuys, CA 91405-4097

Catherine Sawyer, M.S., CCC-SLP
University of Virginia Health Sciences Center
Speech-Language Pathology
Box 430
Charlottesville, VA 22908

Jayne Shepherd, M.S., O.T.R.
Assistant Professor
Occupational Therapy
Box 980008
VMI Building 424
Medical College of Virginia
Richmond, VA 23298-0008

Jo Ann Sowers, Ph.D.
Project Director
New Hampshire Natural Supports Project
Institute on Disability/UAP
University of New Hampshire
10 Ferry Street, Number 14
Concord, NH 00301

Theresa L. Tanchak, M.S., CCC-SLP
Prentke-Romich Company
1022 Heyl Road
Wooster, OH 44691

Michael D. Tashjian, M.A.
Research Triangle Institute
Post Office Box 12194
Research Triangle Park, NC 27709

Ed Turner
Rehabilitation Research and Training Center
   on Supported Employment
Virginia Commonwealth University
Post Office Box 842011
Richmond, VA 23284-2011

Susan Urofsky
14301 Spring Gate Court
Midlothian, VA 23112

Joseph F. Wallace, Ph.D.
Virginia Assistive Technology System
8004 Franklin Farms Drive
Box K-300
Richmond, VA 23288-0300

Mary Kay Webster
Richmond DSB Chair
3105 Park Avenue
Richmond, VA 23220

Paul Wehman, Ph.D.
Rehabilitation Research and Training Center
   on Supported Employment
Virginia Commonwealth University
Post Office Box 842011
Richmond, VA 23284-2011

Foreword

It has been said by leaders of the disability civil rights movement that technology will be the equalizer of the 21st century. Great strides have been made since the passage of the Americans with Disabilities Act of 1990 (ADA) (PL 101-336), which accorded full civil rights to the estimated 49 million persons with disabilities in the United States. As physical and attitudinal barriers crumble, newly empowered citizens are entering the marketplaces, city halls, and public buildings with unprecedented access. Education in regular schools for students with disabilities is beginning to become the norm rather than the exception, and college campuses are beginning to address long-neglected accommodations for students with both physical and mental disabilities. ADA is the law, and merchants, along with public officials, are proclaiming the good sense of accessibility for all people in all walks of life.

The field of employment, however, has not seen such gains. An estimated 68% of people with disabilities of working age (around 15 million people) are unemployed. When President Bush signed the ADA in 1990, his administration estimated the cost of private and public payments to unemployed Americans with disabilities at $200 billion annually. It is hoped that we will build on many of the gains since the enactment of ADA and, through the use of technology, create an employment breakthrough. However, many disincentives to employment of people with disabilities, such as health care coverage, still exist and need to be addressed.

Technology is clearly shaping all our lives. Some of us unlock our car doors by the touch of a button on a little box attached to our keys and open the garage door in much the same way. At work we check our e-mail for urgent messages from people all over the world. We quickly sit down at our computer and transmit responses to places like Richmond, San Francisco, Geneva, or London. Some of us use a keyboard to input our response, while others dictate the response to the computer. At the same time, our children are at school, where their fingers rapidly progress across the computer keyboard. Almost miraculously they are transported to a world beneath the ocean or to a different planet through multimedia software.

Imagine the look on the faces of congresspersons in Washington, when they meet Gus Estrella from Arizona, who will soon, under a United Cerebral Palsy Associations award, begin educating Congress on alternative and augmentative communication devices. However, it will not be the high-tech power wheelchair Gus uses that will amaze them—it will be the way he speaks to them with his Liberator computer. Gus is bilingual and can use his Liberator to speak in either English or Spanish, whichever language the listener is more comfortable with.

Technology applications enhance our independence and productivity, whether or not we have a disability. When a technology application is used by a person with a disability, it is commonly referred to as *assistive technology*. Assistive technology may be high- or low-tech; it may be an item available at a local department store, such as a large-key telephone, or a specially designed product, such as an electric wheelchair equipped with a sip-and-puff control. Unfortunately, many people with disabilities do not have access to any of the thousands of technological devices that might make school, work, and home life easier and more productive. This lack of access is due to several factors. Unless potential users have formal ties to medical or social service systems, they probably do not know whom to call for help. Also, because assistive technology devices are constantly being developed and improved (and some devices are custom made), the cost for high-tech devices can be prohibitive. Consumer loan funds have not been plentiful up to this point, and finding one's way through existing funding streams is difficult. In addition, assessment procedures for assistive technology are not uniform. It is not unusual for a person to be assessed in a medical setting and then learn, when he or she takes the device home, to school, or to work, that it is not effective. Often the very best and latest technology winds up in the closet (a phenomenon called *technology abandonment*) rather than assisting the person to perform critical daily functions or to achieve community access. Often the reason for this abandonment is that the technology users themselves have had little say in selecting the assistive device.

Technology can and must become more of an integral part of the lives of children and adults with disabilities. Making technology truly assistive for people with disabilities requires a radical break from past and present human services practices. The person with a disability and human services program representatives must invest the time, energy, cooperation, and resources necessary to make technology work. Technology must be viewed as any process or means that a person with a disability *chooses* to use to perform a critical function or achieve a desired goal in her or his life. Service systems must publicize their resources and make them more accessible to consumers. People with disabilities must have the primary role in defining what makes technology truly assistive to their lives. This will occur as individuals obtain the information and tools they need and, most importantly, as they have the primary responsibility in defining the role technology is to play in achieving their dreams. The end result will be a better use of valuable time and limited financial resources and more people obtaining technology that is truly assistive and *liberating*.

Throughout the next decade, this "liberation" is likely to unchain more and more of our citizens with disabilities. Combined with civil rights, access, and education, assistive technology can help us transcend the myths and prejudices that have limited us for so many years and usher in a new age of inclusion for those of us who are currently labeled as people with disabilities.

Richard Douglas
Executive Director
President's Committee on Employment
of People with Disabilities

REFERENCES

Americans with Disabilities Act of 1990 (ADA), PL 101-336. (July 26, 1990). Title 42, U.S.C. 12101 et seq: *U.S. Statutes at Large, 104,* 327–378.

Preface

Our first memories of assistive technology may consist of simple devices: glasses, hearing aids, crutches, or wheelchairs. However, as inventors have performed their magic since the early 1980s, more elaborate devices, equipment, and services have found their way into the marketplace. Now, our experiences with technology may include a powerful computer that allows a person to communicate with his family and friends, an adapted van that enables a woman with quadriplegia to drive herself to work, or an environmental control unit that assists a homemaker in performing simple daily living activities.

Since 1988, Congress and the states have addressed the challenges related to increasing the knowledge of, access to, and utilization of technology by users, professionals, and the general public. The Technology-Related Assistance for Individuals with Disabilities Act (Tech Act) of 1988 allowed states to fund local projects to provide assistive technology information and referral services. These projects help to explain what assistive technology is all about and how to find services and devices when they are needed. Experience gained from implementing the first Tech Act gave Congress insight into crafting the Technology-Related Assistance for Individuals with Disabilities Amendments of 1994, which places greater emphasis on consumer responsiveness. There is a renewed focus on improving access for individuals in rural areas and other underserved populations.

For all the promises of how assistive technology can improve the lives of individuals with disabilities, many barriers remain. For example, some devices can be simple to operate, but priced out of the range of a user's financial capacities. Other devices may be so sophisticated that they require hours of individualized training from a service provider. There are many more examples that could be cited; however, frequently the barriers are associated with a lack of information, quality service, or control of the process by the user of technology. These issues, as well as the recent advances in technology, point to a need for a comprehensive resource guide that can answer users' and professionals' questions about assessment, training, implementation, and funding issues related to assistive technology services and devices.

This book brings together a number of nationally recognized authors who discuss the application of assistive technology in various environments: school, work, and community. In addition, each chapter focuses on the need to place the user of technology at the center of the design, training, and implementation process. Case studies demonstrate assistive technology in action, and resource lists guide the reader to particular devices and information. Finally, descriptions of innovative loan programs and other funding options are provided to help users and professionals design strategies for gaining access to technology. The authors hope that this book will provide a foundation for users and professionals as they apply technology to all aspects of daily living.

REFERENCES

Technology-Related Assistance for Individuals with Disabilities Act of 1988, PL 100-407. (August 19, 1988). Title 29, U.S.C. 2201 et seq: *U.S. Statutes at Large, 102,* 1044–1065.
Technology-Related Assistance for Individuals with Disabilities Amendments of 1994, PL 103-218. (March 9, 1994). Title 29, U.S.C. 2201 et seq: *U.S. Statutes at Large, 108,* 50–97.

Assistive Technology

I
POLICY FOUNDATIONS

1

Legislative Foundation of Assistive Technology Policy in the United States

Joseph F. Wallace
Karen F. Flippo
J. Michael Barcus
Michael M. Behrmann

Tracing the path of rehabilitation legislation in the United States since the early 1900s reveals a pattern of law that has been molded by social, economic, and political change. Rehabilitation legislation mirrors many of the upheavals that have been experienced by the general population. From World War I, when the Vocational Rehabilitation Act of 1918 (PL 65-178) was enacted, to the Rehabilitation Act Amendments of 1992 (PL 102-569), rehabilitation legislation and policy have expanded to address both the employment and living concerns of persons with disabilities. Driven by public sentiment, disability policy emerged after World War I because the American citizens believed their government had an obligation to provide medical and vocational rehabilitation services to veterans, as well as to integrate them back into society after the war.

The definition of *persons with disabilities* has expanded to include individuals with physical, mental, and emotional disabilities. In fact, today, approximately 43 million Americans are considered to have disabilities. Current laws and services are the result of continual growth in the population of Americans with disabilities and society's recognition of the barriers that these persons face. For example, high unemployment experienced by individuals with disabilities immediately sends warnings of potential problems to others. These problems include poverty, welfare dependence, lack of work skills, and societal isolation, all of which may individually or collectively exacerbate the effects of a disability.

Societal barriers to employment and inclusion are not individually controlled, but rather are systemic failures. The current philosophy of rehabilitation grew from an understanding of the negative impact that the government's ignorance and inactivity in responding proactively to abilities and needs has had on persons with disabilities.

An individualized, capacity orientation to service delivery directly contrasts with the former vocational rehabilitation model, which was rooted in a medical philosophy of treatment. Previously, individuals with disabilities entered the vocational rehabilitation system to be "fixed." Deficits were identified, and the services revolved around eliminating any problems. The federal/state vocational rehabilitation system was designed as a continuum. That is, for acceptance into services, an individual was expected to have a disability upon entry and emerge "fixed" or "cured" at closure. This practice was frequently challenged by persons with disabilities and their advocates. As a result, rehabilitation legislation in the late 1980s and early to mid-1990s has been strongly influenced by these consumers. Subsequently, capacity-oriented, quality, individualized services directed by the consumer have become the values of the vocational rehabilitation system.

Approximately 1 year following its introduction, the Technology-Related Assistance for Individuals with Disabilities Act of 1988 (PL 100-407) (commonly referred to as the "Tech Act") was passed by Congress. Congressional action in passing this law was historic for two primary reasons. First, the Tech Act of 1988 was the first law to *specifically* address the technology-related needs of persons with disabilities. Second, and of equal importance, is the message that Congress gave to state agencies, the entities responsible for local implementation. This message was for state agencies to develop consumer-responsive systems that are directed and influenced by the technology users themselves.

TECHNOLOGY-RELATED ASSISTANCE FOR INDIVIDUALS WITH DISABILITIES ACT

The framework for the Tech Act of 1988 was provided by advocacy and the powerful, value-laden disability rights legislation that preceded it. Rapid proliferation of technology into every phase of American life in the 1980s also influenced congressional decision making. In the Tech Act of 1988, Congress stated that

provision of assistive technology devices and assistive technology services enables some individuals with disabilities to:

(A) have greater control over their own lives

(B) participate in and contribute more fully to activities in their home, school, and work environments, and in their communities

(C) interact to a greater extent with non-disabled individuals and

(D) otherwise benefit from opportunities that are taken for granted by individuals who do not have disabilities (Tech Act of 1988, p. 1044)

Congress believed that both low and high technology and adaptations would substantially benefit the United States by reducing dependency costs associated with major life areas (e.g., transportation, health care and rehabilitation, telecommunications).

Congressional intent in authorizing the Tech Act of 1988 was to assist states in developing and implementing statewide programs of technology-related assistance for meeting the needs of individuals with disabilities. However, there were several factors that hampered assistive technology service delivery. These factors included resources to pay for assistive technology devices and services, sufficient numbers of trained personnel to assist with service delivery, the promotion of an awareness to the right to service delivery, the publication of resource information, the coordination of existing technology services among state agencies, and the expansion of programmatic services to respond to the needs of persons with disabilities.

The Tech Act of 1988 further defines an *assistive technology device* to be any device, piece of equipment, or product system, whether acquired commercially or off the shelf, modified, or customized, that is used to increase, maintain, or improve functional capabilities of individuals with disabilities. *Assistive technology service* can be defined as any service that directly assists an individual with a disability in the selection, acquisition, or use of an assistive technology device.

Title I of the Tech Act of 1988 authorizes grants to states. As part of the process of developing consumer-responsive systems, states were given the latitude to design their own models that corresponded to the characteristics of their particular populations and existing service systems. Needs assessments, identification and coordination of existing resources, service provision networks, information and referral systems, public awareness, training, and technical assistance are standard components of systems change projects (see Chapter 3). Because individuals with disabilities are expected to perform substantial, valued roles in state projects, many states involved individuals with disabilities and/or their families in project staffs, advisory councils, training, conferences, and committees.

Under the original Tech Act of 1988, 49 states received grants, with the minimum award being $500,000 appropriating approximately $34 million per year. One percent of the total appropriation or $500,000, whichever is greater, was earmarked for projects that provided states with information and technical assistance for developing and implementing statewide programs. Systems change grants, which were allotted for 3 years, had possible 2-year extensions, after which time states were expected to incorporate the new assistive technology system design into their own administrative structures. In the first round of systems change grants in 1989, 9 states received funding, followed by 14 in fiscal year 1990, 8 in fiscal year 1991, 11 in fiscal year 1992, and 8 in fiscal year 1993.

Reauthorization of the Tech Act occurred in February 1994. This action followed 1 year of congressional hearings and deliberations. The second act, the Technology-Related Assistance for Individuals with Disabilities Act of 1994 (PL 103-218), requires states to be more accountable in conducting activities through the systems change projects. Advocacy services take a greater role in assistive technology systems, and national technical assistance requirements have increased.

The Tech Act of 1994 also continues the state grant competitive program for an additional 5 years. States receiving grants are required to engage in activities that are apt to result in systems change. From the onset, Congress encouraged states to develop plans and work toward incorporating assistive technology into state systems in anticipation of the end of federal funding, which usually occurs 10 years after a program begins.

The following sections outline the key provisions of the Tech Act of 1994.

Title I: State Grant Appropriations

In Title I of the Tech Act of 1994, Congress increased its appropriations to states. Fifty million dollars was authorized for fiscal year 1994, with "such sums" as necessary through fiscal year 1998. The majority of states will receive about $750,000 each per year. States are eligible to compete for a 1-year development grant enabling them to plan and begin laying the foundation for regional operation and state systems change, followed by a 2-year extension grant called the "first extension grant," and finally followed by a new 5-year extension grant, or the "second extension grant."

Federal funds will be reduced during a state's second extension grant period. In the fourth year, funds will be reduced to 75% of the grant amount, with a 50% reduction in the fifth year. Federal funding stops at the end of the second extension grant period.

Leadership

State agencies responsible for leading state systems change efforts are expected to possess a wide range of capabilities. One such capability is demonstrated leadership throughout the change process and the achievement of outcomes that result in established consumer-responsive policies and procedures that facilitate access to and use of assistive technology.

These lead agencies are supposed to identify and respond to technology needs of individuals with disabilities, as well as their families, guardians, advocates, and authorized representatives. Another leadership task is to promote consumer confidence, responsiveness, and advocacy in all project activities. Finally, states are expected to display leadership by identifying strategies to build local capacity, developing and conducting both staff and consumer training, and increasing funding options and access to these funds for assistive technology.

Clarification of Definitions

In order to provide more clarity to states in charting and implementing their activities, new definitions were written as part of the Tech Act of 1994. These definitions underscore the critical part consumers have in planning and implementing state and local assistive technology systems.

In particular, the Tech Act of 1994 defines consumer-responsive activities, advocacy services, and systems change and advocacy activities. *Consumer responsive* indicates that activities are to be usable by and easily accessible to individuals with disabilities and, when appropriate, their families, guardians, advocates, or authorized representatives. These activities are meant to respond to the needs of individuals with disabilities in a timely, appropriate manner. The program or activity facilitates the full, meaningful participation of individuals with disabilities (including those from underrepresented and rural populations), as well as their families, guardians, advocates, and authorized representatives, in decisions related to the provision of assistive technology devices and services and in the planning, development, implementation, and evaluation of the comprehensive statewide program of technology-related assistance (Tech Act of 1994, Section 4[5]).

Advocacy services are those services provided to assist individuals with disabilities and their families, guardians, advocates, and authorized representatives in gaining access to assistive technology devices and services. These services are provided through 1) individual case management for individuals with disabilities; 2) representation of individuals with disabilities (other than representation within the definition of protection and advocacy [P&A] services); 3) training of individuals with disabilities and their families, guardians, advocates, and authorized representatives to successfully conduct advocacy for themselves; and 4) dissemination of information (Tech Act of 1994, Section 4[1]).

Systems change and advocacy activities are efforts that result in laws, regulations, policies, and practices or organizational structures that promote consumer-responsive programs or entities and that facilitate and increase access to, provision of, and funding for assistive technology devices and services on a permanent basis. These devices and services are provided to empower individuals with disabilities to achieve greater independence, productivity, integration, and inclusion within the community and the work force (Tech Act of 1994, Section 4[12]).

Protection and Advocacy Services

The states' lead agencies must now supplement the P&A services already existing in their states, which is accomplished through contracted services. States have two options: They can augment funds for the existing P&A organization or request that the U.S. Secretary of Education fund the P&A services directly from each state's allotment.

Contracted amounts are determined by the size of the state's Title I grant, the overall needs of persons with disabilities within the state, state population, and size of the state. Minimum allocations are $40,000, with a $100,000 maximum.

Advocacy efforts are meant to result in changes in laws, practices, and policies, ultimately resulting in consumer-responsive programs and services. States can redesignate a

P&A provider (an organization with the same credentials and competence to perform legal representation similar to the current advocacy services provider) if the provider does not successfully perform its contracted activities (Simpson, 1994). The final result of a consumer-responsive assistive technology system is greater "independence, productivity and integration and inclusion within the community and the work force" (Tech Act of 1994, Section 4[12]).

Systems Change and Advocacy Activities

Congress has directed that states perform at least six specific activities leading to systems change and increased advocacy. These functions are as follows:

1. To develop, implement, and monitor state, regional, and local laws; regulations; policies; practices; procedures; and organizational structures that will improve access to, provision of, funding for, and timely acquisition and delivery of assistive technology
2. To develop and implement strategies to overcome barriers regarding access to, provision of, and funding for devices and services, with priority for identification of barriers to funding through state education (including special education) services, vocational rehabilitation services, medical assistance services, or (as appropriate) other health and human services. Particular emphasis is on overcoming barriers for underrepresented and rural populations.
3. To coordinate activities among state agencies
4. To develop and implement strategies to empower individuals with disabilities and their family members, guardians, and advocates in selecting and obtaining assistive technology
5. To provide outreach to underrepresented and rural populations, including the identification and assessment of needs
6. To develop and implement strategies to ensure the timely acquisition of technology

National Technical Assistance

States' training efforts are augmented by additional funds that are provided through grants or contracts from the National Institute on Disability and Rehabilitation Research (NIDRR). Information and technical assistance offered throughout the United States is expected to include dissemination of critical assistive technology information, such as funding and innovations. Congress has appropriated approximately $1.5 million for national technical assistance. Technical assistance is prescriptive information. This information may include specifics on funding such as developing revolving loan programs, consultation on developing information and referral systems, strategies for increasing consumer involvement, and so forth. In 1989 the Rehabilitation Engineering Society of North America (RESNA) was awarded a contract by NIDRR to provide training and technical assistance to all funded Tech Act states.

Title II: Programs of National Significance

Under Title II of the Tech Act of 1994, Congress authorized the establishment of a national classification system for assistive technology devices and services. This system allows for the uniform collection of data across public programs, by tracking assistive technology use and funding streams and by identifying assistive devices that are eligible for tax credits. Congress has appropriated $200,000 for this classification system in fiscal year 1995. Also under this title, Congress authorized training, technology transfer, recycling demonstration projects (projects that use innovative methods to recycle used assistive technology equipment), business opportunities for persons with disabilities, and initiatives for universal design products.

Title III: Alternative Financing Mechanisms

Paying for assistive technology is one of the major barriers to accessing assistive technology. Congress addresses this problem in Title III of the Tech Act of 1994. One-time matching federal grants of no greater than $500,000 are authorized to each state. These funds will be used to establish a variety of alternative funding approaches for the purchase of assistive technology devices and services. Of course, each state can provide additional funding beyond this $500,000 to establish its programs.

Funding approaches are expected to include different types of public and private loan programs such as interest buy down, revolving loans, and consumer pools. Congress also set aside $250,000 from this authority for technical assistance to states as they develop their financing strategies.

HISTORICAL AND LEGISLATIVE DEVELOPMENT OF ASSISTIVE TECHNOLOGY POLICY

The Tech Act of 1988 (PL 100-407) and the Tech Act of 1994 (PL 103-218) are built upon several major pieces of rehabilitation legislation. The following review represents important policy benchmarks in the evolution of rehabilitation, the development of assistive technology, and the influence of U.S. society's changing values relating to persons with disabilities. The evolutionary process of viewing individuals with disabilities as contributing members of society, of involving them more in self-determination, of the gradual expansion of work-related and other services, and of the movement to steadily serve persons with the most severe disabilities is represented in this historical presentation.

Many of the difficulties that individuals with disabilities face in gaining access to assistive technology have their foundations in the legislative origins of rehabilitation (Enders, 1989). The history of U.S. disability policy can be analyzed through its chronological development. Each time period provides representation of the social perspectives of persons with disabilities—evolving from a caregiver and institutional perspective to one of community inclusion and self-direction. Five broad time periods of policy development are identified and examined through examples of legislation, regulation, and fiscal appropriation, which all provide an understanding of assistive technology issues. The individual policy development initiatives are presented in Table 1.1 by year, development title or legislature, and impact that the specific initiative has had on the disability field.

Berkowitz (1987) describes the history of federal policy relating to disability as an uncoordinated, conflicting set of approaches and incentives. Berkowitz believes that such policy conflicts have their basis in varying historical definitions of disabilities and in the related outcomes that the policies were intended to support, such as Social Security work incentives and disincentives or vocational rehabilitation promotion of retirement versus rehabilitation.

There has been, however, little historical attention at a federal policy level to disability prevention or individual empowerment of persons with disabilities (Haber, 1985). Assistive technology has the potential to lower the barriers that exclude persons with disabilities from society. This is evidenced by young children with severe cerebral palsy who, through the use of power wheelchairs and voice output communication devices, are able to ambulate independently and express their desires across environments. A simple wooden backscratcher can provide persons with muscular distrophy a means to reach an elevator button and press it on

Table 1.1.   Public policy development in rehabilitation and assistive technology

Year	Development	Impact
Pre-1900	Various state-level funding initiatives promoting institutional care	Steady growth of institutional placement of persons with mental and physical disabilities
1918	Vocational Rehabilitation Act of 1918 (PL 65-178)	Pension compensation for war-related disabilities, first federal rehabilitation program
1920	Smith-Fess Act of 1920 (PL 67-236)	First federal rehabilitation program for civilians using state matching funds
1935	Social Security Act of 1935 (PL 74-271)	Established federal/state rehabilitation as a permanent program
1943	Vocational Rehabilitation Amendments Act of 1943 (PL 113)	Extended federal/state rehabilitation services to mental disabilities
1954	Vocational Rehabilitation Act Amendments of 1954 (PL 82-565)	Increased federal rehabilitation funding to states and expanded assistive technology services
1956	Social Security Act Amendments of 1956 (PL 84-880)	Provided Social Security disability allowances
1965	Social Security Act Amendments of 1965 (PL 89-97)	Created direct relationship between Social Security and vocational rehabilitation
	Vocational Rehabilitation Act Amendments of 1965 (PL 89-333)	Increased flexibility in financing and administration of state rehabilitation programs
1972	U.S. Department of Education and Veterans Administration initiated product testing	Established standards for assistive technology product performance standards
1973	Rehabilitation Act of 1973 (PL 93-112)	Increased awareness of disability issues, civil rights of individuals, and promoted disability research
1975	Developmental Disabilities Assistance and Bill of Rights Act of 1975 (PL 94-103)	Shifted focus from employability to "maximum potential"
	Education for All Handicapped Children Act of 1975 (PL 94-142)	Federal support for free appropriate public education, IEP vehicle for gaining needed equipment
1976	U.S. Department of Education established centers of technical excellence	Rehabilitation engineering centers were established to provide disability research and assessment
1978	Rehabilitation Act Amendments of 1978 (PL 95-602)	Established NIHR, promoted rehabilitation engineering centers

(continued)

Table 1.1. (*continued*)

Year	Development	Impact
1986	Rehabilitation Act Amendments of 1986 (PL 99-506)	Defined and expanded rehabilitation engineering role in vocational rehabilitation planning process
	Employment Opportunity for Disabled Americans Act of 1986 (PL 99-463)	Created income set aside for SSI and SSDI recipients to purchase technology
	Education of the Handicapped Act Amendments of 1986 (PL 99-457)	Mandated the design and adaptation of technology for use in teaching students with disabilities; through Part H, created entitlement for infants and toddlers (birth to age 3) and their families to receive assistive technology through early intervention
1987	Developmental Disabilities Assistance and Bill of Rights Act Amendments of 1987 (PL 100-146)	Defined "best practice" supports and services, including assistive technology as priority
1988	Medicaid Amendments for Special Education Related Services (PL 100-360)	Resolved payment dispute between Medicaid and local school districts for needed services
	Technology-Related Assistance for Individuals with Disabilities Act of 1988 (PL 100-407)	Provided financial assistance to states to implement assistive technology coordination
1989	Medicaid Early and Periodic Screening, Diagnosis, and Treatment Amendments of 1989 (PL 101-238)	Mandated that all children under 21 years of age eligible for Medicaid receive broad range of services
1990	Americans with Disabilities Act of 1990 (PL 101-336)	Extended civil rights for persons with disabilities and references assistive technology in each title
	Individuals with Disabilities Education Act of 1990 (PL 101-476)	Public agencies are to ensure assistive technology devices or services are made available
1992	Rehabilitation Act Amendments of 1992 (PL 102-569)	Requires each rehabilitation agency to address assistive technology in every phase of the rehabilitation process
1994	Technology-Related Assistance for Individuals with Disabilities Act of 1994 (PL 103-218)	Requires states to be more accountable in conducting systems change projects; advocacy services take a greater rolo

IEP, individualized education program; NIHR, National Institute on Handicapped Research; PL, public law; SSDI, Social Security Disability Insurance; SSI, Supplemental Security Income.

their own. Assistive technology may also correct the many disabling environments that prevent community inclusion. The traditional rehabilitative policy paradigm has been one of medical orientation. This approach has focused on repairing the broken part, rather than the impact of that specific disability on the individual as a whole. The medical model has promoted a discerning eye to the prevention of possible causes of the disabling condition or to facilitating the independence of the person with a disability.

Pre-1900–1918

Dating back to the mid-1850s, institutions became society's legislated answer for the care of persons with disabilities. This first phase of public policy development was anchored in values that considered persons with physical or mental disabilities to be untreatable and to need lifelong care (Wolfensberger, 1975). They were considered sick and in need of medical intervention or treatment as if they were diseased. Institutions provided a medically oriented alternative by which persons with disabilities were subjected to isolation and to substandard treatment in segregated settings (Kanner, 1964). The first residential facility was founded by Johann Guggenbuhl in 1841 and called the Abendburg. It was located in the mountains of Switzerland and was designed to provide comprehensive treatment for individuals who had mental disabilities. This facility, although initially deemed innovative and resourceful, was forced to close due to mismanagement and intolerable conditions (Beirne-Smith, Patton, & Ittenbach, 1994).

The legislative origins of vocational rehabilitation and assistive technology date back to the early 1900s, with the passage of the Vocational Rehabilitation Act of 1918. This was the first federal program in the United States directed toward rehabilitation, specifically of veterans with disabilities. Previous compensation for war-related disabilities was provided exclusively through pensions. Under this act, the Federal Board for Vocational Education was responsible for developing programs for veterans with disabilities. Employment was required to be a feasible outcome for eligibility under the act (Obermann, 1965). The provision of services and devices (assistive technology) necessary for successful employment training was an approved component of the Vocational Rehabilitation Act. This act can be identified as the first public policy that legislated broad funding for such assistive technology. In addition, the act set the stage for two restrictive criteria that would deny persons with disabilities access to technology in future years: first, the requirement of veteran status and, second, the concept of employment potential. These policy criteria embodied the traditional medical model requiring a veteran-related injury and a certain level of potential employability.

1920–1943

The Smith-Fess Act of 1920 (PL 67-236) provided the first civilian component to vocational rehabilitation in the United States. It legislated $750,000 the first year and $1 million for each of the next 2 years. These funds were to be expended on the rehabilitation of persons with physical disabilities who were either "totally or partially incapacitated for remunerative occupation" (Rubin & Roessler, 1987, p. 26). This act provided a 50-50 match for states, with individual appropriations determined by ratio of state population to total U.S. population, which gave an incentive for states to pass similar legislation. Although the purpose of the Smith-Fess Act was not to provide physical restoration services, a person with a disability could be provided a prosthesis if it could be justified as a supply necessary for the successful completion of training. The training requirement continued to be work-related, pertaining to employment potential. The general provision for physical restoration devices was still a significant unmet need, and the involvement of the individuals themselves in the determination of their needs was not yet a part of the approval process due to the narrow interpretation of the legislation.

The status of the federal/state rehabilitation program as described remained unchanged for the next 15 years and seemed destined for temporary funding (Lenihan, 1977). It was the Social Security Act of 1935 (PL 74-271) that established federal/state vocational rehabilitation as a permanent program. Congress cited vocational rehabilitation of persons with disabilities as "a matter of social justice, a permanent on-going public duty that should not depend on periodic determination of deservability" (Lenihan, 1977, p. 5–7).

As an outgrowth of the wartime demands for manpower, both in the United States and abroad, the Vocational Rehabilitation Amendments Act (PL 113) was passed in 1943. This Act extended federal/state rehabilitation program services to persons with mental retardation and mental illness and expanded the types of physical restoration services that could be provided for persons with physical disabilities. Such restoration services were to be provided only to "those with static defects" (permanent physical disabling condition) (Kessler, 1953, p. 229). The paradox of this legislation was that persons with mental retardation or mental illness, although technically eligible, did not have the educational base or the work history necessary to take advantage of these benefits. This paradox demonstrated the appearance but not the true application of expanded services as may have been intended. It was not until the 1960s that this discrepancy was corrected through the passage of the Vocational Rehabilitation Act Amendments of 1965 (PL 89-333).

1954–1965

The period from 1954 to 1965 represented the time of most notable progress in the legislative arena. This period has been called the Golden Era of Rehabilitation due to a number of significant federal initiatives for persons with both physical and mental disabilities (Rusalem, 1976). Federal funding for rehabilitation increased by more than $150 million by 1965. The primary legislative endeavors responsible for this increase were the Vocational Rehabilitation Act Amendments of 1954 (PL 82-565) and the Social Security Act Amendments of 1956 (PL 84-880) and 1965 (PL 89-97). Each of these laws is discussed briefly.

Vocational Rehabilitation Act Amendments of 1954

These amendments increased federal funding for vocational rehabilitation services to states from a 50-50 match level to a $3 in federal monies for every $2 in state monies. In 1955, the U.S. government increased its overall appropriations to states for rehabilitation purposes to $30 million, and by 1958 this amount rose to $65 million. Significant provisions of the amendments included expanded services allowable for reimbursement (Obermann, 1965), which included the purchase of assistive technology for individuals with disabilities.

Social Security Act Amendments of 1956

This legislation provided Social Security disability allowances for individuals with disabilities. Those allowances were available to any person with a disability who was permanently "injured," older than 50 years of age, and considered incapable of returning to competitive employment (Erlanger & Roth, 1985).

Social Security Act Amendments of 1965

Despite the many income protection advances provided through the amendments of 1956, it was not until the 1965 amendments that Social Security formed a direct relationship with vocational rehabilitation. This legislation stressed that a primary objective was vocational rehabilitation to the greatest number of applicants for the Social Security Disability Insurance

(SSDI) program (Popick, 1967). Congress mandated that SSDI monies were intended to cover the costs of rehabilitating "selected disability beneficiaries" through state rehabilitation agency services.

1972–1978

Assistive technology was introduced as a formal component of rehabilitation during the late 1950s and early 1960s. This introduction came as a result of improved prosthetic appliance and sensory aids that were necessary to assist American soldiers with disabilities who were returning from war zones around the world (Levitan, Magnum, & Marshall, 1976). The increasing need to respond to the soldiers' physical rehabilitation led to multiple research and development projects (DeJong, 1979). These generally were located in various academic and clinical facilities across the United States, and the result was a variety of new products and producers. Consequently, a new field of organized adaptive equipment technology began to emerge (Allan, 1958).

The Committee on Prosthetic Research and Development of the National Academy of Sciences was developed in 1942 and had the responsibility for centralizing the information gathered from these national facilities and projects. It was through the coordinated collaboration of the committee that the specialty field, which interchangeably has been called both "rehabilitative engineering" and "assistive technology," came to be known as a specific, unique discipline.

Product Testing

The U.S. Department of Education and the Veterans Administration took the lead in the early 1970s by establishing programs specifically identified to provide product testing, development of product performance standards, and support for product research and development (DeJong, 1979). During the mid-1970s, the U.S. Department of Education had begun to develop centers of technical excellence at identified academic and clinical facilities across the country. These rehabilitative engineering centers received their funding beginning in the late 1970s through the National Institute on Handicapped Research (NIHR), which is now known as the NIDRR.

Each rehabilitative engineering center had a specifically identified target area from which it coordinated research, development, and training activities. Although valuable data came out of these centers, the utility of the information has been somewhat limited due to variation of content and format standards (Skelley, 1980). The lack of a central organization from which this information could be analyzed, disseminated, and interpreted has limited the potential impact that this information could have for persons who are assistive technology users, designers, and vendors.

Rehabilitation Act of 1973

PL 93-112 and its amendments provided a comprehensive plan for providing rehabilitation services to all eligible individuals, regardless of their disability and its severity. Martin and Gandy (1987) suggest that the primary purpose of the Rehabilitation Act of 1973 was one of "equality of opportunity through its provisions relating to consumer involvement, emphasis on persons with severe disabilities, creation of the National Institute on Handicapped Research, emphasis on program evaluation and the advancement of the civil rights of persons with disabilities" (p. 66). The successful passage of the act in 1973 and of the Rehabilitation Act Amendments of 1978 (PL 95-602) in 1978 has created an increased awareness both of persons with disabilities and of the physical and attitudinal barriers experienced by those individuals. In particular, Section 504 of this legislation provided a clear delineation of rights for persons with disabilities and required employers to take affirmative action in their hiring practices.

Rubin and Roessler (1987) summarize the act into five general mandates that still exist as foundations for future legislative initiatives: 1) to serve individuals who have the most severe disabilities, 2) to promote consumer involvement, 3) to stress program evaluation, 4) to provide support for research, and 5) to advance the civil rights of persons with disabilities. These mandates set the stage for the second phase of public policy change in the United States, which began approximately in the mid-1970s and continued to the mid-1980s. This period is embodied primarily in the deinstitutionalization and community-based transition movements. In reality, this return to the community phase proved to be little more than an ideological shift to a continuum-of-care concept (Taylor, 1988). Taylor states that this concept was built on the "readiness" model whereby an individual with a disability prepared for the next step on the least restrictive alternative continuum and "earned" his or her way through countless programs and levels of decreasing supervision before becoming independent. Many service delivery systems continue to subscribe to this continuum-of-care model. This approach to service delivery creates smaller residential settings that may be equally as restrictive in that they create homogeneous groupings and continue to segregate most persons with severe disabilities.

Developmental Disabilities Assistance and Bill of Rights Act of 1975

Another significant legislative step forward for persons with disabilities came about as a result of the passage of the Developmental Disabilities Assistance and Bill of Rights Act of 1975 (PL 94-103). This legislation describes the person with a disability as a person (not as a client or patient) who has unique abilities to contribute to family, community, and society. The act also states that the disability itself is not to blame for the lack of societal acceptance, but rather social attitudes and environments are to blame. The act furthermore implied that competency, capacity, and contributions are the factors that lead to preferences and choices and that the latter should be respected and individually determined by each person (U.S. Commission on Civil Rights, 1983). The purpose of the act is to help states ensure that persons with developmental disabilities receive "services necessary to enable them to achieve their maximum potential" (U.S. Commission on Civil Rights, 1983, p. 60). This reference to the whole person and his or her maximum potential represents a radical departure from the isolated focus of previous laws on employability.

Education for All Handicapped Children Act of 1975

The other significant piece of legislation passed during the 1970s was the Education for All Handicapped Children Act of 1975 (PL 94-142). This act mandated that U.S. public schools provide free appropriate public education (FAPE) for every child with a disability, irrespective of the nature or severity of that disability (Yanok, 1986). PL 94-142 was propelled by "congressional concern and dissatisfaction with the complete exclusion of millions of handicapped children from the Nation's public schools and with the inappropriateness of educational programs available to additional millions of handicapped children" (U.S. Commission on Civil Rights, 1983, p. 56). A FAPE includes special education (specially designed instruction) and related services, which are provided at public expense, under public supervision and direction, without charge to meet the unique needs of a child with a disability. An appropriate education must take place in the least restrictive environment, with children who have no disabilities, and, if possible, in regular classrooms aided by the use of supplementary aids and services. Related services include supportive services as are required to assist a child with a disability to benefit from special education. Rules and regulations pertaining to the act state that parents, together with a team of professionals involved with the child, are to determine the appropriate placement and educational programming needs for their child. The decisions are recorded in the individualized education program (IEP), which is another mandate of this law.

The Education for All Handicapped Children Act of 1975 did not mention assistive technology as special education or as a related or supplemental service. However, by the early 1980s, schools did begin to recognize the benefits of technology in teaching children with disabilities. Some of these schools provided training and support services for technology to their students and some allowed assistive technology devices and services to be incorporated into individual students' IEPs. In addition, during this same time period, federal research priorities of the Division of Innovation and Development of the Office of Special Education Programs (OSEP) established funding priorities for research and development in the area of special education technology. OSEP also supported contracts such as the Center for Special Education Technology at the Council for Exceptional Children, which facilitated and enhanced national information exchange and professional communication among researchers, developers, and trainers on special education technology issues.

The Rehabilitation Act Amendments of 1978 continued to build on the concept of increasing consumer involvement in service planning through increased attention to research endeavors. The establishment of the NIHR (now the NIDRR) was a result of these amendments and became identified as the primary agency to direct and establish priorities on studies regarding the employment, health, and income of individuals with disabilities. Within the many priorities identified by the NIHR, the emphasis on funding for rehabilitation engineering centers to pursue research and development activities relating to assistive technology ranks high. These research activities included stimulation of industry and evaluation of technology; improved prostheses and orthoses; worksite modifications to enhance employability; development of a new generation of hearing aids; development of nonvocal communication assistance; aids to improve mobility for individuals with low vision; and improvement of the usefulness of functional electrical stimulation.

1980s to 1994

A change in emphasis, from research and development to service delivery, began to occur in the early 1980s. The interface of technology with the many other areas of the vocational rehabilitation process began to be demonstrated through a number of state-level initiatives. For example, the Veterans Administration and RESNA developed performance and disclosure standards for wheelchairs.

Although the 1980s have been typified as a generally conservative political period due to a reduced role of the U.S. government in disability policy, several theoretical and philosophical movements began to take hold and become embodied in legislative initiatives. From the quality of life and community membership movements, a third phase of public policy direction created a new emphasis on functional supports to provide all persons, regardless of the severity of their disability, with a place in their community. This movement represents a full-scale evolutionary change in legislative philosophy from employment to independence to empowerment. The shift toward natural supports and personal dignity was embodied in several major legislative initiatives. These are as follows: the Rehabilitation Act Amendments of 1986 (PL 99-506); the Employment Opportunity for Disabled Americans Act of 1986 (PL 99-463); the Education of the Handicapped Act Amendments of 1986 (PL 99-457); the Developmental Disabilities Assistance and Bill of Rights Act Amendments of 1987 (PL 100-146); the Medicaid Amendments for Special Education Related Services (PL 100-360); Medicaid

Early and Periodic Screening, Diagnosis and Treatment Amendments of 1989 (PL 101-238); the Americans with Disabilities Act (ADA) of 1990 (PL 101-336); the Individuals with Disabilities Education Act (IDEA) of 1990 (PL 101-476); the Individuals with Disabilities Education Act (IDEA) Amendments of 1991 (PL 102-119); and the Rehabilitation Act Amendments of 1992 (PL 102-569). Each of these landmark policy developments will be analyzed with respect to the impact that they are intended to have on persons with disabilities and the relationship to assistive technology.

Rehabilitation Act Amendments of 1986

These amendments (PL 99-506) require state vocational rehabilitation agencies to describe in their 3-year plan the role that rehabilitation engineering services would play in assisting individuals with disabilities throughout the rehabilitation process. This was the first time that rehabilitation engineering had been defined and included as "a range of services and devices which can supplement and enhance individual functions" (p. 4). The role of rehabilitation engineering included careful consideration when determining eligibility, especially in the cases of individuals who might not be otherwise eligible for rehabilitation services.

Rehabilitation engineering also was added to the four mandatory services that state rehabilitation agencies must provide. This suggests that Congress intends to provide funding support to assist persons in the acquisition of assistive technology devices and services. More specifically, Section 508 of the act requires federal agency compliance for equal access to electronic office equipment for federal employees. From a federal accessibility procurement perspective, this section set a new policy direction for improved functional performance for its employees with disabilities.

Employment Opportunity for Disabled Americans Act of 1986

This law (PL 99-463) attempted to create new incentives for persons with disabilities who were receiving Supplemental Security Income (SSI) and SSDI by enabling them to return to work without losing their SSI benefits. One program entitled a Plan for Achieving Self Support (PASS) allowed income to be set aside from a beneficiary's paycheck to purchase assistive technology devices and services with an approved vocational goal and associated timetable. This policy development represents the value of assistive technology for persons with disabilities in achieving the goals of independence and self-sufficiency, and it acknowledges the need for alternative financing necessary for acquisition.

Education of the Handicapped Act Amendments of 1986

These amendments (PL 99-457) contained new provisions regarding the use of technology, as well as mandated the design and adaptation of technology for the use in teaching students with disabilities. Furthermore, the law directed the U.S. Department of Education to promote the use of new technology, media, and materials in the education of students by way of agreements between education agencies and institutions (Behrmann, Morrissette, & McCallen, 1992). In addition, the current use of technology in education for individuals with disabilities was to be studied, and more effective uses were to be determined and developed through research and demonstration projects. In PL 99-457, federal priorities also changed; the primary emphasis on research and development shifted to focus on priorities for training personnel in special education technology.

Although the administration's OSEP funding priorities directed funding to assistive and special education technology research, it was not until PL 99-457 was passed that Congress allocated funding for assistive and special education technology. In addition, OSEP continued to promote assistive and special education technology through administrative policy interpretations. A 1990 policy letter from the director of OSEP clarified the right of a child with a disability to use and be provided with assistive and special education technology devices and services under PL 94-142, as amended in PL 99-457. The letter stated clearly that schools must provide assistive technology in children's IEPs when appropriate. However, this policy was largely ignored as it was not legislated or passed as a formal regulation. It did, however, provide the basis for the legislative language in the next set of amendments to PL 94-142.

Under the Part H (Early Intervention for Infants, Toddlers and Families amendment) program, there was a focus on appropriate statewide early intervention services for infants and toddlers (birth to age 3) with disabilities and their families. The use of assistive, orthotic, and other related devices and services to promote the acquisition of functional skills is discussed in the final regulations issued in 1989.

Developmental Disabilities Assistance and Bill of Rights Act Amendments of 1987

This act (PL 100-146) is an example of value-laden public policy that sought public opinion from individuals with disabilities. Assistive technology was added to this act during its reauthorization as a cited priority for state funding and planning for systems change. Senator Lowell Weicker sponsored this bill, which put three national goals into legislation. These well-defined goals are independence, productivity, and integration. These three concepts embody the positive impact assistive technology can have on the lives of persons with disabilities.

Independence is defined in the act as the extent to which persons with developmental disabilities exert control over their own lives. *Productivity* is defined as the perception of an individual regarding his or her contribution to both his or her own self and community, while achieving self-esteem in the process. *Integration* involves persons with disabilities having access to and using the same services and places in the community as all other persons.

In a 1990 Developmental Disabilities Council national survey of 15,000 adults with disabilities, the respondents were asked if independence, productivity, and integration were important to them and if they felt satisfied in their own levels of achievement in these areas (Peckla, 1990). The results were as follows: 75% responded that it was important for them to be independent, have control, and exercise choice; 35% felt that they had some independence in their lives; 16% were allowed to live where they chose; 78% said productivity is important; 38% felt that they were making a contribution; and 11% stated that they were completely unable to work. Another 75% said that integration is indeed important, yet only 40% felt that they had achieved community integration. These statistics emphasize the need to make assistive technology available to all persons with disabilities and to integrate it into their lives.

Similar state-level findings were discovered in a consumer satisfaction survey conducted in Virginia by the Virginia Commonwealth School of Rehabilitation Counseling in 1989 (Goalder, Martin, Hecks, Gandy, & Jarrell, 1989). More than 50 surveyors interviewed 309 Virginians with a broad range of disabilities using the same instrument described previously. The Executive Summary states that community integration was rated by more than 80% of adults interviewed as being important to their lives. High levels of need were indicated for income and food assistance, financial management assistance, private health insurance, payment for medication, and payment or provision of medical equipment. Although 8 out of every 10 persons with disabilities sampled endorsed independence as an important life value, more than one half of these same individuals characterized themselves as dependent.

This survey reinforces the need for improved funding alternatives to assist persons with disabilities in acquiring assistive technology and related services.

Medicaid Amendments for Special Education Related Services of 1988

These amendments (PL 100-360) passed in 1988 ended a long-standing conflict of assistive technology funding between Medicaid and local school districts. These amendments come under the Medicare Catastrophic Coverage Act of 1988 (PL 100-360). With the Medicaid Amendments, states now have the option of including special education and related services under Part B of IDEA, and services included under Part H of this law are Medicaid-reimbursable services within the state's Medicaid plan. A broad funding option for a full range of assistive technology services was provided through these amendments without adding additional burden to state and local special education budgets.

Technology-Related Assistance for Individuals with Disabilities Act of 1988

The purpose of this law (PL 100-407) was to increase the capacity to provide assistive technology devices and services to individuals with disabilities. Specifically, its purposes were to increase awareness of assistive technology needs for devices and services; increase awareness of existing policies, practices, and procedures; increase availability of and provision of funding mechanisms; increase awareness of the benefits of assistive technology to individuals with disabilities, their families, service providers, employers, and others; increase the ability of public and private organizations to provide assistive technology services and devices; increase coordination among state agencies to provide assistive technology assistance and assistive technology devices and services; and increase the probability that individuals with disabilities, regardless of age or severity of disability, would be able to access and maintain assistive technology devices (PL 407 [2(b)(1)]).

Medicaid Early and Periodic Screening, Diagnosis, and Treatment Amendments of 1989

PL 101-238 requires all states to provide children from birth to 21 years of age who are receiving, or who are eligible to receive, Medicaid with "medically necessary" diagnostic and treatment services for any physical or mental disability identified during screening or assessment. These amendments provide for a broad funding of assistive technology devices and services, even if they are not identified in the state's Medicaid plan.

Americans with Disabilities Act of 1990

PL 101-336 provides direct references to assistive technology within each of the four titles of the act. The ADA extends federal civil rights to protect persons with disabilities from discrimination in the workplace and to provide them with equal access in many other areas, including public services and accommodations, transportation, and telecommunications. This act requires employers who receive federal funding to provide "reasonable accommodation" to persons with disabilities to enable them to perform work for which they are qualified. In Titles I and III, the purchase and modification of equipment needed to perform a job is included in the definition of "reasonable accommodation." ADA is considered a civil rights bill rather than a funding bill, as it attempts to promote the integration of assistive technology as a civil right for all persons with disabilities (West, 1991).

Individuals with Disabilities Education Act of 1990

The passage of PL 101-476, IDEA, provided a new title for PL 94-142. IDEA protects the rights of children with disabilities, recognizes greater variability in the population of persons with disabilities, and emphasizes the child, not his or her disability. In order to promote accountability, IDEA specifically permits states and departments of education to be sued by private citizens for noncompliance. In the past, they had immunity under the 11th Amendment of the Constitution. With regard to assistive and special education technology, IDEA "provides that if a child with a disability requires assistive technology devices or services, or both, in order to receive a free *appropriate* public education, the public agency shall ensure that the assistive technology devices or services are made available to that child, either as special education, related services, or as supplementary aids and services that enable a child with a disability to be educated in regular classes. Determinations of whether a child with a disability requires assistive/special education technology devices or services under this program must be made on an individual basis through applicable individualized education program (IEP) and placement procedures." IDEA also provides funding for research and training on assistive technology, confirming its commitment, which had been initiated by previous administrative and congressional policies, to this area.

There are also implications for assistive technology that are related to other federal initiatives and priorities. For example, recent priorities from the Office of Special Education and Rehabilitative Services have included an emphasis on "transition to work." Children with disabilities will become adults with disabilities, and they must be provided with the opportunities to compete in a technology-based marketplace. Therefore, assistive technology can conceivably be required as a part of the transition plan in the IEP.

IDEA, along with other federal and state legislation, has utilized definitions of assistive technology devices and services that were developed in another important federal legislative initiative, the Tech Act of 1988.

Rehabilitation Act Amendments of 1992

These amendments, PL 102-569, refer to the ADA and the Tech Act of 1988 for definitions of assistive technology, rehabilitation technology, and extended services. This law states that disability is "a natural part of human experience" and uses the term *empower* for the first time in federal disability legislation. The values contained in this legislation confirm a clear redirection in policy for individuals with disabilities. Concepts such as informed choice and self-determination, inclusion, integration, full participation, and support for the involvement of the family are representative of this movement away from the medical and isolationist philosophies of previous years.

The Rehabilitation Act Amendments require each state rehabilitation agency to 1) describe how a broad range of rehabilitation technology services will be provided at each stage of the rehabilitation process; 2) describe how a broad range of such rehabilitation technology services will be provided on a statewide basis; 3) describe the rehabilitation technology training that will be provided to rehabilitation counselors, client assistance personnel, and other related services personnel; and 4) describe the manner in which devices and services will be provided, or how worksite assessments will be made as part of the assessment for determining eligibility and or needs of an individual. This comprehensive directive represents the growing importance that assistive technology will have in the rehabilitation process in the future.

CONCLUSION

The early 1990s have been noteworthy because of the unprecedented progress that has been made in the availability of devices to individuals with disabilities (Enders, 1990). The increased attention to the role of assistive technology in improving the functional needs of these persons can be attributed to many events. The passage of the Tech Act of 1988 and the establishment of technology projects across the United States have been central to this increase in public awareness. The development of technology in the form of new products such as computer accommodations, mobility enhancements, and augmentative communications are just a few of the areas of innovation. It is likely that the momentum currently being demonstrated through the development of new technology will continue to improve the lives of many individuals with disabilities (Roessler, 1986).

REFERENCES

Allan, W. (1958). *Rehabilitation: A community challenge.* New York: John Wiley.

Americans with Disabilities Act (ADA) of 1990, PL 101-336. (July 26, 1990). Title 42, U.S.C. 12101 et seq: *U.S. Statutes at Large, 104,* 327–378.

Behrmann, M.M., Morrissette, S.K., & McCallen, M.H. (1992). *Assistive technology issues for Virginia schools.* Paper submitted to the Virginia State Special Education Advisory Committee, Richmond.

Beirne-Smith, M., Patton, J.R., & Ittenbach, R. (1994). *Mental retardation.* New York: Macmillan.

Berkowitz, E. (1987). *Disabled policy: America's programs for the handicapped.* New York: Cambridge University Press.

DeJong, G. (1979). *The movement for independent living: Origins, ideology, and implications for disability research.* East Lansing: University Centers for International Rehabilitation, Michigan State University.

Developmental Disabilities Assistance and Bill of Rights Act of 1975, PL 94-103. (October 4, 1975). Title 42, U.S.C. 6000 et seq: *U.S. Statutes at Large, 89,* 486–507.

Developmental Disabilities Assistance and Bill of Rights Act Amendments of 1987, PL 100-146. (October 29, 1987). Title 42, U.S.C. 6000 et seq: *U.S. Statutes at Large, 101,* 840–859.

Education for All Handicapped Children Act of 1975, PL 94-142. (August 23, 1977). Title 20, U.S.C. 1401 et seq: *U.S. Statutes at Large, 89r,* 773–796.

Education of the Handicapped Act Amendments of 1986, PL 99-457. (October 8, 1986). Title 20, U.S.C. 1400 et seq: *U.S. Statutes at Large, 100,* 1145—1177.

Employment Opportunity for Disabled Americans Act of 1986, PL 99-643. (October 16, 1986). Title 42, U.S.C. 1382 et seq: *U.S. Statutes at Large, 100,* 3575–3580.

Enders, A. (1989). Funding for assistive technology and related services: An annotated bibliography. *Physical and Occupational Therapy in Pediatrics, 10*(2), 147–173.

Enders, A. (1990). Ensuring technology reaches those who can benefit by it. In RESNA Press (Ed.), *Assistive technology sourcebook* (3rd ed.) (pp. 67–79). Washington, DC: RESNA Press.

Erlanger, H., & Roth, W. (1985). Disability policy: The parts and the whole. *American Behavioral Scientist, 28*(3), 319–346.

Goalder, J., Martin, E.D., Hecks, M., Gandy, G.L., & Jarrell, G.R. (1989). *Life patterns: A report on life and satisfaction of Virginians with developmental disabilities.* Richmond: School of Rehabilitative Counseling, Virginia Commonwealth University.

Haber, L. (1985). Trends and demographic studies on programs or disabled persons. In L.G. Perlman & G.F. Austin (Eds.), *Social influences in rehabilitation planning: Blueprint for the 21st century* (pp. 20–23). Arlington, VA: National Rehabilitation Association.

Individuals with Disabilities Education Act (IDEA) of 1990, PL 101-476. (October 30, 1990). Title 20, U.S.C. 1400 et seq: *U.S. Statutes at Large, 104,* 1103–1151.

Kanner, L. (1964). *A history of the care and study of the mentally retarded.* Springfield, IL: Charles C Thomas.

Kessler, H. (1953). *Rehabilitation of the physically disabled.* New York: Columbia University Press.

Lenihan, J. (1977). Disabled Americans: A history [Bicentennial issue]. *Performance, 27* (pp. 5–7). Washington, DC: The President's Committee on Employment of the Handicapped.

Levitan, S., Magnum, G., & Marshall, R. (1976). *Human resources and labor markets.* New York: Harper & Row.

Martin, E.D., Jr., & Gandy, G.L. (1987). Philosophical and educational considerations: Foundations of the rehabilitation process. In G.L. Gandy, E.D. Martin, Jr., R.E. Hardy, & J.G. Cull (Eds.), *Rehabilitation counseling and services: Profession and process* (pp. 55–66). Springfield, IL: Charles C Thomas.

Medicaid Amendments for Special Education Related Services of 1988, PL 100-360. (July 1, 1988). Title 42, U.S.C. 1395 et seq: *U.S. Statutes at Large, 102,* 683–817.

Medicaid Early and Periodic Screening, Diagnosis, and Treatment Amendments of 1989, Omnibus Budget Reconciliation Act of 1989, PL 101-239. (December 19, 1989). Title 42, U.S.C. 1396 et seq: *U.S. Statutes at Large, 103,* 2253–2273.

Medicare Catastrophic Coverage Act of 1988, PL 100-360. Title 42, U.S.C. 1305 et seq: *U.S. Statutes at Large, 102,* 683–817.

Obermann, C. (1965). *A history of vocational rehabilitation in America.* Minneapolis, MN: Dennison.

Peckla, J. (1990). *Forging a New Era; 1990 Report on Persons with Disabilities.* Washington, DC: National Association of Developmental Disability Councils.

Popick, B. (1967). Social Security and rehabilitation: On the move. *Journal of Rehabilitation, 33*(3), 10–12.

Rehabilitation Act of 1973, PL 93-112. (September 26, 1973). Title 29, U.S.C. 701 et seq: *U.S. Statutes at Large, 87,* 355–394.

Rehabilitation, Comprehensive Services, and Developmental Disabilities Amendments of 1978, PL 95-602. (November 6, 1978). Title 29, U.S.C. 701 et seq: *U.S. Statutes at Large, 92,* 2955–3017.

Rehabilitation Act Amendments of 1986, PL 99-506. (October 21, 1986). Title 29, U.S.C. 701 et seq: *U.S. Statutes at Large, 100,* 1807–1846.

Rehabilitation Act Amendments of 1992, PL 102-569. (October 29, 1992). Title 29, U.S.C. 701 et seq: *U.S. Statutes at Large, 100,* 4344–4488.

Roessler, R. (1986). Technology utilization in rehabilitation. *Rehabilitation Literature, 47*(7/8), 170–173.

Rubin, S., & Roessler, R. (1987). *Foundations of the vocational rehabilitation process.* Austin, TX: PRO-ED.

Rusalem, H. (1976). A personalized social history of vocational rehabilitation in America. In H. Rusalem & D. Malikin (Eds.), *Contemporary vocational rehabilitation* (pp. 29–45). New York: New York University Press.

Simpson, J. (1994, February/March). Tech Act: Reauthorized. *Word from Washington,* pp. 7–9. Washington, DC: United Cerebral Palsy Associations.

Skelley, T. (1980). National developments in rehabilitation: A rehabilitation services administration perspective. *Rehabilitation Counseling Journal, 24,* 24–33.

Smith-Fess Act of 1920, PL 67-236. (June 27, 1920). Title 29, U.S.C. 31 et seq: *U.S. Statutes at Large, 40,* 1379–1380.

Social Security Act of 1935, PL 74-271. (August 14, 1935). Title 42, U.S.C. 301 et seq: *U.S. Statutes at Large, 15,* 687–1774.

Social Security Act Amendments of 1956, PL 84-880. (August 1, 1956). Title 42, U.S.C. 101 et seq: *U.S. Statutes at Large, 49,* 807–856.

Social Security Act Amendments of 1965, PL 89-97. (July 30, 1965). Title 42, U.S.C. 101 et seq: *U.S. Statutes at Large, 79,* 288–410.

Taylor, S. (1988). Caught in the continuum: A critical analysis of the principle of least restrictive environment. *Journal of The Association for Persons with Severe Handicaps, 13*(1), 41–53.

Technology-Related Assistance for Individuals with Disabilities Act of 1988, PL 100-407. (August 19, 1988). Title 29, U.S.C. 2201 et seq: *U.S. Statutes at Large, 102,* 1044–1065.

Technology-Related Assistance for Individuals with Disabilities Act of 1994, PL 103-218. (March 9, 1994). Title 29, U.S.C. 2201 et seq: *U.S. Statutes at Large, 108,* 50–97.

U.S. Commission on Civil Rights. (1983). *Accommodating the spectrum of individuals with disabilities.* Washington, DC: Author.

Vocational Rehabilitation Act of 1918, PL 65-178. (June 27, 1918). Title 16, U.S.C. 486A–486W, *U.S. Statutes at Large, 40,* 617.

Vocational Rehabilitation Amendments Act of 1943, PL 113 (July 6, 1943). Title 29, U.S.C. 3141 et seq: *U.S. Statutes at Large, 57,* 374–380.

Vocational Rehabilitation Act Amendments of 1954, PL 82-565. (August 3, 1954). Title 36, U.S.C. 155 et seq: *U.S. Statutes at Large, 68,* 652–665.

Vocational Rehabilitation Act Amendments of 1965, PL 89-333. (November 8, 1965). Title 1, U.S.C. 101 et seq: *U.S. Statutes at Large, 79,* 1282–1294.

West, J. (1991). *The Americans with Disabilities Act: From policy to practice.* New York: Milbank Memorial Fund.

Wolfensberger, W. (1975). *The origin and nature of our institutional models.* Syracuse, NY: Human Policy Press.

Yanok, J. (1986). Free appropriate public education for handicapped children: Congressional intent and judicial interpretation. *RASE, 7,* 49–53.

2

Development of Assistive Technology Systems
Evaluation of Federal Initiative

Becky Hayward
Michael D. Tashjian
Paul Wehman

Sam was in a motorcycle accident at the age of 24, which resulted in a severe traumatic brain injury and accompanying physical disabilities with cognitive deficits. He has right-side hemiplegia with little use of his upper right extremities; there is some left-hand ataxia with limitations of fine motor behavior. His walking skills are limited, and he has poor balance. Sam becomes tired quickly and has limited short-term memory.

Sam's vocational evaluation after his injury regarding reentry into the competitive work force was dismal; however, he continued to be interested in finding some type of work, particularly in the area of data processing. Two years after his injury, Sam was referred for supported employment services and an assistive technology workup. After assessing his skills and interests, the assistive technology staff helped Sam to acquire a job as a data entry operator at a bank in his community. His duties consisted of taking incoming calls from local vendors and routing orders to the appropriate distribution centers via a computer terminal. He earned $6.75 per hour and worked 32 hours per week.

Sam had several problems to overcome before he could be a successful data entry operator. For example, he was unable to keep up with the high rate of incoming calls because of his physical and cognitive limitations. Contributing to his slower work speed was his inability to press the shift key while pressing other keys simultaneously. Also, Sam experienced periods of increased extraneous movement caused by his ataxia and limited motor skills.

The supported employment specialist arranged for the assistive technology staff to visit the worksite. One adaptation that the staff suggested was a wooden lapboard built to fit Sam's desk chair. This board expanded his work space and stabilized his ataxia. A map of the city was laminated, and tabs were added to the edge of the pages of the guidebook to make turning them easier. Finally, with the assistance of a design expert a shift-key adaptation was added to the computer keyboard that allowed uppercase letters to be typed with one hand.

The development of this chapter was supported in part by Contract No. HN910-24-001 from the U.S. Department of Education, National Institute on Disability and Rehabilitation Research (NIDRR). The opinions expressed are solely those of the authors, and no official endorsement by NIDRR should be inferred.

Sam has been a data entry operator for almost 3 years and has earned more than $15,000. More important, he has begun to gain access to a variety of recreational outlets within the community and has made new friends at work and in the apartment complex where he now lives.

The use of a supported employment specialist and an assistive technology team working together for the common purpose of integrating Sam into the work force is an example of how a local system can be effective in helping a consumer with a severe disability. However, two questions remain: First, how many similar systems have been established locally across the United States? Second, how many of the 50 states are able to gather and organize the appropriate resources to assist persons such as Sam who are in need of the newest technologies?

Sowers and Powers (1991) talk about the many commercially made technologies that are available to persons with physical disabilities. They indicate, for example, that computer technology will become a major area of focus for those individuals involved in delivering assistive technology services. They estimate that 75% of all employment during the latter 1990s and early 2000s will involve the use of computers. Sowers and Powers provide a number of different ways that the computer can be modified using assistive technology (e.g., keyguards, large and small keyboards, voice-activated input and output innovations). Furthermore, they note that telephone technologies, environmental controls, and robotics are additional devices that persons with assistive technology needs will be able to gain access to. Other specialized devices that will be greatly utilized include height-adjustable wheelchairs, circular rotating desks, and automatic page turners. These examples are only some of the additional types of devices that will be used in community living situations and employment (Behrmann & Schepis, 1994; Wehman, Wood, Everson, Goodwyn, & Conley, 1988).

The reader may be asking why these different devices and technologies are presented in the context of a systems change chapter. The reason is that no system is viable unless it has the content to deliver. That is, a system is nothing more than a shell, having little value without product content. An assistive technology system needs to have innovative devices and appropriate ways to deliver those devices, or they will lose their utility to consumers.

This chapter discusses and explores how to develop and/or change systems that are not effective in delivering human services to persons with severe disabilities. Specifically, there are two main goals of this chapter. The first is to provide a focus on how to deliver assistive technology services to persons who have severe disabilities. These persons may be individuals who have severe traumatic brain injuries, such as Sam, or who have severe cerebral palsy or who are elderly, having degenerative arthritis. There are many types of people who could benefit from the advances that have been made in assistive technology. These advances, however, are of limited value if they cannot be directly delivered to the persons in need. The second goal of this chapter is to describe the efficacy of the Technology-Related Assistance for Individuals with Disabilities Act of 1988 (PL 100-407) on creating assistive technology systems in the 49 funded states (Arizona is not funded). A variety of evaluation outcomes are described based on an analysis of different states.

CRITICAL ELEMENTS OF ESTABLISHING A SYSTEM

American Heritage Second College Edition (1985) defines a system as "a group of interacting, interrelated, or interdependent elements forming a complex whole" (p. 1234). There are numerous ways to approach the development of a statewide system. However, after reviewing a number of different references and materials (Gardner & Chapman, 1993; Wehman & Moon, 1988), five major components or elements have been identified:

1. Create employment and community living opportunities.
2. Develop local service providers and related personnel.
3. Establish state systems.
4. Build consensus in participation.
5. Manage statewide development of assistive technology systems.

These are generic elements in the sense that they can be used in both a local or state area, as well as in urban, suburban, or predominately rural areas. A description of each of these five components follows.

Create Employment and Community Living Opportunities

In order to make a system viable, opportunities must be present. For example, in order to ensure that assistive technology resources can be timely and useful, employment and community living opportunities must be available within the state.

Promote Private and Public Sector Jobs

Private and public sector jobs need to be developed for persons with disabilities. It is not enough to assume that these jobs will simply emerge without a strong effort to promote and plan meetings with business and government officials. The public sector, in particular, is an untapped source of employment, and most public sector positions are required to be highly accessible and open to hiring persons with disabilities.

Provide Incentives to Generate Local Employment Opportunities

In some communities, tax credits, subsidies, and other financial incentives are provided to businesses to purposely enhance employment of persons with disabilities. There are also other ways to establish hiring incentives that are not always financial in origin. For example, public recognition may be an additional incentive that can be used to open the doors for employment.

Promote Independent Living and Supported Living Options

A viable assistive technology system will be receptive to an array of independent living and supported living options. No one particular type of residential option can be forced on consumers. Most individuals with disabilities prefer to live in their own homes with as much support as possible; however, what is most important in establishing the assistive technology system is that there are, in fact, an array of independent living options available within the system.

Provide Barrier-Free Transportation and Accessibility to Community Facilities

The Americans with Disabilities Act (ADA) of 1990 (PL 101-336) provides for enhanced accessibility through transportation and open facilities (those considered easy for people with physical disabilities to move through) (Turner, 1994; Wehman, 1992). Unfortunately, most transportation options and community facilities traditionally have not been accessible. The establishment of a viable assistive technology system will be a substantial means of increasing this type of accessibility. It is almost impossible for persons with disabilities to become empowered if they cannot move freely within the community. The greatest strength of assistive technology will be to enhance this mobility.

Develop Local Service Providers and Related Personnel

Even with the establishment of an array of opportunities in a given state, such as those mentioned in the previous section, a system cannot function effectively without competent providers.

Identify Training Needs and Personnel

Most individuals currently working in the rehabilitation area know very little about assistive technology. Many communities have not assessed the assistive technology needs of consumers, which makes it difficult to determine the appropriate training needs and provide specialized personnel.

Provide Program Development and Start-Up Grants

One way to establish capacity for assistive technology in local communities is to provide small grants. These grants can be used to "seed" innovative ideas and also as leverage to obtain other resources. A viable assistive technology system will be greatly enhanced by coordinating program elements that already exist within the community.

Provide Coordinated Technical Assistance

In an effective assistive technology system, there will be an opportunity for both service providers and consumers to request technical assistance. This can be helpful in designing the necessary materials or equipment for consumers. In addition, information and referral systems can be established so that assistance can be most efficiently provided based on the level of need.

Establish State Systems

Once steps are taken to create viable employment and living opportunities and a cadre of trained personnel is established within the state, it will be necessary for systems and subsystems to be coordinated. Lack of this coordination often causes many systems to break down. Most states have some employment and living opportunities available and some trained personnel; however, a coordinated focus of effective and efficient subsystems is lacking (Hayden & Abery, 1994).

Identify Target Populations and Establish Funding Agencies, Responsibilities, and Authority for Assistive Technology

In order to develop a statewide system, target populations of persons who need assistive technology must be identified. This can be done, of course, if a number of local programs have already completed the necessary planning. There are a variety of funding agencies that might be responsible for funding. These could include the state department of rehabilitative services, the health department, or developmental disability agencies.

Establish Funding Formulas in Systems Across Agencies

Once the system is established, funding formulas and ways for consumers and agencies to gain access to money will be necessary. This information must be communicated to all potential recipients of services. A Request for Proposal format or a formula arrangement based on the number of persons participating in a given program may be used.

Implement Referral Service Planning and Coordination System

One of the most overlooked aspects of any system is ensuring that there is a continual flow of consumers for the service. Although most needs assessments will sufficiently identify numbers of persons who could use services, this does not mean that these persons will discover the system and use it on a regular basis. Although this may seem paradoxical, it happens all too often. Consumers are unaware that services are available, or they may find them too expensive or difficult to gain access to. A referral service planning coordination system is an important means of communication about the services and access to those services.

Develop and Maintain Systems for Quality Assurance

Most persons who have worked in human services systems are aware that, even though the systems have been created, the level of quality is often poor. Typically, some of a system's program activities are effective and well received; yet in other areas of the system, they are either nonexistent or highly inconsistent in the way they are delivered. A viable system of assistive technology will have built-in safeguards for quality assurance. These safeguards should be driven by consumer satisfaction and regular feedback concerning the services (Albin, 1992).

Build Consensus in Participation

Even with the previous three elements, if there is not a strong grass roots interest in using the resources that are offered, the system will lie dormant. Therefore, concurrent with the establishment of a system, it is essential that consensus is developed and that participation by the users occurs.

Include Creative Participation of Individuals with Disabilities and Their Advocates

Persons with disabilities are the end users of an assistive technology system. To fully utilize this system, the end users must have ownership in it and be aware of what the system can do to help them. If a person in a wheelchair does not know that there is accessible public transportation in the neighborhood, this transportation will remain underutilized.

Provide Public Information

Placing advertisements in the community, in newspapers, and on television and radio is another way to distribute information on assistive technology systems. The more that persons in the community know about the availability of such a system, the greater the likelihood for its use.

Manage Statewide Development of Assistive Technology Systems

The best system of assistive technology must still be managed and controlled, whether the state is the size of Rhode Island or California. There are safeguards and quality assurances that need to be implemented, along with a structure that allows for careful organization of all activities and resources.

Establish and Maintain Planning and Monitoring Processes

A process for operating the system needs to be developed, written down, and communicated to the end users and service providers. There must be rules and regulatory procedures to be followed.

Maintain Implementation Processes

One function of appropriate monitoring will be that of maintaining effective implementation across the system. Getting the system up and in place is one thing; maintaining its momentum, funding, resources, and quality is quite another. For example, in many states, the economic downturn has adversely affected the implementation of established supported employment systems.

The previously described system process for assistive technology is essentially a prototype of a human services system that can be established in any state or region. It is essential for implementation that all five of these elements be developed concurrently with participation from multiple participants who represent many different interests. The consensus of these participants must be coordinated in such a way that the system continues to grow and evolve. Although the system might only be 20%–30% developed, if coordinated in the right way it will still be tremendously useful to consumers.

The following section describes how assistive technology systems are developing in various states. Figure 2.1 shows when 49 states, Puerto Rico, and American Samoa were funded. Obviously, a large government investment has been made in assistive technology. The question remains as to how effective these assistive technology systems have been. Are states responding appropriately? Are assistive technology systems working for consumers? The balance of this chapter is devoted to reporting the results of an in-depth study that examines the answers to these questions.

EVALUATION OF THE FEDERAL INITIATIVE ON ASSISTIVE TECHNOLOGY

The Technology-Related Assistance for Individuals with Disabilities Act (Tech Act) of 1988 (PL 100-407) required the U.S. Secretary of Education to conduct a national evaluation of state grants funded under the act and to submit a report to Congress in 1992. The National Institute on Disability and Rehabilitation Research (NIDRR) of the U.S. Department of Education awarded a contract to the Research Triangle Institute (RTI) in October 1991 to conduct

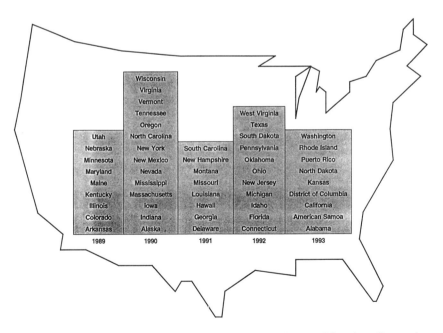

Figure 2.1.   Funding sequence of the 49 states, Puerto Rico, and American Samoa for systems change.

the study. The remainder of this chapter summarizes the findings of this study regarding the activities and effectiveness of the assistive technology program and individual state projects in implementing comprehensive, consumer-responsive, and statewide programs.

Study Context

Since the initial passage of the Tech Act of 1988, federal policymakers have expressed concern about the availability of technology-related assistance to persons with disabilities. This concern has led to several important federal initiatives designed to apply technological innovations to address the needs of persons with disabilities toward increased personal, social, and economic independence. For example, in 1972 the Rehabilitation Services Administration established the Rehabilitation Engineering Centers program to develop assistive technology for persons with disabilities. A continuing perception of the need among persons with disabilities for technology-related assistance has also resulted in specifications in the Rehabilitation Act Amendments of 1992 (PL 102-569). These specifications require the state and federal vocational rehabilitation (VR) service program, the largest federally supported rehabilitation program, to develop the capacity to identify and meet the technology-related needs of its clients.

Despite these and other initiatives, assistive technology services and devices remain unavailable to large numbers of individuals with disabilities and their families. Moreover, state and federal agencies, as well as public and private sector service providers, often lack the awareness, information, and skills needed to implement mandates to incorporate assistive technology services into individualized education programs and rehabilitation plans and to adequately address client needs for technology-related assistance. To improve this situation, Congress enacted the Tech Act of 1988 to build national capacity to provide appropriate technology-related assistance, including devices, services, information, and expertise, to all persons with disabilities. The specific purposes of the Tech Act of 1988 are to

- Support grants to states for implementation of statewide, comprehensive, and consumer-responsive programs of technology-related assistance.
- Reduce federal barriers to financing of needed technology.
- Improve federal capacity to provide technical assistance and other capacity-building support to the states.

Although the enabling legislation recognizes a federal role in removing federal barriers, providing technical assistance, and otherwise supporting state efforts, primary responsibility for planning and implementing the technology-related assistance program rests with the individual states. In 1989, NIDRR awarded a contract to the Rehabilitation Engineering Society of North American (RESNA) to provide training and technical assistance to states that succeeded in securing an NIDRR grant. The Tech Act of 1988 also requires the agency, office, or other entity that will apply for and administer the NIDRR grant to be designated by the governor of a state. Thus, state technology assistance projects are being implemented and administered within a variety of structural and organizational contexts.

Title I of the statute provides that NIDRR award 3-year development grants to states on a competitive basis for a minimum of $500,000 per year. In 1989, the first nine state grants were awarded and are referred to as Phase I projects. An additional 14 grants were awarded in the program's second year (Phase II projects) and eight more grants in fiscal year (FY) 1991 (Phase III projects). Eleven projects funded by FY 1992 were not included in the national evaluation. States that demonstrate sufficient progress in developing statewide systems of technology assistance during the first 3 years are eligible to apply for 2-year extension grants.

The overriding purpose of each state project supported under the Tech Act of 1988 is to develop a statewide, comprehensive, consumer-responsive program of technology-related assistance for all persons with disabilities. More specifically, the act lists seven objectives to be pursued by each project:

(A) increase awareness of the needs of individuals with disabilities for assistive technology devices and services;

(B) increase awareness of policies, practices, and procedures that facilitate or impede availability or provision of assistive technology devices and assistive technology services;

(C) increase the availability of and funding for the provision of assistive technology devices and assistive technology services for persons with disabilities;

(D) increase awareness and knowledge of the efficacy of assistive technology devices and assistive technology services among individuals with disabilities, the families or representatives of individuals with disabilities, individuals who work for public agencies and private entities that have contact with individuals with disabilities (including insurers), employers, and other appropriate individuals;

(E) increase the capacity of public and private entities to provide technology-related assistance, particularly assistive technology devices and assistive technology services, and to pay for the provision of assistive technology devices and assistive technology services;

(F) increase coordination among state agencies and public and private entities that provide technology-related assistance, particularly assistive technology devices and assistive technology services; and

(G) increase the probability that individuals of all ages with disabilities will to the extent appropriate, be able to secure and maintain possession of assistive technology devices as such individuals make the transition between services offered by human service agencies for between settings of daily living (PL 100-407 §2[b][1])

As a review of these objectives indicates, the program is intended to have a strong systems change orientation, with increases in awareness, knowledge, and coordination of the outcomes of grantee activities. However, states have considerable flexibility in determining how best to pursue the legislated objectives of the program. Some states may emphasize an explicit *systems change approach* that places a priority on removing policy and financial barriers and improving coordination among consumers, service providers, and government agencies. Other states may opt for a *service delivery approach,* which dictates that the bulk of project resources be used to purchase devices, provide assessments, or otherwise attempt to address immediate consumer needs for technology assistance. This approach holds the view that changes in the system will follow increased service capacity. Still other states may implement a project that incorporates both systems change and direct service components.

In addressing one or more of the seven statutory purposes identified in the preceding paragraph, grantees are authorized to conduct specific activities and perform certain functions also identified in the enabling legislation. In all, the Tech Act of 1988 describes 11 functions and 7 activities that state projects may pursue. However, in addition to those activities and functions specifically identified within the act, grantees are also authorized to conduct any activity that is necessary for developing, implementing, or evaluating the program. Thus, states retain the flexibility necessary to implement a project that best responds to the unique needs and conditions of persons with disabilities.

Evaluation of Assistive Technology Systems

The national evaluation of state grants, conducted by the U.S. Secretary of Education and funded under the Tech Act of 1988 (Section 107[a] and [b]), was submitted to Congress in 1992. NIDRR awarded a contract to RTI in October 1991 to conduct the evaluation, which was designed to

- Evaluate the effectiveness of the technology assistance program and individual state projects in implementing technology-related assistance programs that are comprehensive, consumer-responsive, and statewide.
- Assess the effects of these programs on individuals with disabilities.
- Develop recommendations for consideration by NIDRR regarding improvement of the technology assistance program.

To ensure that these purposes were fully addressed, a preliminary conceptual framework for the evaluation was developed with several broadly focused research questions to guide subsequent study activities.

- What configuration of services and activities have grantees undertaken to meet the purpose of the act, and what effects can these configurations, or models, be expected to have on availability and use of technology-related assistance?
- How are the programs operating in the field, and how do organizational and contextual factors affect their likelihood of success?
- To what extent has implementation of technology-related assistance programs improved the likelihood that persons with disabilities will accomplish their goals in education, employment, independent living, and community integration?
- What are the most effective strategies for ensuring the institutionalization of comprehensive, statewide, and consumer-responsive programs of technology assistance throughout the United States, and what actions might NIDRR and Congress consider to ensure that the purposes of the act are accomplished?

In the following section, an overview of the methods employed to obtain and analyze the information needed to respond to these questions is provided.

Evaluation Methods

The RTI evaluation was initiated with a comprehensive review of existing documentation for the 31 state projects funded under the Tech Act of 1988 through FY 1991. The authors' examination of the projects' original and continuation applications, progress reports, and self-evaluation plans enabled them to develop preliminary profiles of the intended focus, organization, activities, and expected outcomes of each assistive technology project. To facilitate preparation of these profiles, matrices were developed that associated each planned project activity with one or more of the seven purposes of the technology assistance program. These activities, matrices, and preliminary project profiles formed the basis for the articulation of models, or configuration of activities, that are now being used by funded projects to address the purposes of the Tech Act of 1988.

To ensure the quality and usefulness of these early study activities, as well as all subsequent study tasks and products, a work group was established. This work group comprised expert consumers and consumer representatives who were experienced with national and state assistive technology programs. Their job was to critique study procedures and products.

After document review and pretests of procedures, a protocol was developed for on-site data collection and site visits of each of the 23 Phase I and Phase II states. The purpose of these visits was to obtain detailed information on program organization, administration, funding, staffing, activities, effects, and so on. At each site, interviews were conducted with program staff, subcontractor staff (as appropriate), advisory council members, and other relevant state officials; project records and documentation were reviewed; and project operations were observed.

In four of the states (two Phase I and two Phase II), detailed case studies were conducted of project implementation and outcomes to examine the projects' effects on persons with disabilities. An assessment of the extent to which persons with disabilities were involved in program planning, implementation, and decision making regarding program objectives and activities and the extent of benefits derived as a result of program activities and services was also an important component of the data collection.

At the conclusion of each site visit, reports were developed that expanded on the preliminary profile of the site and provided a comprehensive discussion of project focus, staffing, funding, organization, location, activities, services, target populations, consumer involvement, and future plans. In addition to identifying actual project status and outcomes in each area, each report identified outcomes that the project might reasonably achieve by the end of its first 3 years of operation. Finally, the information obtained was synthesized across all 31 projects to develop an overview of the program, as it exists in the United States, to assess its effects on persons with disabilities, and to develop recommendations regarding program improvement for consideration by NIDRR.

A final component of the study was to assess grantee responses to the self-evaluation requirements imposed by the statute. Of particular interest in this component were 1) the nature and extent of self-evaluation activities planned by the projects, 2) the types of information collected to support the projects' self-evaluation, and 3) the projects' use of self-evaluation findings in monitoring their accomplishment of goals and objectives. The evaluation's key findings regarding the programs' operations and activities follow.

Organizational Location and Administration

A project's organizational location, although less influential to a project's success than a host of other factors (e.g., preexisting capacity in assistive technology), often does have major effects on its ability to accomplish the Tech Act's objectives within the time frame and using the resources established by Congress. For example, most projects, whether rehabilitation or education, located in state agencies reported that state-level policies, procedures, and restrictions have constrained project implementation and operations. Budget problems in some states have forced hiring freezes; civil service requirements have affected projects' latitude to hire staff in many states; and state purchasing regulations have constrained several projects' ability to buy office equipment, assistive technology for demonstration labs, or rental space. State agencies that already had strategies for overcoming such problems were generally able to implement these strategies for the assistive technology projects, suggesting that the appropriateness of location in one or another state agency probably depends on the overall quality and sophistication of that agency's officials. Location in an independent agency or at a university, which may provide a generally desirable distance from a particular service agency, may limit consumer awareness of project activities. Consumers were least likely to have had involvement with, or even to be familiar with, a project located in a university. Again, it is likely that the limitations of organizational location may vary according to type of recipient but that all imply both advantages and disadvantages in terms of progress toward the Tech Act's intent.

The strategy of extending services across the state through use of subcontracts with provider organizations or through locating project staff in regional centers has been moderately successful in expanding projects' "reach." However, most projects have not succeeded in achieving an assistive technology system that is truly statewide, as called for in the statute. Most respondents indicated the intent to make additional efforts in this area, although many were not optimistic that current levels of funding would permit full achievement of this goal.

Staffing

The scarcity of individuals experienced in the field of assistive technology prior to the establishment of the program is reflected in the difficulty that projects experienced in identifying, recruiting, and hiring staff. Frequent changes over the life of most grants in the types of job functions needed, resulting in expansion of individuals' roles or hiring of new individuals, emphasize the developmental aspects of the program. The success that most projects eventually experience in obtaining and retaining committed individuals who have learned their functions on the job suggests that the program has met at least one of the statute's purposes—increasing national capacity to meet the assistive technology needs of individuals with disabilities.

Funding

The Tech Act of 1988 stipulates a limited time period for the establishment of assistive technology systems that will meet the needs of all individuals. The fact that most projects experienced carryover in their early years suggests that Congress may want to implement an incremental scale of funding as projects engage in start-up activities, with first-year budgets substantially lower than the current $500,000 minimum. Assuming that the projects receive NIDRR funds for 5 years, each of the assistive technology projects will have received, on average, between $2.75 and $3.25 million in federal funds. Although some projects have obtained additional funds from individual states or other sources, fiscal problems in most states have generally precluded allocation of additional financial resources to the projects, although many have provided in-kind support (e.g., space, equipment). Furthermore, nearly all projects report that state financial conditions will preclude continuation of most of their current activities following the 5-year period of support. This means that systems change needs to be in place by the end of 5 years if a project's benefits are to continue over time.

Insufficient funding of assistive technology is still a critical barrier for many persons with disabilities, and without changes in public and private insurance policies it is unlikely that most states will have substantial success at creating a resource base to ensure devices and services to persons who will need them in the future. Continued federal support may be required for persons with disabilities to acquire the devices and services that they need to meet their personal and employment goals.

Consumer Involvement and Responsiveness

These findings suggest considerable project success in involving consumers as project staff and decision makers and in being responsive to consumer needs. However, consumers offered varying perspectives regarding the progress and outcomes of state assistive technology projects. One reason for this variance is related to each project's choice of focus. Many persons with disabilities have endured years of difficulty in their attempts to obtain and maintain assistive technology. The award of assistive technology grants raised expectations that individual assistive technology problems would be solved rather than developing strategies to improve the situation over time. Many consumers recognized that the grants could not support the purchase of equipment; however, some of their ideas for project activities could improve consumer responses to the projects and could enhance faith in the system's likelihood to become what it needs to be. Consumers' suggestions in this vein included establishment of demonstration and try-out services that would permit individuals to borrow devices for a period of time to determine their appropriateness before making a commitment to purchase. A case management system would assign staff to work directly with consumers on a case-by-case basis to assist them in identifying and obtaining funding for assistive technology.

These perspectives suggest that full involvement of consumers in project decision making might result in some rethinking of project activities and services. The Tech Act of 1994 (PL 103-218) emphasizes protection and advocacy and directs states to financially support these activities. States are also charged with operating consumer-responsive systems that include a more stringent evaluation process to ensure this responsiveness.

Project Focus

A key question of the evaluation was whether a systems change or service delivery model can do a better job of implementing activities that will ultimately result in full access to appropriate assistive technology devices and services for individuals with disabilities. A primary factor in answering this question is the time frame in which systems change and service delivery activities are implemented. Implementation of a service delivery model within the full 5 years of NIDRR funding essentially involves the purchase or provision of assistive technology devices and services for individuals with disabilities, resulting in an immediate response to consumer needs for as long as funding is available. However, a "pure" service delivery project can only be successful for as long as it is able to provide devices (i.e., for as long as funding is available). If the state does not assume fiscal responsibility for the project beyond the 5 years of NIDRR funding, provision of devices and services will most likely be discontinued. The extent to which a service delivery model can affect a state's capacity beyond NIDRR funding is limited to the extent to which consumers are able to influence other delivery systems to assume the project's function of providing devices and services—that is, the extent to which consumers have been empowered as their own advocates for systems change through receipt of project training and assistance during the period of NIDRR funding.

Successful implementation of a systems change model is contingent on a project's ability to establish new patterns of technology-related assistance and bring about changes in extant systems within the 5 years of NIDRR funding. Perhaps the most important accomplishment of such a project would be creation of viable sources of funding for assistive technology along with a service system that would support effective use of assistive technology devices by consumers.

Similar to service delivery projects, if the state does not assume fiscal responsibility for the project beyond the 5 years, systems change activities will cease; and, if a project has not been successful in implementing permanent changes within the 5-year funding period, there would be little to no benefit remaining from the project. Consequently, for the duration of NIDRR funding, implementation of a service delivery model seems to ensure better access to assistive technology devices and services for individuals with disabilities than does implementation of a systems change model. The extent to which a systems change model can affect capacity beyond the 5 years of NIDRR funding depends on the success of the individual project in advocating for change in the existing service delivery system.

Because of the youth of the program overall, the implications of focus for the grantees' achievement of the outcomes intended by Congress are not yet clear, as this discussion suggests. Future examination of the program can be expected to yield information on which approach appears better in terms of its likelihood to eventuate in permanent availability of sufficient assistive technology information and services to meet the needs of all persons with disabilities.

As a final note, projects pursuing one or the other project focus, as well as those contemplating changes in focus, should solicit the perspectives of consumers prior to final decisions on this issue. As noted by most consumers who participated in focus groups conducted as part of this evaluation, at least some attention to services may be key to a project's effectiveness.

Although many participants in the focus groups agreed with the importance of systems change, they also expressed a great need for services, including mechanisms for try-out periods, training in the use and maintenance of devices, and assistance in locating funding sources. Based on these perspectives and on the authors' analyses of other information collected in the evaluation, many states, particularly those with relatively limited initial capacity in assistive technology, should be encouraged to devote a portion of the grant's resources to service delivery.

Activities and Services

Regardless of the projects' primary focus on systems change or service delivery, in the early stages of the program all grantees have devoted considerable effort and resources to knowledge dissemination and awareness activities. This emphasis suggests that many projects have seen their primary responsibility to "get the word out" concerning technology assistance, with more direct systems change efforts to follow increased awareness. Certainly, the systems change projects have placed considerable emphasis on knowledge development as an avenue to improving their states' assistive technology systems.

In addition, projects that have emphasized service delivery have reported their intent to educate or empower consumers, while providing direct services to a limited number of individuals based on resource availability. The theory has been that consumers will then demand changes in the system and will be better advocates for such change with legislators and other policy makers than are assistive technology project staff. At the same time, however, knowing about technology but not being able to obtain it creates a frustration that some consumers perceive as more intense than not knowing about its existence in the first place. Thus, the program as implemented so far is characterized by a tension between responding to immediate needs for assistive technology services and pursuing longer-term benefits through changes in the overall delivery system, the full implications of which, for permanent statewide assistive technology systems, are not yet clear.

Target Populations

Most projects acknowledge that comprehensiveness—reaching all disabilities and all ages, races, ethnicities, and genders—and extension of services statewide are goals that have yet to be accomplished. Among the groups that pose a continuing challenge to many projects are elderly persons, individuals in rural areas, and persons who do not speak English. In addition, states with large Native American populations are struggling to devise strategies to improve their ability to reach these persons. Most states have been more successful at reaching children and persons of working age, particularly to the extent that the latter are known to the service system, including VR, independent living centers, and other rehabilitation service providers. Finally, many consumers reported problems in transporting assistive technology across service agencies. For these reasons, projects may need to place increased emphasis both on outreach to groups that are difficult to reach and on coordination throughout the service system.

Effects and Effectiveness

Overall, the state technology grantees have conceived and implemented a wide range of innovative strategies to address the purposes of the statute. Most grantees have made substantial progress toward these purposes. As noted earlier, the youth of the program, along with delays experienced by most projects in getting under way once they received the grant, has limited projects' achievement of their intended outcomes at this point in their grants. Most have experienced more success in achieving consumer involvement, and hence consumer responsiveness, than they have in establishing an assistive technology system that is statewide and comprehensive. Although it is too early to determine the relative efficacy of systems change versus service delivery approaches, the weight of current evidence suggests that, to meet the needs of persons with disabilities, projects will likely be more successful to the extent that they implement a combination of strategies, retaining some resources for services to individuals while focusing substantial attention on attempts to affect a system that is more responsive to the assistive technology-related needs of persons with disabilities. However, given current fiscal realities, additional federal support will likely be important to the projects' eventual success.

RECOMMENDATIONS FOR PROGRAM IMPROVEMENT

The RTI evaluation of the technology assistance program supports a number of recommendations regarding potential improvements in the program's operations that may increase the likelihood of its accomplishing the purposes of the Tech Act of 1988. These recommendations reflect our sensitivity to the current age of the program, as well as to the fiscal problems that have limited the amount of resources that states can contribute to assistive technology projects, ongoing state-level reorganizations, and other issues that can be expected to affect the operations of the state technology assistance grants.

Recommendations Based on Site Visits and on Reviews of Documents and Policies

The following recommendations are made based on data collected at site visits and on the reviews conducted on documents and policies concerning assistive technology:

- Minimize the inefficiencies associated with project initiation problems. Grants might be restructured in the following ways:
  - Inclusion of an initial period for planning and development to be time limited and funded at reduced levels
  - For projects located in state agencies or state-supported institutions, negotiation of exemptions from state requirements governing hiring and purchasing that interfere with efficient project operations
- Reduce fiscal inefficiencies associated with delayed project initiation. Implement an incremental scale of funds, with the first or second year of operations funded at less than the current $500,000. Full funding should occur in year two or year three depending on project progress.
- Increase the likelihood of meeting the needs of current consumers. NIDRR might consider revision of program requirements such that grantees are encouraged to focus a portion of resources on service delivery during the grant's early years, with the possibility of reducing the proportion allocated to direct services as system capacity increases.
- Identify activities that are useful to consumers in obtaining needed assistive technology including low-interest loan funds, try-out programs, and consumer-to-consumer networks for sharing information and equipment. Projects should be encouraged to allocate a portion of their resources to these activities.
- Ensure permanent availability of assistive technology devices and assistive technology services needed by persons with disabilities. Provisions for continuing federal support should be considered.

- Assist individuals with disabilities to identify and obtain needed funding. Federal attention should be directed toward appropriate revisions in Medicaid and Medicare provisions and in requirements governing the private insurance industry. In addition, states should be encouraged to consider adopting case management approaches for addressing the technology-related needs of individuals.

Recommendations Based on Focus Groups with Consumers

For persons with disabilities, obtaining and using assistive technology is generally a lifelong process requiring substantial energy and resourcefulness. This process comprises a number of steps, which are repeated as individuals grow and change in their needs and priorities, as technology develops, and as the environment becomes more accessible. They include identification of the potentially appropriate assistive technology device or equipment; training in its use; a try-out period during which the individual uses the assistive technology in his or her home or work environment to determine its compatibility; purchase of the device or equipment; ongoing maintenance and repair, including access to substitutes during repair as needed; and eventual replacement, which begins the process again.

The difficulty experienced by many persons with disabilities and reflected in all 11 of the focus groups is the pervasiveness of gaps in the assistive technology system and in the service system for persons with disabilities. Such gaps can occur at various points in the process, depending in part on personal characteristics, such as age, type of disability, or income level, and in part on the relative richness or poverty of human and fiscal resources in a state or locality. Major gaps in the assistive technology system generally included 1) lack of financial support to acquire necessary technology; 2) absence of mechanisms for matching equipment to individuals and the limited options that persons with disabilities have in selecting devices that best meet their needs; 3) insufficient awareness of assistive technology by service providers, employers, and parents; and 4) difficulty in obtaining maintenance and repair services in a timely and cost-efficient manner. Focus group findings (Research Triangle Institute, 1992) regarding the specific activities and accomplishments of state assistive technology projects designed to address these gaps suggest a number of recommended improvements:

Regarding the State AT Projects

- State AT projects should provide AT-related case management services to persons with disabilities. Case managers should have "information on appropriate referral sources, what is available, where to obtain training, payment structures, what Medicaid buys, what private insurance buys, what the state buys, and what nobody buys. If we don't have this information, we're in trouble." Schools and human services agencies need this information, and according to participants, the grants should be organized to provide this service.
- While many projects employ funding specialists who work to change policy and practice, what projects should be doing is employing funding specialists who work directly with consumers to arrange funding for needed AT, if more comprehensive case management is infeasible.
- Projects should implement demonstration try-out centers. (While most of the projects have demonstration labs, few have implemented procedures to permit consumers to try out equipment in time frames and environments that would permit informed choices.) To match available technology to individuals, consumers need to see the equipment, be trained to its use, take it home and try it out for a

month, and then be able to return it if it does not meet the individual's needs. Such centers could be implemented through partnerships with vendors and human service agencies, which could provide demonstration try-out equipment and fund training. Such an arrangement would help to ensure that the centers would survive following termination of NIDRR funding.

- Projects should establish mechanisms to obtain and evaluate feedback from actual and potential consumers on a regular, formalized basis. Such mechanisms might include telephone interviews with a sample of persons with disabilities residing in the state, in addition to the needs assessment and satisfaction surveys many projects already conduct.
- Projects should establish consumer-to-consumer information networks to facilitate sharing of information and experiences about AT and to enhance opportunities for personal loans, trades, or purchase of AT equipment between consumers. Electronic bulletin boards, such as those already in place in some states, are a good mechanism through which to create such a network.
- Projects should provide more training to parents, employers, and service providers. Parent training should focus on their rights to demand that schools provide services and devices that will ensure a free and appropriate education. Employer training is needed to increase knowledge of how to purchase equipment that is not unduly expensive and that fully addresses the needs of the consumer in the work place. Service provider training should focus on general awareness of the uses and benefits of AT as the field continues to evolve.

Regarding the Availability of AT to All Persons

- To protect the interests of consumers, Congress should implement national standards for AT equipment, perhaps along the lines of FCC or FDA approval, that certifies the soundness and durability of AT.
- National initiatives to educate employers as expeditiously as possible are needed as ADA is implemented. Consumers fear that employers will be enticed into making uninformed decisions regarding technology in the work place, that they will "buy junk that won't be useful." (Research Triangle Institute, 1992, pp. 17–18)

Recommendations Concerning Project Self-Evaluation Activities

The demands of planning and implementing assistive technology projects often leave project staff with little time to conduct evaluations. The purposes of the required evaluations should be more explicit to maximize the usefulness of time available for evaluations. Neither the legislation nor the supporting regulations provide much clarification on this issue for assistive technology grantees. Hence, project staff or external individuals responsible for self-evaluations should have clear guidance from NIDRR about the types of evaluations to be conducted, when they should be conducted, and their particular uses. For example, it seems evident that the first 2 years of the project would be best spent identifying the project elements that appear to be most effective and efficient. Following this trial period, summative assessments designed to evaluate the impact and quality of fully functional and stable projects should be undertaken.

In summary then, we recommend that NIDRR

- Encourage applicants to respond fully to existing federal requirements governing the contents of project self-evaluation plans and provide additional guidance on the appropriate types of indicators and measures.
- Require funded projects to include revised self-evaluation plans that reflect early implementation experiences and identify specific elements of the original plan and why they have been changed in each year's continuation application.
- During the first 2 years of the project, require the self-evaluation activity to be formative in nature and designed to facilitate project implementation. Third-year evaluations should include a summative component that will provide an adequate basis for the assessment of a project's impact on persons with disabilities and subsequent NIDRR decision making regarding the award of extension grants.

CONCLUSION

Since 1988, when the Tech Act was enacted, almost every state in the United States has planned and engaged in a vigorous campaign to improve the availability of assistive technology to persons with disabilities. This chapter describes essential elements of local and federal systems change, discusses progress made toward this end, and provides recommendations for future federal and state activities that will put the spirit of the Tech Act of 1988 into practice.

REFERENCES

Albin, J. (1992). *Quality improvement in employment and other human services.* Baltimore: Paul H. Brookes Publishing Co.

Americans with Disabilities Act of 1990 (ADA), PL 101-336. (July 26, 1990). Title 42, U.S.C. 12101 et seq: *U.S. Statutes at Large, 104,* 327–378.

The American Heritage Dictionary Second College Edition. (1985). Boston: Houghton Mifflin Co.

Behrmann, M., & Schepis, M. (1994). Assistive technology assessment: A multiple case study review of 3 approaches with students with physical disabilities during the transition from school to work. *Journal of Vocational Rehabilitation, 4*(3), 202–210.

Gardner, J., & Chapman, M. (1993). *Developing staff competencies for supporting people with developmental disabilities* (2nd ed.). Baltimore: Paul H. Brookes Publishing Co.

Hayden, M., & Abery, B. (Eds.). (1994). *Challenges for a service system in transition: Ensuring quality community experiences for persons with development disabilities.* Baltimore: Paul H. Brookes Publishing Co.

Rehabilitation Act Amendments of 1992, PL 102-569. (October 29, 1992). Title 29, U.S.C. 701 et seq: *U.S. Statutes at Large, 100,* 4344–4488.

Research Triangle Institute. (1992). *National Evaluation of State Grants for Technology-Related Assistance for Individuals with Disabilities Program, Final Report, Volume 1: Evaluation Findings and Recommendations.* Research Triangle Park, North Carolina: Author.

Sowers, J., & Powers, L. (1991). *Vocational preparation and employment of students with physical and multiple disabilities.* Baltimore: Paul H. Brookes Publishing Co.

Technology-Related Assistance for Individuals with Disabilities Act of 1988 (Tech Act), PL 100-407. (August 19, 1988). Title 29, U.S.C. 2201 et seq: *U.S. Statutes at Large, 102,* 1044–1065.

Technology-Related Assistance for Individuals with Disabilities Act of 1994, PL 103-218. (March 9, 1994). Title 29, U.S.C. 2201 et seq: *U.S. Statutes at Large, 108,* 50–97.

Turner, E. (1994). Consumers and the Americans with Disabilities Act. *Journal of Vocational Rehabilitation, 4*(3), 202–210.

Wehman, P. (1992). *Life beyond the classroom: Transition strategies for young people with disabilities.* Baltimore: Paul H. Brookes Publishing Co.

Wehman, P., & Moon, M.S. (Eds.). (1988). *Vocational rehabilitation and supported employment.* Baltimore: Paul H. Brookes Publishing Co.

Wehman, P., Wood, W., Everson, J., Goodwyn, R., & Conley, S. (1988). *Vocational education for multihandicapped youth with cerebral palsy.* Baltimore: Paul H. Brookes Publishing Co.

3

Virginia Systems Change_____
Case Study

Kenneth Knorr
Susan Urofsky
Joseph Ashley

Since the 1970s, assistive technology has emerged as having the potential to open unlimited community living and employment opportunities for persons with disabilities. Individuals who had been faced with seemingly insurmountable barriers concerning accessibility, communication, and mobility became able to optimize their intellectual and physical capabilities through technology applications. For example, a person unable to communicate verbally could convey ideas and desires using a voice synthesizer. Adaptive computers could be operated by voice, by devices mounted in the mouth or on a headset, and even with the blink of an eye.

These high-technology adaptations enable individuals to control their home environment (i.e., lock and unlock doors, turn appliances or lights on and off) and carry out complex job tasks, such as computer programming or computer-assisted drafting. Low-technology solutions such as reaching devices, rubberized cloths to open jars, and ramps that enable individuals to gain access to buildings, are easily available either off the shelf or customized.

VIRGINIA ASSISTIVE TECHNOLOGY SYSTEM

In 1990, Governor Douglas Wilder designated the Virginia Department of Rehabilitative Services (VDRS) as the lead agency responsible for developing an assistive technology systems change plan and applying for a grant to implement these plans under the Technology-Related Assistance for Individuals with Disabilities Act of 1988, or the 1988 Tech Act (PL 100-407).

Once the grant was received, VDRS began to develop the framework for increased public awareness, service delivery, and enhanced public policy, and the internal service delivery capacity to respond to its clientele's assistive technology needs. Through this state project, VDRS envisioned accomplishing the following goals:

1. Include diverse public and private stakeholders in systems change.
2. Increase accessibility and affordability of assistive technology.
3. Provide accurate, user-friendly information.
4. Stimulate individual and organizational innovation.

5. Develop consortia and networks to carry out project goals locally and regionally.
6. Provide ongoing resources once federal funding ends.

In 1991, the Virginia Assistive Technology System (VATS) was created to spearhead Virginia's systems change. The mission of VATS is to improve access to assistive technology information, devices, services, and funding for Virginians of all ages and abilities. The state project focused on systems development that would transcend federal time frames and limitations and be supported by permanent structures and products, such as regional consortia and an automated information and referral database. In addition to increasing the accessibility and affordability of assistive technology, stimulating consumers, advocates, and provider networks to use assistive technology was also a desired by-product (see Table 3.1).

Stakeholder Involvement

In order to develop a lasting consumer-responsive system, the Virginia Council on Assistive Technology (VCAT) was formed to take an active, meaningful role in project development and guidance. VCAT comprises 25 diverse stakeholders, an advisory board with more than one half of its membership consisting of persons with disabilities and their family members, who initially came together to focus on a common mission of assistive technology systems change. Also included on the council are service providers, vendors, employers, educators, advocates, and agency representatives. The VCAT consults, advises, and is fully integrated into all project activities. Individual council members have participated on interview panels, helped formulate project goals and objectives, developed action plans and requests for proposals, selected grant recipients, and assisted with project evaluation. Members actively participate in the three task groups that guide the VATS' work scope: the information and referral system, resource development, and community integration.

Information and Referral System

In response to a significant issue identified through surveys and requests from VCAT, an information and referral (I&R) system was established. The mission of the I&R system is to increase the availability of information on assistive technology to all Virginians with disabilities. This system seeks to bridge the gap that exists between consumers and assistive technology-related devices and service providers. VCAT's I&R task group helped to design the system, devise a recommended questionnaire format to ensure that service provider information is collected in a consistent manner, and select the I&R manager. It also guides the activities of the I&R staff, ensuring that the system is consumer responsive and promotes systems change. To that end, national databases on assistive technology devices and services, such as ABLEDATA, have been integrated into a centralized statewide microcomputer database. Currently, the database contains approximately 17,000 assistive technology devices and services.

The statewide I&R system is housed in Richmond and is accessible by various means. They are as follows:

- A toll-free number answered by an information specialist, allowing any person within Virginia to call for assistance and instruction on how to gain access to information
- A toll-free number allowing any person within Virginia with a computer and modem to directly connect with the system
- Walk-in sites at the four assistive technology resource consortia (ATRC) and a public access workstation at the central VATS office

Table 3.1. Systems change activities

The intent of the Tech Act of 1988 (PL 100-407) is to promote systems change activities. Described as follows is a list of the minimum components of a systems change grant and the ways in which the state of Virginia has chosen to implement them.

1. *An involved stakeholder.* VCAT guides all the activities of VATS. Members represent each stakeholder with an investment in systems change in Virginia. The stakeholders themselves bring together consumers, practitioners, and agencies committed to that end.
2. *Uniform statewide assistive technology policies.* Virginia passed a resolution directing state and local agencies that provide assistive technology to ensure that clear, consistent assistive technology policies and procedures are developed. The policies are to be uniform across agencies and are intended to remove barriers and provide for consumer choice.
3. *An advocacy component.* VATS has a full-time position designated to provide technical assistance to current and potential assistive technology users and families to assist them in advocacy efforts to obtain assistive technology. ATRC also provides technical assistance in advocacy.
4. *Regionally based technology centers.* Four ATRC have been established in Virginia, designed to respond to the needs of consumers at the local level, including the introduction of a consumer consultative network that will pair consumers with their peers in an attempt to help them negotiate through the various systems.
5. *Personnel training.* A personnel preparation training program was designed to increase the numbers of individuals who can perform paraprofessional rehabilitation technology services for Virginians with disabilities. A program outcome is to build local capacity to deliver assistive technology services.
6. *Financial support to enable consumers to afford technology.* VATS is committed to the development of methods to assist consumers in financial access to technology. A supplemental award from NIDRR was received to expand on research efforts and identify various loan alternatives for other states.
7. *Up-to-date service and product information.* VATS has developed an extensive on-line database of services, products, and funding sources that are available to persons with disabilities.
8. *A consumer-to-consumer network.* An EEBBS links consumers seeking used devices with consumers who want to sell or donate their devices.
9. *Policies ensuring compliance with Section 508 of the Rehabilitation Act of 1973 (PL 93-112).* The development of a policy statement bringing Virginia into compliance with Section 508 represents the first statewide policy in Virginia that provides public employees with disabilities equal access to electronic equipment.
10. *Strategies to fund or promote innovation.* VATS has committed substantial funding to stimulate creative assistive technology initiatives.
11. *A minority outreach program.* VATS cosponsored the national pilot testing of RESNA TA's Project Reaching Out, designed to develop culturally sensitive materials about assistive technology for minority groups and service providers who work with minority populations.

ATRC, assistive technology resource consortia; EEBBS, equipment exchange bulletin board system; NIDRR, National Institute on Disability and Rehabilitation Research; RESNA, Rehabilitation Engineering Society of North America; TA, technical assistance; VATS, Virginia Assistive Technology System; VCAT, Virginia Council on Assistive Technology.

The I&R system averages approximately 200 contacts from consumers each month from the on-line database and the information specialists. I&R staff also provide technical assistance, presentations, and demonstrations on request to both consumers and service providers.

A directory of funding alternatives was developed by VATS. The directory is available in hard copy and on-line through the I&R database and is accessible free of charge through the project's toll-free number. This directory, the first of its kind in Virginia, informs consumers of available funding resources and services and how to gain access to them. It concisely overviews the assistance available from government agencies, independent living centers, civic and service organizations, and private insurance companies. To aid potential recipients in their efforts to obtain assistance, detailed guidance on the application and appeals process is also provided.

VATS was aware that in Virginia there was no single, coordinated point of contact for individuals needing to exchange assistive technology devices, information, and ideas. Many organizations such as hospitals, nonprofit groups, and independent living centers serve as local access points for similar services. These organizations have welcomed the prospect of VATS coordinating the posting and maintaining of equipment exchange information. VATS has chosen to address this need through the development of a user-friendly equipment exchange bulletin board system (EEBBS) and a mentor/consumer consultation program implemented at the regional level. The information relating to assistive technology devices includes equipment for sale, rental, and giveaway.

The EEBBS runs on a stand-alone microcomputer and is provided in two formats: 1) a toll-free voice number connected to the VATS I&R specialist to take equipment exchange inquiries, and 2) and direct computer access. The EEBBS is designed to allow consumers to leave messages and electronic mail for other consumers. This simulated "trading post" empowers consumers and, at the same time, removes the burden of having to use a state agency as an arbitrator of equipment exchange agreements.

Assistive Technology Resource Consortia

With the knowledge that a state the size of Virginia could not be covered effectively from a single office in Richmond, four regional ATRCs were created as an integral part of the VATS network. These regional resources carry out many of the same functions, such as training, public awareness, and I&R, as the central office. They also facilitate assistive technology demonstration opportunities and respond to their region's specific needs.

A Request for Proposal (RFP) for the establishment of the ATRC was developed with input from the VCAT. In an attempt to leverage maximum resources and to encourage coalition building and collaboration, the RFP insisted that a consortia of organizations and entities be established prior to grant submission. The RFP also requested that the proposal include plans for funding the consortia beyond the federal funding cycle. Seven proposals were received from across the state, and four consortia were selected with the assistance of review panels comprising assistive technology users, VCAT members, vendors, and service providers. All four ATRC began operating in 1992.

Each consortium consists of a group of organizations, with one designated as the lead entity. Three of the ATRC have a university for the lead entity; the fourth ATRC has a state rehabilitation center as its lead agency, and it works closely with another state university. All ATRC involve persons with disabilities as advisers or staff. Consortium members include area agencies on aging, advocacy groups, centers for independent living, local vocational rehabilitation offices, rehabilitation centers, human resources I&R systems, the United Cerebral Palsy Center, the Children's Hospital, state agencies, and others.

Training and Public Awareness

The community integration task group of the VCAT guides the development and implementation of public awareness activities. Activities are varied and correspond to the diverse interests of VATS' public. Television stories have been aired in an attempt to generate public knowledge of assistive technology. In addition, VATS and ATRC staff give numerous presentations and I&R demonstrations across Virginia. Highlights of project activities are featured in a regularly published newsletter entitled *Connections*.

From its beginning, VATS has contracted with the Virginia Commonwealth University's Rehabilitation Research and Training Center (RRTC) on Supported Employment to provide training and technical assistance. RRTC and VATS staff have worked together to develop training curricula for three specific audiences: consumers, service providers, and employers. These sessions were constructed as prototypes with the expectation that the ATRC would tailor the curriculum for their own audiences and deliver similar trainings in their regions.

Another collaborative venture between the RRTC and VATS was designing and conducting a personnel preparation program for paraprofessional rehabilitation technologists and technology users. The objective of this program is to build local capacity to deliver low-tech assistive technology services. This program is being offered through a few of the state's community colleges.

VDRS counselors received training on using VATS' I&R system. I&R training was initiated to encourage lasting systems change by bringing the project knowledge to the desks of persons who work directly with consumers. By the end of 1995, all state rehabilitation offices and centers for independent living will be equipped to serve as I&R satellites, resulting in more person-to-person I&R involvement.

VATS has held four annual assistive technology conferences featuring best practices from Virginia and across the United States. A significant number of the conference participants are assistive technology users. Participants representing all the major stakeholders are given an opportunity to define their needs and to collaborate with others who share their investment in enhancing the VATS.

Policy Development Activities

In addition to the formation of task groups, two major policy initiatives have been undertaken. These are state compliance with Section 508 of the Rehabilitation Act of 1973 (PL 93-112) and a statewide policy on assistive technology. The development of a policy statement bringing Virginia into compliance with Section 508 ensures that public employees with disabilities have equal access to electronic equipment (computer-related accommodations, telephone adaptive hardware, assistive listening devices). Technical assistance is provided by VATS and VDRS staff to support this effort.

Also, representatives from 11 state agencies that provide services to persons with disabilities authored a statewide policy statement on assistive technology for legislative approval. A resolution, HJR 697, was enacted by the state legislature. HJR 697 directs state and local agencies that provide assistive technology to their clientele to ensure that clear, consistent assistive technology policies and procedures are developed. These are to address information and referral; types of devices and services provided through the agency; conditions of eligibility and extent of coverage; fiscal responsibilities; methods to inform individuals of their rights; consumer evaluations; service provider and vendor standards; and the identification of unserved and underserved populations.

Loan Financing Model Development

Early in the project, VATS conducted preliminary national research on assistive technology loan financing models in operation across the United States. Alternatives currently under consideration in Virginia include a revolving loan model and an interest buy-down model as described in Chapter 13. VATS received a supplemental award from its primary funding source, the National Institute on Disability and Rehabilitation Research (NIDRR), to pursue national loan model research across both public and private loan programs that may have application to the 1988 Tech Act states. Loan programs that support disaster relief, student aid, housing, and financial assistance are examples of possible models for research. The outcome of this research was the identification of loan financing models that address administrative, financing, and oversight alternatives, which states may use to address the needs of their citizens.

Creative Initiative Awards

VATS annually funds Creative Initiative Awards. The purpose of this grant program is 1) to promote the independence, productivity, and quality of life of persons of all ages with disabilities through improved access of unserved and underserved Virginians with disabilities to assistive technology products, services, and information; and 2) to provide small seed money grants to stimulate innovation.

Review panels, comprising consumers, council members, various agency staff, and other stakeholders, selected the final recipients. These grants generally support the work of people who typically are not grant writers. Many of these ventures are replicable and encourage collaboration among agencies and organizations, thus encouraging an expansion of the network designed to improve access to assistive technology.

Business Accommodation Response Teams

A model for a business accommodation response team (BART) has been piloted. The primary objective of BART is to have a central point of contact for Virginia employers and to respond to their job accommodation requests within 72 hours. Teams are made up of consultants, including job placement specialists, rehabilitation engineers, employment specialists, occupational and physical therapists, and rehabilitation counselors. The project is developing a registry of professionals who are willing to provide consultation and respond quickly to employer and employee problems. However, it is uncertain whether the BART pilot will be incorporated into the VDRS system.

Resource Development Activities

In 1993, VATS staff were asked to provide testimony to the House Subcommittee on Select Education and Civil Rights as it was preparing for reauthorization of the Tech Act (PL 103-218). A summary of VATS' position follows:

1. As other strategies are identified to sustain the Tech Act projects, federal dollars will be necessary for the short run.
2. Funding authorities need to document and articulate indices of performance.
3. Projects should be funded based on merit and be held accountable for their dollars.
4. In order to stimulate creativity and flexibility, a competitive grant process should continue.
5. State projects should be expected to have an advocacy component and adhere to standards established for this purpose. However, these activities should be self-directed by each individual state project.

6. Given the diversity of approaches to the administration of these projects, each state should be allowed to choose what is best for it.

For systems change to be fully effective and lasting, continuity must be there beyond federal funding. VATS recognizes the need to pursue alternative funding for long-term continuation of the statewide system beyond the federal funding cycle. Paul Hearne, Director of the Dole Foundation, spent several days with VATS staff brainstorming possible approaches. The following approaches may be undertaken to help secure funding:

- Conduct a feasibility study and determine the level of commitment to continue the major activities, such as ATRC, capitalization of the loan fund, I&R system, and creative initiative grants. Interviews will be conducted with legislators, consumers, and private sector and public officials.
- Identify potential funding sources specific to program components with strategies to solicit resources in conjunction with the purposes of each component.
- Interpret and analyze interviews to determine the amount of support needed in terms of resources (i.e., dollars, staff, equipment).
- Recommend strategies and realistic time frames for the accomplishment of goals.

VIRGINIA DEPARTMENT OF REHABILITATIVE SERVICES

VATS' activities at the state and local level helped to increase VDRS' awareness of assistive technology needs. As the implications of these needs for departmental clients became clearer, the department initiated significant organizational restructuring and resource allocation to enhance the quantity, quality, and consistency of its statewide technology services. This effort strongly involved the interdisciplinary staff of various department units and diverse stakeholders.

Consistent with the Tech Act (PL 100-407) and the Rehabilitation Act Amendments of 1992 (PL 102-569), technology assessments are being built into each phase of the vocational rehabilitation process. For example, clients may use adaptive computers to communicate during intake and to participate in vocational evaluation testing. As a result, clients with more severe disabilities will be more likely to be found eligible for services, and employers will be assisted with cost-effective job accommodations.

To the extent possible, capacity development, staff training, and community awareness are being kept in sync. Rehabilitation engineering is now available in each of the department's four regions. Mobile technology teams have been formed using the occupational, physical, and communication therapy resources of Woodrow Wilson Rehabilitation Center (WWRC), Fisherville, Virginia, a comprehensive residential center with both health and vocational programs. All service delivery vocational staff are receiving introductory training, specially designed by the department, on assistive technology devices and services and how to use technology specialists. To ensure quality technology solutions for individual clients, technologists participate in grand rounds where proposals are evaluated to ensure that consumer needs are adequately addressed and that they are presented with more than one viable option.

Stakeholder Involvement

Because technology is a relatively new, dynamic, and rapidly changing aspect of rehabilitation, there are unique opportunities for developing a collaborative system. Stakeholder participation on both the individual and systems level ensures that assistive technology meets the needs of consumers. In Virginia, much emphasis is placed on developing client-centered teams and interactive systems.

Addressing individual consumer needs may require coordination of a technology team, with therapists addressing issues such as positioning, range of motion, and aptitude and with rehabilitation engineers or specialists in computer adaptations constructing or adapting low- or high-tech devices. A consumer focus for such teams ensures that client needs and preferences are paramount and that energy and talent work in concert. The team must recognize that even low-tech applications and modest computer adaptations can create consumer anxiety if there is not adequate support and training on their use. This leads to persons abandoning equipment and solutions that are actually very workable.

On a systems level, optimizing technology requires coordination among public and private providers, funding sources, advocates, users, and professionals from various disciplines. As noted, VATS is guided by a stakeholder council that has moved beyond support for first-generation products, such as the I&R system, to broader system concerns. Additional focus for the future will be on self-sufficiency for the regional resource centers, practitioner education and capacity building, and various methods for enabling consumers to test and make supported purchases of needed equipment and services.

Developing Integrated Rehabilitation Technology Services

The VDRS believes that a practical application of both low- and high-tech services can assist individuals with disabilities in taking full advantage of opportunities provided through the Americans with Disabilities Act (ADA) of 1990 (PL 101-336). Technology application is also essential to fully implement the Rehabilitation Act Amendments of 1992 (PL 102-569). These amendments include integrating rehabilitation technology into critical phases of the rehabilitation process. Keeping pace with changing technology and ensuring its application and integration into service delivery offers a threefold challenge:

1. Services must address informed consumer choice.
2. Cost-effective services must be made available and accessible throughout the state.
3. Professionals with the appropriate orientation, experience, and training are needed to deliver the service.

To address these three challenges, the VDRS has mobilized the resources of its various units and drawn on its experience in developing programs that increase independence and employment opportunities for individuals with severe disabilities. WWRC, which is a division of VDRS, houses occupational, physical, and speech/audiology therapy departments as well as rehabilitation engineering departments. Through these services, WWRC has developed expertise in both vocational and medical rehabilitation.

The department views WWRC as a potential assistive technology hub, where specialized and complex services can be provided and technology specialists can supplement regional resources. The department has also developed rehabilitation engineering capacity in each of its regions. Quality assurance, coordination, and ADA assistance are assigned to a newly created technology unit.

USING ASSISTIVE TECHNOLOGY FOR COMMUNITY LIVING AND EMPLOYMENT

Through a long history with computer technologies and rehabilitation engineering services, VDRS has positioned itself to utilize emerging technologies to improve vocational and community living opportunities. For example, in 1972, WWRC worked with IBM Corporation to develop the initial prototype of the "Data Processing for the Handicapped Project" that helped persons with severe disabilities become competitively employed as computer programmers.

This project established a model for collaboration among VDRS, business, and industry. Business initiated the project, IBM provided crucial staff support, and WWRC contributed vital resources such as physical and occupational therapy. Because of this cooperation, the project has been very successful. During the initial 5 years of the project, 100% of the graduates entered into competitive employment immediately after completing their training program. The opportunities provided as the result of an applied technology program were apparent.

Currently, assistive technology is being made available to VDRS clients in other programs with positive results. Examples are the personal assistance program and supported employment for persons with physical disabilities. Technology enables individuals with disabilities to become more independent and eases their transition into the workplace.

Personal Assistance Services

The personal assistance services (PAS) program in Virginia is a cooperative effort of VDRS and centers for independent living. The program enables individuals to employ attendants to assist them in carrying out activities of daily living, such as bathing, eating, and dressing. Nevertheless, program developers recognized that through the application of assistive technology people will be able to carry out more daily living activities themselves. Each client is assessed by a rehabilitation engineer to determine if assistive technology, such as home modification or adaptive devices, could facilitate greater functional capacity.

Application of technology has been found to not only increase individual self-sufficiency but also to cost-effectively reduce the amount of hours of personal assistance required by 15 of the 33 individual consumers in the pilot project. The $17,000 of assistive technology devices purchased resulted in a reduction of personal care attendant hours during a 3-year period equivalent to $40,000 (Adams, 1993). This combination of personal assistance services and assistive technology allowed individuals to be more independent in their home settings and resulted in sustained employment for some individuals who were in jeopardy of institutionalization.

Supported Employment

Similar to the PAS program, assistive technology benefits participants in the supported employment for persons with physical disabilities program. Primary applications have been in the form of job accommodations and enhanced worksite accessibility. A follow-up survey of program participants (Parent, 1992) found that worksite modifications and assistive technology were critical employment supports for some individuals. Twenty-eight percent of the individuals surveyed indicated that they had their worksites modified, and 18% indicated that they received some kind of assistive technology to help them on the job.

Reported modifications included job reorganization, equipment modification, and structural adaptations and additions. Assistive technology devices such as mobility equipment, rehabilitation appliances, augmentative communication devices, and equipment modifications were used. Parent (1992) noted that practical applications highlight the importance of assistive technology as an additional supported employment tool for persons with physical disabilities.

DEVELOPING AGENCYWIDE TECHNOLOGY CAPACITY

Prior to developing extended capacity, VDRS offered rehabilitation engineering services through WWRC and two regionally located engineers. In addition, WWRC employed a mobile trailer with fabrication capacity to take rehabilitation engineering services to rural areas of Virginia.

One of the first steps in expanding assistive technology services agencywide was to make assistive technology efforts more cohesive throughout the agency. An internal task force reviewed rehabilitation engineering services and noted issues that needed to be addressed to ensure consistent access to these important services and to integrate rehabilitation engineering into the vocational program through a more systematic process.

Similar problems encountered with other specialized services influenced the organizational structure adopted by VDRS in 1990. A division was created to address the unique issues associated with independent lifestyles and vocational opportunities for individuals with chronic, long-term rehabilitation problems, and to address services that were of a special nature and were not available statewide. The reorganization study correctly predicted the future importance of small service delivery units that consisted of professional, highly technical staff located in units that would include rehabilitation engineering. Although small in nature, these units were viewed as strategic assets by external environments that would become more important in the future (Zody, 1990). One such unit is the technology and accommodations services unit. It consists of a lead rehabilitation engineer who coordinates services with other engineers located in the VDRS regions, a computer systems engineer with statewide responsibility, and an accommodations coordinator.

REHABILITATION ENGINEERING

Rehabilitation engineering was the first technological element to be fully addressed by VDRS. A lead rehabilitation engineer now focuses on the development of consistently available high-quality rehabilitation engineering services that are integrated into the rehabilitation process. Rehabilitation engineering is viewed as an agencywide resource; engineers with somewhat different specialties are based in regional offices and at WWRC. From a statewide perspective, this staffing structure ensures engineering expertise. It also allows for optimization by using the unique strengths of each engineer as part of an overall team.

Grand Rounds

VDRS is committed to consistent, high-quality service delivery that assures consumers and rehabilitation counselors that well-developed options will address shared needs. One mechanism to ensure sharing the wealth of expertise of the rehabilitation engineering staff is the grand rounds, which are convened on a weekly basis. All cases initiated within the week are presented by the six rehabilitation engineers for review by their peers, who provide feedback on proposed solutions and issues to be addressed. This process of reviewing cases allows engineers, with their own specialty, to critique and offer solutions.

Quality Assurance

Protocols are also being developed and tested to formally address quality assurance. To this end, 36 rehabilitation programs from 23 states were contacted to review existing protocols. Of the groups that responded, 50% of the university-based programs and 75% of the hospital-based programs reported having developed quality assurance protocols. These programs monitored several quality assurance activities, such as the client's level of satisfaction with the services, the durability of the equipment provided, training provided to clients and the rehabilitation team, and the amount of problems that arise as a result of service delivery.

VDRS then decided to develop its own process by building on the strengths of these existing procedures because no one protocol completely addressed agency needs. Internal stakeholder groups, which include consumers and employers, will review the rehabilitation engineering process and identify the important aspects of service delivery. This information will be gathered on a regional basis and developed into a consolidated protocol for improving rehabilitation engineering services throughout the agency.

Rehabilitation Technology Liaisons

Rehabilitation technology liaisons have been identified within each of the four VDRS regions. These individuals will assist counselors in ensuring that rehabilitation technology is considered in all aspects of the rehabilitation process. When there is a question about the need for rehabilitation technology services, a team consisting of the lead rehabilitation engineer and an occupational therapist, physical therapist, and speech/audiology therapist from WWRC will be available by telephone to discuss issues related to the individual. This rehabilitation technology team will provide a screening consultation to help address issues through local resources.

Complex cases will be scheduled for mobile clinic service by the individual's rehabilitation technology liaison. These clinics will be available in each region and will utilize the regional rehabilitation engineer working with a team of WWRC therapists to provide comprehensive assistive technology evaluations. Mobile clinics will be staffed by the rehabilitation technology screening team.

Preconsultation screening ensures that the rehabilitation technology team will have all necessary equipment available at the regional site for evaluations. Rehabilitation technology needs of agency clients can be addressed in the most efficient manner possible using the expertise of WWRC and other agency personnel.

Computer Accommodations Laboratory and Outreach

Another aspect of WWRC is the computer accommodations laboratory (CAL), which uses a collaborative team to identify a match of a client's functional abilities with appropriate hardware and software to accomplish specific vocational and independent living objectives. Although primarily provided at WWRC, evaluations are also arranged at the individual's home and worksites when appropriate. The CAL team includes a computer systems engineer as a team leader and may include other professionals such as vocational evaluators and occupational, physical, and speech therapists, depending on the individual's needs.

In addition to participating in the matching of clients' needs with adaptive computer solutions, the computer systems engineer serves as a liaison between manufacturers of specific hardware and software. This role allows the agency to develop new vocational opportunities and press for the development of off-the-shelf technology for the client. The computer systems engineer also ensures the compatibility of hardware and software of computer-based adaptive technology throughout the state. The computer systems engineer works with evaluators and instructors to integrate adaptive computer technology information into the vocational evaluation and training processes.

The agency views rehabilitation technology as important in the development of service approaches that make vocational opportunities and independent living a reality for individuals with disabilities.

THE FUTURE OF VATS

Congress has now directed Virginia's tech projects to focus the scope of their activities to ensure that systems change occurs in programs that provide disability-related benefits and funding. Two new issues were added in the new Tech Act of 1994 (PL 103-218), which include aggressive outreach to underrepresented and rural populations and development of systems that ensure timely acquisition and delivery of assistive technology devices and services, particularly with respect to children. Four additional areas of importance that will be addressed by the project are:

- The development, implementation, and monitoring of state, regional, and local laws, regulations, policies, practices, procedures, and organizational structures
- The development and implementation of strategies to overcome barriers regarding access to, provision of, and funding for such devices and services
- Coordination of activities among state agencies in order to facilitate access to, provision of, and funding for assistive technology services
- The development and implementation of strategies to empower individuals with disabilities and their family members to successfully advocate for increased access to, funding for, and provision of assistive technology devices and services, and to increase participation, choice, and control of such individuals with disabilities and their family members in the selection and procurement of assistive technology devices and services

All these activities are reflected in project goals. For example, the ATRC plan to conduct public strategy forums for consumers and service providers at both the local and regional levels. The ATRC will also provide training and limited technical assistance to state and local agencies in assistive technology policy development and implementation. These activities are aimed at underrepresented, rural populations. To ensure coordination among the agencies, a task group in each region functions as a problem-solving body. Their activities are entirely accessible to both consumers and service providers and, in turn, these groups provide policy interpretation and mediation. Each consortium intends to develop and maintain a consumer consultative network in its region, consisting of a directory of individual consumers who are willing to share their expertise and experiences.

VATS has a contractual agreement with the state protection and advocacy (P&A) agency. The focus of the agreement is related to P&A issues specific to consumer acquisition of assistive technology from the Virginia Departments of Education, Rehabilitative Services, Medical Assistance Services, and the Visually Handicapped. One of the most important activities that responds to the mandates of the Tech Act of 1994 is personal advocacy training, which emphasizes consumer rights, how to provide technical assistance, mediation techniques, and appeal procedures. The state P&A agency serves as a consultant to consumers when they are trying to acquire assistive technology. Direct legal services are also offered to consumers, and both VATS and the P&A agency will jointly pursue legal reform in major areas.

CONCLUSION

The VDRS has established an ambitious agenda. Although much has been accomplished, emerging needs (such as the establishment of an assistive technology evaluation system in each region and the implementation of a statewide loan financing model during an era of declining resources) continue to challenge the creativity of staff and stakeholders. VDRS welcomes its system development role through the VATS project and values the many stakeholders who have made substantial contributions. Department staff learn more every day from consumers and stakeholders regarding the potential for assistive technology to enhance quality of life and employment opportunities for persons with disabilities. Thus, working to increase access to assistive technology for Virginians with disabilities of all ages is a challenge well worth undertaking. VATS welcomes its role as a catalyst for change.

REFERENCES

Adams, M. (1993). *Comprehensive cost effectiveness measurement of a consumer directed personal assistance services program* (46th national conference). Washington, DC: President's Committee on Employment of People with Disabilities.

Americans with Disabilities Act (ADA) of 1990, PL 101-336. (July 26, 1990). Title 42, U.S.C. 12101 et seq: *U.S. Statutes at Large, 104,* 327–378.

Parent, W. (1992). *Assessment of the supported employment for persons with physical disabilities: Findings and recommendations.* Richmond: Virginia Commonwealth University, Virginia Institute for Developmental Disabilities.

Rehabilitation Act of 1973, PL 93-112. (September 26, 1973). Title 29, U.S.C. 701 et seq: *U.S. Statutes at Large, 87,* 355–394.

Rehabilitation Act Amendments of 1992, PL 102-569. (October 29, 1992). Title 29, U.S.C. 701 et seq: *U.S. Statutes at Large, 100,* 4344–4488.

Technology-Related Assistance for Individuals with Disabilities Act of 1988, PL 100-407. (August 19, 1988). Title 29, U.S.C. 2201 et seq: *U.S. Statutes at Large, 102,* 1044–1065.

Technology-Related Assistance for Individuals with Disabilities Act of 1994, PL 103-218. (March 9, 1994). Title 29, U.S.C. 2201 et seq: *U.S. Statutes at Large, 108,* 50–97.

Zody, R. (1990). *Organizational recommendations: A report to the commissioner of the Virginia Department of Rehabilitation Services.* Blacksburg: Virginia Polytechnic Institute, Institute for Public Management.

II

APPLICATIONS OF TECHNOLOGY

4

Augmentative Communication_____

Theresa L. Tanchak
Catherine Sawyer

The ability to communicate is the most powerful tool humans possess, and it opens many doors; the inability to do so can close just as many doors. One nonspeaking individual illustrates this in the following statement:

> Speech has always been one of the biggest obstacles in my endeavour to make ordinary contact with people. It has been the one aspect of my handicap that has caused me the bitterest pain, for without speech one is practically lost, curtained off from other people, left wishing to say a million things and not able to say one. Writing is all very well, but there are some emotions that cannot be conveyed, that cannot be 'felt' through the written word alone. Writing may be immortal, but it does not bridge the gap between two human beings as the voice may, and oh, I would rather have an hour's fierce argument with a pal or a few moments of soft chatter with a girl than write the greatest book on earth. (Brown, 1954, p. 161)

In this chapter, we provide basic information about augmentative and alternative communication (AAC), an introduction to the tools and techniques available for AAC, evaluation guidelines for individuals seeking AAC, and information regarding training and follow-up. One section of this chapter is devoted to discussing more advanced applications of AAC technology, and resource information for AAC is provided.

Augmentative and alternative communication refers to means, other than speech, that can be used to send a message from one person to another. Understanding AAC requires discerning the difference between augmentative and alternative communication, the goal of AAC intervention, and the determination of candidacy for AAC. This chapter provides introductory information regarding AAC; a discussion of the tools available for AAC; and best practices for evaluation, system selection, and training.

Augmentative communication refers to any approach designed to enhance an individual's already existing speaking skills. The intervention is not designed to replace existing communication abilities, but rather to support them. That is, techniques are designed to function in concordance with an individual's own abilities. This type of intervention is most often provided to individuals who have limited oral communication abilities. Conversely, *alternative communication* refers to those communication approaches that are an individual's primary means of communication. This approach is utilized when an individual possesses no oral communication abilities. Although AAC tools and strategies are often the same, their purposes differ. Most individuals use devices and strategies in an augmentative sense, because only persons with severe disabilities have no usable oral communication abilities.

AAC is an area of rehabilitation aimed at individuals with severe expressive communication disorders. An AAC system serves as a *communication prosthesis*, a device specifically designed to replace critical communicative functions normally fulfilled by speaking and/or writing. The prosthesis serves to replace a missing or malfunctioning body part—in this case, the structures for oral communication.

The purpose of AAC intervention is to provide individuals with a functional effective communication system that will enable them to gain control over their environment and their lives. Intervention should provide an individual with greater access to and participation in educational, vocational, and social opportunities and allow him or her greater participation in his or her own medical care. The goal of intervention is to restore or provide a person with the ability to express his or her needs, thoughts, and feelings through the use of specifically designed devices, techniques, and training.

CANDIDATES FOR AUGMENTATIVE AND ALTERNATIVE COMMUNICATION

AAC intervention is appropriate for individuals of all ages, with varying degrees of physical and/or cognitive limitations, who are nonspeaking or whose speech is not viable as a primary mode of communication. Populations who may benefit from augmentative communication include the following:

- Persons with congenital disabilities, such as cerebral palsy, mental retardation, autism, developmental apraxia, and sensory impairments
- Persons with acquired neurogenic disabilities, such as aphasia, apraxia, dysarthria, sequelae from traumatic brain injuries, or spinal cord injuries
- Persons with acquired structural changes from laryngectomy or glossectomy procedures
- Persons with progressive disabilities, such as amyotrophic lateral sclerosis, multiple sclerosis, muscular dystrophy, Parkinson's disease, or acquired immune deficiency syndrome (AIDS)
- Persons with temporary speech loss due to a tracheostomy or ventilator placements

These population groups include persons in hospitals, intensive care units, emergency rooms, nursing homes, rehabilitation programs, school systems, community agencies, or local medical/health offices. Children as young as 12 months of age who show delay in the development of speech sounds should be referred to a speech-language pathologist for assessment and diagnosis. Adults of any age, even those with terminal illnesses in hospice care, may benefit from AAC assessment.

The need for augmentative communication is identified by individuals within a person's environment. Referrals are initiated generally by physicians, teachers, family members, allied health professionals, or concerned friends who recognize communicative dissonance or a critical decision-making point in the life of the individual. *Communicative dissonance* is defined as a significant discrepancy between what an individual is able to understand and what he or she is able to express (Shane, 1986). A *critical decision-making point* is a point at which communication needs are unmet, have changed, or will change substantially in the near future (Yorkston & Karlan, 1986). Some examples of critical decision-making points include an individual with cerebral palsy who is about to leave school to pursue vocational options or future educational opportunities, an individual who has suffered a stroke and is unable to speak, an individual who is recovering function following a traumatic brain injury, or conversely, an individual who is gradually losing function because of a progressive disorder such as amyotrophic lateral sclerosis (ALS) or multiple sclerosis (MS).

The AAC tools available are so varied and flexible that they can be tailored to meet the communication needs of both young and old persons. The speech-language pathologist is available to provide assessments and determine etiology of speech impairments, prognosis for improvement of speech, and the need to refer further for augmentative communication evaluation. The following section provides a discussion of the available augmentative communication systems and their various components.

AUGMENTATIVE COMMUNICATION SYSTEMS

Augmentative communication systems fall into three major areas: natural communication techniques, graphic and manual signs, and communication aids (Magnusson, Hanson, Hubbard, & Skelly, 1988). Most systems prescribed to individuals are multimodal. A *multimodal system* is a system that combines a variety of techniques available to an individual. Thus, an individual's communication system may include gestures, facial expressions, residual speech, and a communication aid. Following is a discussion of the major areas of communication systems and further discussion regarding high-tech devices.

Natural Communication Techniques

Natural communication techniques are naturally occurring behaviors that are used to communicate (Magnusson et al., 1988). These techniques include nonstandard gestures, vocalizations, facial expressions, nonverbal signals, and speech and are used in everyday life. Incorporation of these techniques into an individual's prescribed communication system is essential for maximizing communication performance. Service providers must remember never to take away abilities or to discourage someone from using the natural techniques available to him or her to augment communication. These techniques must be encouraged to support communication.

Graphic and Manual Signs

Although used by persons with hearing impairments, sign language systems can be explored to support the communication skills of an individual in need of augmentative communication (Magnusson et al., 1988). Examples of sign language systems include American Indian sign language (Amerind, a language composed of gestures made mostly with the hands and fingers, used by American Indians; Tomkins, 1969) and American Sign Language (ASL). Examples of graphic symbols include pictures, picture sets, symbol systems, blissymbolics, letters, and words (Figure 4.1). These may all be used as one component of an individual's total communication system.

Communication Aids

Communication aids range from low-tech communication aids to high-tech commercially available aids. Low-tech aids may be purchased or clinician-made. These include communication boards, communication notebooks, and picture wallets. High-tech aids are available commercially from a number of manufacturers. The systems vary widely in regard to their purpose and capabilities. Many of these systems have speech output and system programming capabilities.

High-tech electronic communication aids have three basic variables: encoding method, access method, and means of output.

Encoding Method

The encoding method is the way in which information is represented on the system for message programming and retrieval. With few exceptions, most information is represented

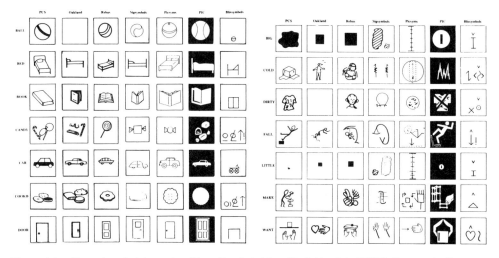

Figure 4.1. Examples of pictographs. (From Vanderheiden, G., & Lloyd, L. [1986]. Communication systems and their components. In S.W. Blackstone [Ed.], *Augmentative communication: An introduction* [pp. 49–161]. Rockville, MD: American Speech-Language-Hearing Association; reprinted by permission).

graphically on a communication aid overlay. These representations take the form of real objects, photographs, line drawings, detailed pictures, colored symbols, letters, or words. The person's chronological age, as well as his cognitive, visual, and physical skills, should be considered when choosing the most efficient method of encoding information.

Information can be encoded using different formats. Some devices utilize *levels* or *pages* to divide vocabulary units. The person using the system must go from one level or page to another to retrieve information. Thus, he or she needs to remember where specific vocabulary is located and demonstrate cognitive flexibility regarding the distribution of information as it changes. On a low-tech system, the levels or pages are generally on separate sheets and need to be changed manually. For example, changing levels can be accomplished by turning pages of a communication book or changing to a different communication board. The levels of a high-tech system are adjusted electronically. Some devices have a dynamic screen that offers new vocabulary units when the levels change, while others have all levels represented on one overlay. Some systems are configured so that a change in levels necessitates a change in the overlay. The design of a level system should be individualized based on a person's cognitive skills and vocabulary demands (see Case Study 4.1).

Another method for organizing vocabulary is *abbreviation expansion*. The vocabulary units are assigned letter and/or number codes. For example, the phrase "I'm having a really good time" could be encoded using the letters "IHG," while the phrase "I'm getting bored" could be encoded using the letters "IGB." Number codes, used in older systems to represent single words, are not frequently used in systems today. The inefficiency of this technique, coupled with the cognitive demands, rendered it marginally useful. Persons using the abbreviation expansion method of encoding information must have some knowledge of letters and numbers and must have sequencing skills. It is advisable that individuals be proficient with spelling to use this encoding method successfully.

Word prediction is a means of vocabulary retrieval that is used with spelling. As a person spells out a word, the technology presents a list of words that begin with those letters spelled. The person must read through the list to find the desired word. Some word prediction programs update vocabulary lists based on frequency and recency of word use and rules of grammar. A person must demonstrate spelling proficiency as well as the cognitive flexibility to

Case Study 4.1: Jake

Jake is a 36-year-old male with severe spastic cerebral palsy. Although he had no usable speech, he communicated with others via facial expressions and vocalizations. Jake had a restricted receptive vocabulary, possibly due to the fact that he did not attend school and was, therefore, illiterate. However, his cognitive skills were strong. He did have friends in the community and went with his mother to visit them once a week, but he spent most of his time home with his mother and other family members. Obviously, Jake was in need of a communication system that would allow him to communicate with others in his home and community. He was evaluated by an AAC team consisting of physical and occupational therapists, a speech-language pathologist, and a rehabilitation engineer. This evaluation indicated that Jake had no control over his extremities but had fairly good head control. In fact, he was able to use an optical headpointer to motion to targets approximately 1 inch in size. The Light Talker (Prentke Romich Company) was recommended for trial because it allowed for optical headpointer access and could be used with pictures rather than traditional orthography. Subsequently, this system was procured for a rental period of 4 weeks.

Jake needed a great deal of practice with the headpointer. He was able to use the headpointer with 100% accuracy on a 32-square location overlay (symbol size of 1½ inches); however, he had a great deal of vocabulary to represent. The decision was made to use a 128-square overlay (symbol size of ⅝ inch) and to place the pictures on the overlay so that there was a blank space between each picture. This reduced the number of incorrect activations, while still allowing Jake enough pictures to represent the vocabulary he wanted. Communication scripts were used to develop vocabulary in themes that corresponded to his various everyday activities. Approximately 10 themes were developed with vocabulary units during the rental period. Color coding of themes was used to assist Jake in recalling the icons that represented his themes. Jake was taught a site word vocabulary that allowed him to read the feedback provided by the liquid crystal display (LCD) and identify which theme he was in at all times. With practice, Jake's accuracy with the optical headpointer improved, and pictures eventually could be placed side by side without sacrificing accuracy or communication efficiency. Jake demonstrated the ability to learn system operations and to use the system communicatively within his home and community. He demonstrated excellent potential to continue to learn new vocabulary and communicative skills with the system. Purchase was recommended following the rental period.

Vocabulary development continued along communication themes. However, the need for greater vocabulary flexibility eventually was identified. The Minspeak™ vocabulary software program Language, Learning, and Living™ (LLL™) was selected for evaluation. LLL™ is a word-based vocabulary system designed for adolescent and adult individuals with developmental disabilities and associated learning difficulties. It was designed so that individuals could communicate at their own level of language competence. Jake's potential to learn this vocabulary system is currently being assessed. He is being taught the vocabulary in the system and how to combine words and generate novel sentences to com-

(continued)

municate ideas without restrictions. If he demonstrates potential to utilize this software program to enhance his communication skills, it will be integrated with the core phrase vocabulary he has already developed. The device will then be customized to meet his own unique vocabulary needs.

This case illustrates the implementation of an AAC system for an individual with a developmental disability. It discusses customizing vocabulary and the overlay to account for individual needs.

alternate between spelling a message and reading a word list. Having to alternate between tasks may slow message generation and decrease communication efficiency.

Minspeak™ (Prentke Romich) is a semantic encoding technique in which the user assigns icons, or symbols, to communication messages. Icons can have multiple meanings and can be combined in sequences. Information is organized by communication environments, or "themes." If a person has good sequencing abilities, all the communication messages will be available using a single overlay. An individual may use one icon to represent the theme and another to represent the message. Individuals must have representational skills to use icons for communication. To utilize the full power of Minspeak™, thought organization skills of categorizing and sequencing are desirable.

Access Method

The access method is the method used by the individual to interface with the device. There are two primary means of access: direct selection and scanning. *Direct selection* is accomplished when an individual gains direct access to the desired target with a finger (by pointing), headstick, optical headpointer, infrared light, or other modified pointing system. This is the fastest method of access but could also be the most fatiguing for an individual with physical limitations. Yet, when feasible, direct selection should be the method of choice.

Scanning is an indirect access method for those who lack sufficient motor control over any part of their body needed to use direct selection. Scanning can be accomplished using a single switch, dual switch, or multidirectional switch. Scanning can be done in a row–column format, in which the system scans by row until the user activates the switch, then proceeds to scan across the column until the target is reached. This can be an arduous process for both speaker and listener. Communication aid manufacturers have introduced time-saving features for those who must use scanning to gain access to their systems. Group scanning, referred to as quadrant scanning or group–row–column scanning, is available on some systems. This allows the system to scan groups prior to resorting to row–column scanning, thus avoiding unnecessary scanning of unneeded portions of the system and allowing the user a more direct route to the target. Predictive scanning has also been introduced. Using this method, the system scans only to locations that have programmed messages. It avoids scanning empty locations or locations that are not part of a symbol sequence. Systems are available that provide auditory prompting during scanning to assist persons with visual impairments. Some persons may be able to use proportional scanning via a joystick to gain access. The access method chosen is dependent on physical, visual, and cognitive abilities. A person may need more than one way to gain access to a system as changes in position occur. For example, an individual may utilize an optical headpointer while seated in a wheelchair, but need to use a single switch when positioned in a bed.

Means of Output

Communication systems may have two primary means of output—visual and/or auditory. Visual output may be transient, as with communication boards and LCDs, or may be permanent in the form of a printed copy. Auditory output may take the form of digitized speech or synthesized speech. *Digitized speech* is digitally recorded human speech. *Synthesized speech* is computer-generated speech that is produced using a speech synthesizer. Both digitized and synthesized speech can be made gender and age appropriate. Finally, systems may combine these two forms of output. Some devices offer LCD output with synthesized speech and a built-in printer if a permanent record is needed.

Types of Communication Aids

Augmentative communication aids can be classified into one of three categories: simple systems, dedicated devices, or multipurpose systems (DeRuyter & Becker, 1988). *Simple systems* are low-tech aids and techniques used for communication, such as communication boards, communication books, and gestural systems. *Dedicated devices* are those that serve the purpose of communication only, including the Canon Communicator (Canon, Inc.) (see Case Study 4.2), the AlphaTalker, the Walker Talker (Prentke Romich Company) (Figure 4.2), the Parrott, the Macaw (Zygo Industries, Inc.), and the Digivox (Sentient Systems Technology, Inc.; see Figure 4.3). *Multipurpose systems* are those that serve more than just com-

---

Case Study 4.2: Kate

Kate is a 40-year-old female who sustained a closed head injury many years ago. Kate had severe dysarthria that affected her articulation and phonation. She did, however, have some usable speech. She also had moderate to severe cognitive-linguistic impairments affecting thought organization, problem solving, and memory. Kate lived at home with her mother and worked in a sheltered workshop. Kate had limited need for a communication system at home as her mother could understand most of her speech; however, the individuals in her workshop could not. She needed a system that would augment her communication with her peers. Kate was in a wheelchair but had sufficient physical abilities to gain access to a system using direct selection with the index finger on her right hand. She and her mother indicated that she did not need a system with spoken output; instead, they were interested in a portable system with printed output.

The Canon Communicator (Canon, Inc.) was recommended based on her abilities and needs. She was able to spell messages and create a printed output to augment her speech production as needed. The system had the technology for a limited number of programmed messages, and it was highly portable, a feature desired by Kate. The augmentative evaluation also consisted of a thorough speech evaluation. Speech intelligibility was assessed and determined to be significantly better when produced at a higher volume. However, Kate fatigued quickly when attempting to speak louder than a whisper. A voice amplifier was assessed. This made her speech more intelligible. Thus, a voice amplifier was prescribed for Kate in addition to the Canon Communicator.

This case is an example of how a variety of techniques can be used to enhance communication skills. Kate used a multimodal system, consisting of a voice amplifier for her natural speech production and a Canon Communicator to augment her speech.

munication. They are designed to change functions easily and, in addition to communication, serve educational, vocational, or recreational purposes (DeRuyter & Becker, 1988). For example, a system may be used for interpersonal communication as well as for interfacing with a computer for educational use. Another example is a system that can interface with an environmental control unit to increase the user's independence. Other systems can also be used as computers themselves, allowing users to create and edit file documents via word-processing capabilities. Examples of multipurpose systems include the RealVoice (Adaptive Communication Systems, Inc.) (see Case Study 4.3), the Touch Talker/Light Talker (Prentke Romich Company) (see Figure 12.2), the Liberator (Prentke Romich Company) (Figure 4.4), the Dynavox (Sentient Systems Technology, Inc.), and the VOIS 160 (Phonic Ear, Inc.). Integrated systems using commercially available computers and specialized communication software are also considered multipurpose systems.

Case Study 4.3: Juan

Juan is a 24-year-old male diagnosed with dystonia muscularum deformans, a rare progressive neurological disorder. Juan's dystonia was characterized by poor motor control with random involuntary movements, which were most pronounced in the facial and lingual muscles. Juan exhibited severe dysarthria with only 25% speech intelligibility. He had a high school diploma, and his cognitive-linguistic skills were within normal limits. Juan was referred for an augmentative communication evaluation during a vocational assessment.

Juan was interested in pursuing vocational opportunities in public relations. He was in need of a communication system with voice output to allow him to communicate with others. Because he was ambulatory, he needed a system that would be portable. He also was interested in a system with print capabilities that would allow him to compose legible messages. Of primary importance in selecting a system for Juan was his medical diagnosis; that is, his form of dystonia was considered to be slowly progressing. The assessment team needed to consider that his motor abilities were expected to worsen over time. Thus, he needed a system that he could continue to use as his physical abilities changed.

The RealVoice (Adaptive Communication Systems, Inc.) was the system that best met Juan's needs. The system is portable and has both spoken and printed output modes. Furthermore, it has the technology for multiple input modes. Juan was able to gain access to the system via the keyboard; however, the system could be configured for optical headpointing or scanning in the future. The system was flexible enough to accommodate anticipated changes in his physical abilities. Juan was proficient with abbreviation expansion encoding and quickly developed a core vocabulary for the system. Purchase of the system was recommended following a successful rental period. Presently, Juan is employed in a community grocery store and utilizes the RealVoice, in addition to his limited speech, for functional communication.

This case study illustrates the implementation of an AAC system for an individual with a progressive disability. It highlights the need to consider system flexibility in accommodating worsening physical abilities. It also illustrates how an individual can use an AAC system to support natural speech in functional and vocational endeavors.

Figure 4.2. The Walker Talker (Prentke Romich Company).

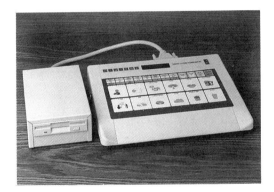

Figure 4.3. The Digivox (Sentient Systems Technology, Inc.).

There are other system variables that need to be considered when evaluating the use of a particular system for an individual. Some of these variables include weight and portability of the device, mounting capabilities of the device, durability of the system, system warranty, service and technical support from the vendor of the system, and price of the system. The next section discusses in-depth the evaluation process for augmentative communication and the variables needing consideration.

ASSESSMENT AND SYSTEM SELECTION

Once the need for augmentative communication intervention is identified, the next step is to seek out assessment services. Augmentative communication is a highly specialized area of expertise that requires both training and experience. Because it is a relatively new area with constantly changing technologies, the majority of practicing professionals did not receive extensive training in this area during their graduate programs. Some service providers have acquired the necessary knowledge through continuing education and independent study. Thus, it is important that professionals conducting such assessments be knowledgeable in this area. Further, the augmentative assessment involves consideration of many issues. The process is so complex that not all issues fall within one professional discipline. That is why the best AAC services are provided by teams of professionals working within an interdisciplinary framework. Team members should possess expertise in widely divergent areas and special knowledge about skills for AAC, and they should join together to make decisions based on

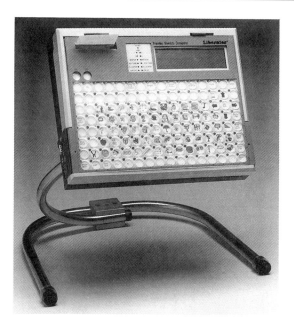

Figure 4.4.   The Liberator (Prentke Romich Company).

shared information. The decision-making process facilitates the development of integrated assessment and intervention plans.

AAC teams can be found in a variety of places, including schools, rehabilitation centers, hospitals, and private practices; however, not all facilities have teams. When seeking evaluation services for AAC, several issues should be considered. A list of questions to guide individuals seeking services is provided as follows:

- Are services provided as a team?
- Who is involved in evaluations, and what other professionals may be consulted?
- What follow-up services will be provided?
- What communication options are typically recommended?
- Is intervention to improve speech recommended?
- Are involved team members familiar with a variety of devices and techniques?
- Is AAC equipment at the facility?
- How long has the team been working together?
- Has the team seen persons with similar disabilities?
- Is there a waiting list for evaluations?
- Is funding assistance provided?
- How successful is the team at securing funding?
- Is training assistance available?
- How much does the evaluation cost?

The best programs will be those with strong team approaches, comprehensive evaluation and follow-up, and the capability to choose from a wide range of AAC aids and techniques.

Team Members or Consultants

The list of possible experts who may serve as team members or consultants to the team can be long, depending on the kind of information that is needed. Team members and the areas they might evaluate include the following:

Speech-Language Pathologist

- Coordinates team
- Assesses understanding of language, use of language, and interaction patterns with different communication partners
- Assesses muscle control for speech, pronunciation of speech sounds, and prognosis for improvement
- Evaluates use of nonverbal communication
- Determines appropriate vocabulary for use with AAC systems
- Recommends types of specialized communication aids and techniques

Occupational Therapist

- Evaluates muscle control of different body parts with and without special equipment
- Assesses visual acuity, visual scanning, visual perception, and visual fields
- Assesses seating

Physical Therapist

- Assesses seating and positioning
- Evaluates muscle strength, range of movement, flexibility, balance, and coordination
- Addresses mobility issues and system transportation

Physician

- Checks general health and medical prognosis
- Determines appropriateness of medical or surgical treatments

Educator

- Contributes information on classroom performance and academic performance
- Defines communication skills needed to complete academic and vocational courses and to interact with classmates

Social Worker

- Explores an individual's total living situation
- Determines need for additional community resources

Psychologist

- Evaluates individual learning potential
- Assesses need for individual and family counseling

Rehabilitation Engineer

- Evaluates usefulness of customized devices or provides modification to commercially available equipment

Computer Programmer

- Determines the usefulness of existing computer programs
- Explores the possibility of modifying existing programs or developing new programs

Vocational Evaluator or Rehabilitation Counselor

- Assesses an individual's potential to hold a job
- Assists with identification of career goals

Audiologist

• Evaluates and recommends treatment of a hearing loss

Of course, the individuals and their families are of primary importance and are at the center of the team. The composition of professionals on the evaluation team is dictated on an individual basis and depends on a person's needs. For children, the core assessment team will most likely consist of a speech-language pathologist, an occupational therapist, a physical therapist, and an educator. For adults, the teacher on the core assessment team is typically replaced by either a vocational evaluator or a physician.

Evaluation

As with any evaluation, a thorough history of the person must be obtained before initiating an augmentative communication evaluation. This information should be collected by the team coordinator and shared with the other team members accordingly. First, the person's *history of communication*, including his or her present methods of communication, previous modes of communication, and the record of success or failure of each and his or her preferred communication partners, should be clearly defined. This information allows the team to understand the individual's prior communication experiences and may avoid unnecessary repetition of strategies during the assessment itself. Much of this information can be provided by the individual and his or her family or caregivers, who may often bring previously used communication tools to the evaluation to assist the team in understanding what already has been used.

Second, the *educational history* of the individual also should be available to the team. The assessment team should know the child's present placement in school, whether he or she is involved in mainstream education in a regular classroom or whether he or she is placed in a nongraded self-contained classroom for individuals with severe disabilities. The current individualized education program (IEP), with annual goals and progress toward each goal, provides valuable information about teaching strategies used by the school and the student's response to each. The IEP also gives the team a good idea of how the student functions in the present placement. Phone calls to teachers or to school speech-language pathologists involved in the child's care may be warranted to obtain further subjective information regarding a child's educational functioning. For adults no longer enrolled in school, it is helpful to know about their school experience. Many adults with severe congenital disabilities never had the opportunity to attend school and thus have little knowledge of academics. Meanwhile, other adults did attend school and learned a great deal. Knowing the educational history of an adult with an acquired disability allows the team to infer what that individual's premorbid level of functioning may have been. This is particularly useful in determining an individual's literacy skills and learning abilities.

Third, information should be sought regarding the person's *social history*. This includes information on how the individual spends time, preferred activities, who he or she interacts with the most, how often he or she go into the community, and overall experiences. This information lets team members know the communication opportunities present in the individual's life and the flexibility needed in a system.

Finally, the person's *medical history* should be requested. Knowing the etiology of the individual's disability and the individual's prognosis is essential. The evaluation of an adult with a stable disability such as cerebral palsy will be much different than the evaluation of an adult with a progressive disability (such as ALS or MS). Similarly, it is essential to know whether an individual's abilities are expected to improve and whether any medical treatment is being received that may affect the use of a communication system.

The critical historical information delineated in this section should be obtained and shared prior to the assessment so that adequate planning and preparation can take place. Another element of information critical to the selection of augmentative aids and techniques is the identification of *communication needs*. Needs assessment involves the identification of specific communication tasks that the individual must perform in order to function optimally in particular communication environments (Yorkston & Karlan, 1986). There are published needs inventories in some of the resources listed in the appendix at the end of this chapter. The identification of communication needs may take place during an interview of the individual and significant others immediately prior to the initiation of the evaluation. This interview actually serves four different functions (Yorkston & Karlan, 1986). These functions are as follows:

1. Allows individuals to compile and prioritize needs
2. Provides information that can be used to establish a series of specific, objectively defined intervention goals
3. Enables team members and those they serve to reach a consensus with regard to goals and expectations
4. Educates individuals and their caregivers regarding communication possibilities and available options that they may not have previously considered

The needs interview truly directs the evaluation. Once the needs are identified, the augmentative communication specialist can then evaluate the individual using the devices or techniques that may potentially meet those needs. The needs interview may also uncover any unrealistic expectations by individuals and family members, and direct attention to more realistic, attainable goals. Accomplishing this prior to initiation of the actual evaluation will prevent unnecessary conflict during the process. Finally, it is a forum to educate individuals and caregivers regarding available communication options. For example, a person may not know that systems are available with both spoken output and printed output or that a system can be portable enough to be carried easily by an ambulatory individual with mild physical disabilities. Once a clear understanding of communication needs is reached, the evaluation may begin.

The evaluation consists of a thorough assessment of many components. The professionals work individually and as a group to evaluate the person. An explanation of assessment areas follows.

Motor Abilities

The evaluation should include consideration of motor abilities. The physical therapist and the occupational therapist may see the person concurrently in order to assess the individual's seating and positioning. The person needs to be in the most upright posture possible in order to maximize functional abilities. Minor wheelchair or seating modifications may be accomplished during the evaluation itself to ensure best possible results. For example, the person may benefit from wheelchair side supports, which will improve sitting balance, thus allowing greater arm control for system access. Once an appropriate seating system is in place, head and trunk control, extremity control, and range of motion are then assessed to identify the most reliable access site. The speech-language pathologist may become involved with this portion of the motor assessment. The question being addressed is whether the individual is capable of direct selection, single or multiple switch access, or other modes of input. Access sites should be examined with respect to accuracy and reliability of movement, range of control, speed of movement, and endurance. The motor assessment should include determination of the best means to transport the AAC system. Team members need to consider balance and motor abilities for persons who ambulate or wheelchair configurations for persons unable to walk.

Sensory Abilities

The occupational therapist is able to provide a complete assessment of an individual's visual abilities. The therapist may assess visual acuity, visual scanning, visual perception, and visual fields. The information obtained from the visual assessment is essential to determining the best placement of the system, the optimal symbol size and shape, the best location for symbols on the system, and whether color contrast should be used to maximize visual skills. For example, an individual with a visual field cut who has difficulty seeing stimuli placed on his or her right side should have a system positioned slightly left of midline with symbols clustered toward the left of the system. If visual acuity is an issue, larger symbols with clear shapes are preferable to small symbols with extensive detail. The speech-language pathologist may provide a hearing screening to ensure adequate hearing for use of an AAC system. If a hearing screening is failed or there is a known hearing loss, an audiologist should provide a complete assessment to determine the extent of the loss, any impact it may have on interactions, and the potential benefits of amplification.

Cognitive-Linguistic Abilities

The speech-language pathologist typically takes the lead in assessing cognitive-linguistic abilities. The assessment should identify cognitive and language strengths and deficits and determine how these strengths and weaknesses affect AAC selection and use (DeRuyter & Becker, 1988). The evaluation should consist of a variety of measurement tools including standardized tests, nonstandardized procedures, and informal clinical observations (DeRuyter & Becker, 1988). Standardized assessment instruments may be utilized to measure receptive vocabulary, auditory comprehension, auditory or visual memory, reading comprehension, and spelling abilities. Standardized tests may be adapted to meet the physical abilities of the individual who cannot speak. For example, open-ended formats may be changed to yes/no or multiple-choice formats and response requirements may need to be modified. Thus, caution must be exercised when interpreting results of modified standardized batteries. Normative information is not used; however, results do yield important clinical information about the person's abilities.

Nonstandardized procedures are used strictly to obtain clinical information. These procedures can be used to assess higher cognitive processes related to AAC use, such as sequencing, organization, functional memory, mental flexibility and abstraction, and representational abilities. The information obtained will influence system selection, configuration, symbol selection, and use (DeRuyter & Becker, 1988).

Clinical observation also serves to identify communicative behaviors in functional situations (DeRuyter & Becker, 1988). The client should be observed throughout the evaluation interacting with familiar and unfamiliar listeners. When possible, children should be observed in classroom settings as well as in social settings. Data on these interactive pragmatic behaviors can be recorded using pragmatic rating instruments. Information obtained from clinical observation can be used to select training targets with an AAC system regarding development of certain interactional capabilities or improvement of existing abilities from a nonstandard level to a verbal level.

Symbol and System Selection

Once information is obtained regarding communication needs and motor, sensory, and cognitive-linguistic abilities, the actual system assessment may begin. The team considers the individual's needs in relation to characteristics of high- and low-tech systems and selects several for assessment. Systems are configured according to needs and are presented for assessment using nonstandard procedures. The most appropriate symbol set is chosen based on previously acquired information and nonstandard assessment with various options. For example, an individual who is illiterate is not going to do well with orthographic symbols, whereas an individual who is highly literate may find such a symbol set to be the most successful. Likewise, an individual with adequate representational abilities and some skills in organizing and sequencing may find symbols that lend themselves to symbol sequencing to be most appropriate. In particular, the individual's ability to encode information using symbols is assessed, as well as his or her abilities related to characteristics of symbol sets. Questions that need answers include the following:

- Is the person able to assign meaning to symbols?
- Is the person able to recall meanings assigned to symbols?
- Is the person able to recognize symbols used to represent messages immediately? after a delay?
- Is the person able to combine symbols to express meanings?
- Is the person able to recall symbol sequences appropriately?
- Is the person able to categorize vocabulary using symbol combinations?

Finally, it is useful to structure a situation within the evaluation in which the person is required to use symbols and a system to communicate a message functionally.

Once the evaluation is completed, the individual, family, and evaluation team have determined the potential to learn an augmentative system. A complete system recommendation should be made following the evaluation. This recommendation will include best symbol set, optimal symbol layout, system specifications, and implementation guidelines. The individual's success in everyday life has yet to be determined. The process must not stop here. If a high-tech electronic communication system is recommended, the team may recommend trial rental of the system prior to purchase. This is an excellent practice. It gives the person the opportunity to try the system in various environments and with different communication partners. It provides added assurance against waning motivation and ultimate abandonment of the system. It also allows for additional assessment beyond the initial evaluation for borderline individuals. This is particularly beneficial for persons with cognitive impairments who may require much structure and repetition to learn a new task. Finally, a successful rental period can be used to demonstrate benefits of improved communication to third-party payers, thus easing the struggle to obtain funding. A recommendation by the team for or against purchase of the system should be made following appraisal of the rental period.

Success of the recommended system is dependent on many factors. Probably the most heavily weighted factor is the quality of the training and follow-up a person receives. The best system recommendations can lead to failure if the person and caregivers receive inadequate training on the system.

TRAINING AND FOLLOW-UP

Appropriate training is essential for successful implementation of a new communication system. Because an individual receives a system does not mean that functional communication will immediately follow. Communication learning takes time and assistance from individuals familiar with the system operation and the person's abilities. Finally, the system received is not the "final product," that is, the system will need frequent changing and updating to continually meet the individual's communication needs as life situations change. Communication systems are designed to be dynamic; thus, training and follow-up after receipt of a system are as important as the evaluation and recommendation procedures.

Providers of Training

Training should be provided by a qualified professional who is knowledgeable regarding the system recommended and the abilities of the individual user. Often, training is provided in the facility in which the evaluation was conducted. If training in that particular location is not feasible because of distance from the home, the evaluating team may arrange for training in the person's community. In this instance, training may be carried out by the local school system, community resource agency, speech-language pathologist, regional hospital or rehabilitation center, or qualified representatives of the communication aid manufacturer. The evaluating team should work in conjunction with the trainer to ensure recommendations from the evaluation are appropriately implemented.

In some cases, it is necessary to "train the trainer" regarding operations of systems; not all professionals can be experts in all systems. Thus, it is common for individuals responsible for system implementation in the community to attend training sessions or seminars sponsored by the vendor of the particular communication system or provided by the evaluating facility. Some vendors of communication systems offer further support to those training the individuals and may even arrange appointments to work with the person themselves to foster a successful beginning. The most successful training teams are those that include the vendor of the system. The vendor should be able to provide technical support and serve as an available resource throughout the training period. It is important to ask about training at the time of the evaluation and to determine what assistance the facility will provide in arranging this training.

Basis of Training

Users of AAC systems need to learn to be competent communicators. Many individuals have not had the opportunity to communicate in a standard understandable way. Just as children learn the rules of language and interaction, AAC users must learn to interact appropriately and efficiently using the new system. Training to use an augmentative communication system, whether high or low tech, should include four main areas: individuals need to learn how to operate their system technically, how to use the encoding technique, how to use the system to communicate in real environments, and how to employ compensatory strategies to circumvent AAC system restrictions (Light, 1989).

The individual must be taught the technical skills needed to operate the system. First, the individual needs to learn to gain access to the system. For example, an individual using single-switch scanning needs to learn the motor pattern to activate the switch and needs to understand the scanning concept. If scanning acceleration techniques of quadrant scanning or predictive scanning are used, these also need to be understood. For individuals using direct selection access via a headpointer, the skill of gaining access to the desired target with the infrared light needs to be practiced. Individuals also need to learn the various features of their unique system, including power switches, volume controls, output mode selections, and other operational variables. It is essential to teach users to look for and interpret the feedback offered by the system. They need to learn to read the display or search for other means of feedback from the system. This allows the individual to participate in active problem solving and troubleshooting and to become more independent in managing the use of the system. An individual's mastery of the technical aspects of the system can be evaluated best in terms of the accuracy and speed with which messages are formulated (Light, 1989).

Individuals need to develop a mastery of language. This includes knowledge of their native language (spoken in the home and community) and mastery of the linguistic code required by the AAC system (Light, 1989). If they have not already, they must develop the receptive language skills required to function within their environment. Furthermore, they must learn the language codes used in their systems. For individuals using icons, they must learn the icons themselves and how to use them singularly and in sequence to communicate meaning. Individuals using traditional orthography or sign language must learn those symbols and must associate meaning to them. Individuals need to learn how to combine symbols (e.g., letters, words, icons) to formulate meaningful strings of information.

The AAC system user must develop knowledge, judgment, and skill in the social rules of communication. The individual must understand discourse strategies, interaction functions, and communicative functions (Light, 1989). Using the AAC system, the individual must learn appropriate ways to initiate, maintain, and terminate interactions. Users should understand rules of turn taking and should be proficient in using techniques for appropriately interrupting. They should be able to use the pragmatic intent of sharing, requesting, protesting, and denying information. These skills are all context dependent and can be evaluated in terms of their appropriateness and effectiveness (Light, 1989). The following skills may enhance the communicative competence of an individual using an AAC system: "a positive self image, an interest in others and a desire to communicate, active participation in conversations, responsiveness to partners, and the ability to put partners at ease" (Light, 1989, p. 140). Teaching the individual to utilize these strategies appropriately is essential to communicative success.

Finally, individuals who use AAC need to develop compensatory strategies to allow them to communicate effectively within restrictions (Light, 1989). For example, AAC users who are not literate may have vocabulary restrictions, or users who employ indirect access methods may find themselves under time constraints during interactions. One compensatory strategy may be inclusion of a vocabulary unit meaning "Please be patient, this may take a second" for an individual who needs extra time for message formulation. Another strategy may be use of the phrase "What I want to say is something like this" for an individual with limited vocabulary available on the system. A strategy can be developed to allow the AAC user to quickly take a turn in a group conversation. For example, a quick phrase saying "Do I have a story for you!" can be used to secure a conversational turn in a fast-moving interaction. Strategies such as these will vary depending on the restrictions placed on individuals and the environments in which they are communicating.

Essential as this information is, training must not focus only on the user. It is important to provide appropriate training to communication partners in the person's environment. These partners should be empowered to support the communication skills of the person using the communication system. In order to effectively support the communication of persons using AAC systems, caregivers require knowledge and skills in two areas: 1) interaction strategies; and 2) system operation, maintenance, and development (Light, 1990). Teaching interaction strategies involves instructing the communication partners in providing opportunities for the person to initiate interactions, to respond to the person's communicative attempts, to pause frequently, and to avoid overuse of yes/no questions (Light, 1990).

Knowledge of system operation and development is equally important. As mentioned previously, the communication system should be dynamic. That is, it needs to change to meet the person's changing needs. Caregivers are the ideal facilitators of this change as they are often with the individual and are frequently most familiar with communication needs. Caregivers should know the symbols and transmission techniques, understand positioning requirements, be confident in ongoing vocabulary development, be able to operate and program systems, know strategies for troubleshooting, and know resources locally and nationally to contact for assistance (Light, 1990). Once again, this information should be received from the professional or team of professionals responsible for training.

Follow-Up

Training should not be the end of the individual's contact with service providers. One of the largest problems in the field of AAC is system abandonment. This can occur for many reasons. Some individuals may experience changes in their life situations or in their communicative needs and find that the system is no longer functional. Children, as they grow older and learn new skills, may need to advance to a different system. Some adults may experience changes in their physical, cognitive, or sensory status and need to make system adjustments. All these scenarios can lead to system abandonment if appropriate follow-up services are not provided.

Appropriate follow-up services can be provided by the initial evaluating facility, the agency providing the training, or the communication aid manufacturer. Service providers should maintain regular contact with communication system users for at least the first 2 years after completed system implementation to ensure the successful use of the system. Depending on the individual's circumstances, regular contacts may continue beyond that point. For example, an adult with a progressive disability such as ALS may need adjustments in system configuration over time to account for changes in physical or cognitive abilities. In another situation, an adult using a system may change jobs, necessitating new vocabulary and possibly new strategies for success in a new vocational situation.

Children present unique challenges in training and follow up. The device prescribed for a 2-year-old child may not meet communication needs or allow for the development of language skills in later years. Ongoing contact with the service providers is beneficial in identifying the need to upgrade a communication system. Children also change classes, teachers, and schools, which creates the challenge of teaching the communication system and interacting strategies to a new set of people. Service providers should be available to ease any such transitions, making them positive experiences for both the children and teachers. Children will have significant difficulty using systems successfully in a "hostile environment" of individuals who do not understand the system and who offer no support in learning about it.

Follow-up services are essential; policies should be explained when an individual initially seeks evaluation and training services. Individuals should also know that some manufacturers offer "trade-up" policies should a child outgrow the initial communication system. Appropriate follow-up can eliminate the problem of AAC system abandonment and prevent many problems experienced by AAC users after the initial implementation period.

One component of evaluation follow-up is the identification of funds to purchase a recommended system. Although money should not be a primary consideration in the selection of an augmentative system, the source of money for such systems is an issue. Recognizing this, there may be a tendency toward purchasing a less expensive communication system than the one recommended. This practice will inevitably result in failure. The service provider should be able to provide a solid explanation regarding why a particular system was recommended over another less expensive alternative. There is no place for or benefit from compromise based on cost or convenience. The optimal system should be identified, and then funding for that system should be pursued. Both the evaluation team and communication aid manufacturer should be available to assist in the pursuit of funds.

CUSTOMIZING AND APPLYING AUGMENTATIVE COMMUNICATION SYSTEMS

All AAC systems need to be customized for individuals. The task of a service provider is to fit the communication system to the person, not to fit the person to the communication system. Often, individuals exhibit certain abilities and characteristics that make customizing a challenge. These are the situations that require a great deal of thought and creativity on the part of the service provider. This section describes some advanced system customizing strategies that will account for a variety of user characteristics. System applications are discussed throughout the chapter using case studies.

The first task of customizing a system is creating a vocabulary set. This should be accomplished with the user and caregivers as much as possible. There have been many techniques developed for vocabulary selection. One such technique is communication scripting (Glennen, 1990). With this technique, vocabulary is derived from interactions that take place in natural situations. Scripts are written for interactions that happen during the day, and the dialogue is programmed into the user's communication system. Scripting provides a core vocabulary of words or phrases and teaches the person how to use language in context. It ensures that the system will be used interactively for communication, not just for making rote requests.

It is essential that vocabulary in a system be motivating to the individual. Although individuals who cannot speak do need to communicate their basic needs, this is not the only purpose of the AAC system. In addition to the phrases requesting that wants and needs be met, motivating phrases about topics of interest or humorous phrases should exist. The form of phrases should be colloquial, not stilted. For example, it is more likely that a child would say "I'm dying of thirst!" than "I would like a drink of water, please." Some clients, both children and adults, like to share jokes and riddles using their systems; therefore, vocabulary should be appropriate to an individual's age and cognitive level. A good way to test vocabulary appropriateness is to spend time listening to conversations taking place with people in the person's peer group. If information is encoded in phrases, these phrases should include a wide variety of words. This is useful in teaching new vocabulary to children and showing them appropriate ways of using the new words.

In addition to phrases, individual words should be available within the vocabulary set. This allows the individual to create novel utterances by combining words. This ability ensures that the system will be generative, as is any language system. Augmented speakers need the freedom to construct messages that accurately reflect their thoughts using available phrases and words. Consideration should be given to the arrangement of vocabulary on the overlay. Ideally, units should be arranged semantically and grammatically. This allows the speaker to learn language, including rules of grammar, semantics, and pragmatics, as well as remain competitive with his or her speaking peers. Vocabulary units, words and phrases, should be arranged for conversation and language learning. Examples of word-based vocabulary programs available include Words Strategy™; Interaction, Education, and Play +™; Language, Learning, and Living™ (Prentke Romich Company) (see Case Study 4.4); and VoisShapes (Phonic Ear, Inc.).

Vocabulary in communication systems should allow the user a range of pragmatic interactions and intents. There should be vocabulary available to initiate interactions, introduce topics of conversations, maintain topics, and terminate interactions. The person should have access to vocabulary that will allow for making requests, sharing information and commenting, and negating. Too often, vocabulary sets are designed that allow an individual to request something to eat, but offer no means to indicate likes or dislikes. Core vocabulary should offer the user a variety of comments.

Finally, vocabulary should be applicable to multiple situations. Units of vocabulary should be reusable. For example, the phrase "Good morning, Mrs. Smith" can be used only when the user sees Mrs. Smith. A more generic phrase that would be reusable is "Good morning, how are you?" This phrase can be used in a variety of settings with different people. For example, some communication systems allow speakers to create generic phrases that can be

Case Study 4.4: Shauna

Shauna is a 13-year-old female diagnosed with cerebral palsy. She had no functional oral speech and limited use of her limbs. She spent most of her day in a wheelchair. Shauna was taught sign language by her speech-language pathologist for use in her classroom and home environments. Her attempts at signing were crude because of poor fine motor skills. Individuals familiar with Shauna were able to interpret her signs; however, unfamiliar listeners had difficulty. Classroom activities revealed that Shauna was able to associate communication messages with symbols but was unable to accurately point to a picture on a communication board. Furthermore, she could use a switch to activate computer software to learn language.

Shauna was evaluated by an AAC team, consisting of physical and occupational therapists, a speech-language pathologist, a physician, and a psychologist, at a children's hospital. The Light Talker with Minspeak™ and IEP +™ software were recommended. IEP +™ is a software program designed for Minspeak™ devices. This program was designed to meet children's interactive, educational, and play needs. Interactive needs are met with a substantial single-word vocabulary set that allows the child to practice with words and experiment with formulating sentences. Educational needs are met with a basic vocabulary set that meets the child's preacademic and early elementary school needs. Play needs are addressed with stories, songs, and rhymes preprogrammed to teach communication through play.

Shauna remained in the same classroom for persons with disabilities for 3 years. She gradually learned the IEP +™ vocabulary needed for her academic and social growth. In addition, she customized the device by adding new information. The goals on Shauna's IEP were written with a language focus; for example, one goal was for Shauna to request assistance with her lessons when needed. With the AAC system, Shauna's receptive and expressive vocabulary, reading skills, and pragmatic skills improved. Thus, she was gradually mainstreamed into some regular education classes.

Next year, Shauna will move to the middle school and will be in a class for individuals with learning disabilities. Attending a new school, she will need to improve her communication efficiency to meet the greater academic and social demands. School personnel are investigating upgrading Shauna's system to one that has a quicker access method, internal printer, notebook and text files, math functions, greater memory capacity, computer interfacing, larger LCD, and more user prompts to facilitate system use. They are also planning to upgrade her software from IEP +™ to Words Strategy™. Words Strategy™ is a software application program that organizes vocabulary by grammatical class. It is designed for the rapid retrieval of messages and allows users to construct personalized sentences using words and phrases. The Liberator™ (Prentke Romich Company) is being considered for Shauna's next device because it meets her needs and would function with the Word Strategy™ application program.

(continued)

Shauna's classroom teacher has organized a 2-week summer workshop for the teachers who will be working with Shauna during the next school year. The school will rent a Light Talker from the Prentke Romich Company for the workshop to allow hands-on practice with the device. In addition, Shauna and her mother will participate each afternoon so that the teachers can better understand her specific needs. Also participating in the training will be the middle school occupational and physical therapists, speech-language pathologists, and a classroom aide. The regional consultant from the Prentke Romich Company will be available 1 day during the workshop to address specific technical questions and to offer ideas for application of the system and the vocabulary software into Shauna's school day.

This case illustrates how a child can use a system to learn language and vocabulary. It shows how a child's communication needs change as he or she grows and how it may be advisable to consider upgrading a communication system to allow further language development. Finally, this case is an example of a team working together to positively implement a system and to successfully transition the child into a new environment.

customized using special functions (similar to "filling in the blank"). This feature lets the speaker quickly gain access to frequently used phrases, customizing them to unique situations. The phrase "That was a really good _____" could be used to describe a movie, a book, a meal, a trip, a game, and so on. These are just a few guidelines for vocabulary development. Each AAC user should be considered individually, and the vocabulary needs of each person should be structured to meet each person's unique requirements.

There are other characteristics of AAC users that may call for additional system customization. Many adults who use AAC have limited overall experiences and often have no formal education. Their world knowledge is of things that exist and events that happen around their home and within their immediate community. These individuals often have significant restrictions in their vocabulary. This can be a factor in system training because they are not familiar with concepts such as "levels" to a communication system, "menus" that offer choices, or "communication themes." These concepts are not consistent with the life experiences of the individual. Thus, it is important to teach these concepts in concrete ways, using language that corresponds with things familiar in their environment. For example, "levels" can be taught by comparing the system levels to shelves in a closet, and "themes" can be taught using a dresser with many drawers as an analogy. Changing some of the jargon and the abstract concepts associated with system use to more familiar terms and concrete examples can make training simpler and more successful.

In addition to limited experiences, many AAC users have impaired cognitive functioning from a congenital or an acquired disability, which may affect their abilities to sequence steps to processes or to recall information. Configuration of the system overlay may be altered to make use easier. For example, pictures in sequences can be placed in proper order on the overlay to assist teaching sequencing. Color coding of sequences or themes can also be useful. Pictures on an overlay can be embellished to cue the user regarding the vocabulary associated with the picture.

Many individuals who use AAC are illiterate. This is true of adults who did not attend school because of their disability and of children who have not yet learned to read. AAC systems can be configured to enhance literacy learning and to lessen the limitations in system use from not being able to read. For adults who are illiterate and are learning a new AAC system, it may be useful to teach a site word vocabulary for words necessary to system operation. This is particularly useful for systems that have an LCD that gives feedback to the user in traditional orthography. A site word vocabulary of pertinent words allows the user to interpret the feedback from the system, thus increasing efficiency of system use. For children, pictures can be placed on a communication board or overlay with the written word. This allows the child to see the word and associate it with the corresponding picture. For children and adults learning to read, the alphabet may be a component of their system. If this is the case, the letters can be presented in alphabetical order. Furthermore, pictures can be arranged so that the first letter of the item pictured corresponds with the letter of the alphabet. These are only a few suggestions for customizing systems to account for literacy training.

One final instance in which extensive customization may be necessary is impaired vision. Users of AAC can have perfect vision or be legally blind. For persons with severe visual impairments, systems can be configured to maximize residual visual skills. Color can be used to facilitate system use. The use of sharp contrasts or bright colors can make it easier for an individual to see stimuli on the communication system. If an individual has better vision in one quadrant than in the others, stimuli on the communication system may be placed where the client's vision is best. Textures or raised lettering can be used on overlays to make locating targets easier. If the system offers an auditory feedback feature, it may be used to facilitate system use. Finally, size of stimuli on the system can be manipulated for the user.

This is just a brief discussion of a few instances in which extensive device customization may be needed. A thorough knowledge of the communication system and the features it offers is essential to customizing the system to best meet the needs of the client.

RESOURCES

Resources are available at the regional, state, and national levels to address augmentative communication systems. There are professional organizations committed to individuals who cannot speak, and there are corporations that provide services and products to this population. Professional organizations may serve as resources for identifying service providers and for legislative advocacy. A list of organizations concerned with augmentative communication issues appears in the appendix at the end of this chapter.

The communication aid manufacturer has a critical role in system implementation. Cooperation and support from the manufacturer is essential to optimal integration and ongoing success with the prescribed system. In fact, many manufacturers offer support services. Inquiry regarding the following services will assist consumers in locating a vendor that will best meet the client's needs. Ask if the manufacturer offers the following:

- Regional consultants with clinical expertise in language and augmentative communication systems
- Toll-free telephone support offering experienced technical advice 24 hours per day
- Rental options available for extended evaluation and trial implementation, with credit of rental fees toward purchase price
- Free service loaner available during repair period
- Timely servicing of devices
- Trade-up policy from one device to another

- Seminars by qualified professionals
- Periodic mailings to consumers
- Resources for training, funding, and consumer networking
- Printed or published training materials

CONCLUSION

This chapter provides basic information on AAC to inform both consumers and caregivers alike. There are many different communication options available to individuals who cannot speak, and thorough knowledge of such options is essential in providing comprehensive assessment and intervention. Although this information is readily available, the responsibility for applying this information and thoughtfully seeking services rests with the consumer. The best team of professionals cannot forge a positive outcome if motivation and support are lacking. Consumers and caregivers must ask questions and assist the AAC team in identifying effective communication modes and strategies. Most important, consumers must be diligent about training and follow up to ensure ongoing success of the system. Excellent services *are* available and accessible.

REFERENCES

Brown, C. (1954). *My left foot.* London: Secker and Warburg.

DeRuyter, F., & Becker, M. (1988). Augmentative communication: Assessment, system selection, and usage. *Journal of Head Trauma Rehabilitation, 3*(2), 35 44.

Glennen, S. (1990). *Vocabulary selection strategies for AAC aids.* Paper presented at RESNA, Washington, DC.

Light, J. (1989). Toward a definition of communicative competence for individuals using augmentative and alternative communication systems. *Augmentative and Alternative Communication, 5,* 137–144.

Light, J. (1990). *Empowering facilitators to support the communication of individuals using augmentative communication systems.* Miniseminar presented at the annual convention of the American Speech-Language-Hearing Association, Seattle, WA.

Magnusson, D., Hanson, J., Hubbard, W., & Skelly, B. (1988). In S.W. Blackstone, E.L. Cassatt-James, & D.M. Bruskin (Eds.), *Augmentative communication implementation strategies* (pp. 7.17–7.31). Rockville, MD: American Speech-Language-Hearing Association.

Shane, H. (1986). Goals and uses. In S.W. Blackstone (Ed.), *Augmentative communication: An introduction* (pp. 29–48). Rockville, MD: American Speech-Language-Hearing Association.

Tomkins, W. (1969). *Indian sign language.* New York: Dover.

Vanderheiden, G., & Lloyd, L. (1986). Communication systems and their components. In S.W. Blackstone, (Ed.), *Augmentative communication: An introduction* (pp. 49–161). Rockville, MD: American Speech-Language-Hearing Association.

Yorkston, K., & Karlan, G. (1986). Assessment procedures. In S.W. Blackstone (Ed.), *Augmentative communication: An introduction* (pp. 163–196). Rockville, MD: American Speech-Language-Hearing Association.

Appendix

AUGMENTATIVE COMMUNICATION SYSTEM HARDWARE MANUFACTURERS

Ablenet
1081 Tenth Avenue S.E.
Minneapolis, MN 55414
(800) 370-0956

Adaptive Communication Systems, Inc.
P.O. Box 12440
Pittsburgh, PA 15231
(800) 247-3433

Adamlab
Wayne Co. Intermediate School District
Data Processing
33500 Van Born Road
Wayne, MI 28184
(313) 467-1415

Baum, USA
17525 Venture Boulevard, Suite 303
Encino, CA 91316-3843
(818) 981-2253

Apple Computer, Inc.
Office of Special Education
20525 Mariani Avenue
Cupertino, CA 95014
(408) 996-1010

Linda Burkhart
8503 Rhode Island Avenue
College Park, MD 20740
(301) 345-9152

Canon USA, Inc.
One Canon Plaza
Lake Success, NY 11042
(516) 488-6700

Computability Corporation
40000 Grand River, Suite #109
Novi, MI 48050
(800) 433-8872

Consultants for Communication Technology
508 Bellevue Terrace
Pittsburgh, PA 15202
(412) 761-6062

Creative Switch Industries
P.O. Box 5256
Des Moines, IA 50306
(515) 287-5748

Crestwood Company
P.O. Box 04606
Milwaukee, WI 53204-0606
(414) 461-9876

Daedalus Technologies, Inc.
#7-12171 Bridgeport Road
Richmond, B.C., Canada, V6V 1J4
(604) 270-4605

Don Johnston Developmental Equipment
Box 639
1000 N. Rand Road, Bldg. 115
Wauconda, IL 60084
(800) 999-4660

Dragon Systems, Inc.
90 Bridge Street
Newton, MA 02158
(617) 965-5200

Du-It Control Systems Group
Chapel Bridge Park, 8765 TR 513
Shreve, OH 44676
(216) 567-2906

Dunamis, Inc.
3620 Hwy. 317
Suwanee, GA 30174
(800) 828-2443

Edmark Corporation
6727 185th Avenue N.E.
P.O. Box 3218
Redmond, WA 98073-3218
(800) 426-0856

Epson America, Inc.
2780 Lomita Boulevard
Torrance, CA 90505
(800) 421-5426

Flaghouse, Inc.
150 North MacQuesten Parkway
Mount Vernon, NY 10550
(800) 221-5185

Franklin Learning Resources
122 Burrs Road
Mt. Holly, NJ 08060
(800) 525-9673

Grid Systems Corp.
47211 Lakeview Boulevard
P.O. Box 5003
Fremont, CA 94537-5003
(800) 222-GRID

IBM
National Support Center for Persons
with Disabilities
P.O. Box 2150
Atlanta, GA 30301-2105
(800) 426-2133

Innocomp
33195 Wagon Wheel Drive
Solon, OH 44136
(216) 248-6206

Innoventions
P.O. Box 621642
Littleton, CO 80162-1642
(800) 854-6554

Kurzweil Applied Intelligence, Inc.
411 Waverly Oaks Road
Waltham, MA 02154-8465
(617) 893-5151

LC Technologies, Inc.
4415 Glenn Rose Street
Fairfax, VA 22032
(703) 425-7509

Luminaud, Inc.
8688 Tyler Boulevard
Mentor, OH 44060
(216) 255-9082

Mayer-Johnson Company
P.O. Box 1579
Solano Beach, CA 92075-1579
(619) 259-5726

Microtouch Systems
55 Jonspin Road
Wilmington, MA 01887
(508) 694-9900

Nanopac
4833 S. Sheridan Road, Suite 401
Tulsa, OK 74145-5718
(918) 665-0329

Phonic Ear, Inc.
3880 Cypress Drive
Petaluma, CA 94954-7600
(800) 227-0735

Pointer Systems, Inc.
One Mill Street
Burlington, VT 05401
(800) 537-1562

Prentke Romich Company
1022 Heyl Road
Wooster, OH 44691
(800) 262-1984

Sentient Systems Technology, Inc.
2100 Wharton St.
Pittsburgh, PA 15203
(800) 344-1778

Switchworks
P.O. Box 64764
Baton Rouge, LA 70896
(504) 925-8926

TASH, Inc.
Unit 1, 91 Station Street
Ajax, Ontario L1S 3H2
CANADA
(416) 686-4129

Therapeutic Toys, Inc.
Cinta, 91 Newberry Road
East Haddam, CT 06423
(800) 638-0676

Tiger Communication System, Inc.
155 East Broad Street #325
Rochester, NY 14604
(716) 454-5134

Toshiba America Information Systems, Inc.
9740 Irvine Boulevard
P.O. Box 19724
Irvine, CA 92713-9724
(800) 999-4273

Toys for Special Children
Steven E. Kanor, Ph.D.
385 Warburton Avenue
Hastings-on-Hudson, NY 10706
(914) 478-0960

Unicorn Engineering
5221 Central Avenue, Suite 205
Richmond, CA 94804
(800) 899-6687

Words+, Inc.
P.O. Box 1229
4370 17th Street West, Suite 202
Lancaster, CA 93534
(800) 869-8521

Zygo Industries, Inc.
P.O. Box 1008
Portland, OR 97207-1008
(800) 234-6006

PROFESSIONAL ORGANIZATIONS

American Speech-Language-Hearing Association
10801 Rockville Pike
Rockville, MD 20850
(301) 948-9626

The Arc
500 East Border Street
Suite 300
Arlington, TX 76010
(817) 261-6003

Autism Society of America
1234 Massachusetts Avenue, N.W.
Suite 1017
Washington, DC 20005
(202) 783-0125

Communication Aid Manufacturers Association
1022 Heyl Road
Wooster, OH 44691
(800) 262-1984

Council for Exceptional Children
1920 Association Drive
Reston, VA 22091
(800) 336-3728

International Society for Augmentative and Alternative Communication
P.O. Box 1762, Station R
Toronto, Ontario M4G 4A3
CANADA
(416) 421-8377

National Easter Seal Society
2023 West Ogden Avenue
Chicago, IL 60612
(312) 243-8400

RESNA—Association for Advancement of Rehabilitation Technology
1101 Connecticut Avenue, N.W.
Suite 700
Washington, DC 20036
(202) 857-1199

Speech-Language-Hearing Association of Virginia
P.O. Box 35653
Richmond, VA 23235
(804) 379-5258

The Association for Persons with Severe Handicaps (TASH)
7010 Roosevelt Way, N.E.
Seattle, WA 98115
(206) 523-8446

United Cerebral Palsy
Community Service Division
1522 K Street, N.W.
Washington, DC 20005
(800) USA-2UCP

Virginia Augmentative/Alternative Communication Association
3600 Monument Avenue, #9
Richmond, VA 23230
(800) 848-8008

5

Mobility

Getting to Where You Want to Go

Beth Bader Gilson
Diane S. Huss

Mobility is basic to human development. People move about in their environments because they want to, they need to, or because they are bored and want a change of scenery. People need a means of getting around in order to do many things including learning, interacting with each other, earning a living, participating in the community, and escaping from life-threatening situations. For some people, the ability to move independently is taken for granted. Yet for other persons, mobility is not a given, and a variety of assistive devices are needed to make mobility possible.

During people's lives, there are times when their mobility is temporarily affected (e.g., when someone sprains an ankle, fractures a leg or a hip, pulls a muscle in the lower back, or becomes weak after a prolonged illness). However, for 38% of the 43 million Americans with disabilities, mobility limitations are not temporary (National Institutes of Health, 1990). Maintaining mobility is a continuous, lifelong issue for this population of persons with permanent, or chronic, disabilities.

It is assistive technology that provides the support, motion, and access that individuals with temporary or chronic disabilities need for mobility. Canes, crutches, walkers, scooter boards, bicycles, wheelchairs, motorized scooters, and adapted automobiles and vans are examples of assistive devices that allow persons with disabilities of all ages to live, learn, work, and play where and when they want.

THE FIRST "STEP"

To decide what type of assistive technology is needed to facilitate an individual's mobility, he or she must undergo an assessment. This assessment includes evaluating the person's physical ability (his or her muscle strength, ambulation capabilities, stamina, and energy level); determining the activities in which the person currently participates, as well as in which he or she wants to be involved; identifying the accessibility of the environments in which the person wants to function; and considering the age of the individual and the stability of his or her condition, which may have an impact on future needs.

Evaluate the Person's Physical Ability

The evaluation of an individual's physical ability is usually conducted by medical personnel. Physical and occupational therapists, exercise physiologists, orthotists (for braces and splints), prosthetists (for artificial limbs), and physicians provide input when assessing an individual's need for and ability to benefit from a particular assistive mobility device. These professionals should evaluate muscle strength, posture, sensation, vision/perception, and the individual's skeletal system, as well as central and peripheral nervous system functioning, before making a recommendation for either supported walking or seated mobility devices. In addition to strength and general physical condition, the assessment process also must determine the individual's energy level and stamina. Finally, it is critical to ensure that the device selected is the one that the person can use effectively and efficiently from a physical, cognitive, and motivational perspective.

Identify Functional Activities

In order to assess the activities of a young child that require mobility, the evaluation begins with talking at length with the family and other caregivers and spending time observing the toddler. Once children are able to communicate, either verbally or through augmentative communication (see Chapter 4), it is important that they identify the activities that they are involved in and indicate where they take part in them (Holder-Brown & Parette, 1992). Children should also be asked to identify other places that they want to go but cannot go without assistance.

Many times it is assumed that adults can identify what they need through a simple interview conducted by a service provider. A single conversation cannot reveal all the information about the person's capabilities or the specifics about the environments that are involved. Also, people sometimes do not use the same terminology as the person conducting the assessment. Sometimes, adults such as persons with cognitive disabilities who use nonverbal means to communicate do not speak at all. Although they cannot use words to describe what it is that they want or where they want to go, they can show preference and provide information to others who take the time to observe. Most important, it should be remembered that people will not always reveal everything about their disability to someone who has not had time to gain their trust. Therefore, it is vital for service providers to take the time to observe and get to know the person who needs a mobility device, rather than to move quickly and obtain a piece of equipment that may or may not meet the person's needs.

Determine Environmental Accessibility

Family, friends, teachers, and coworkers can assist the individual with a disability in identifying and evaluating environmental accessibility issues. Entrances and exits to buildings need to be evaluated in terms of ramps (slope and length); steps (number, height, and depth); railings (left or right side); and doorways (width). Floor coverings, both carpets and bare floors, in building interiors need to be assessed as well as hallways and doorways (width), location of bathrooms (reasonable distance and size), and methods of gaining access to other floors (stairs or elevators). Climate and expected weather patterns (snow and ice in winter, heat and humidity in summer) should be taken into consideration in regard to safety and operating requirements of the various devices. Finally, it is important to assess outdoor and recreational areas that the person uses or wants to use, looking at sidewalks, curbs, dirt paths, gravel drives, and uneven grassy surfaces.

Evaluate Need Based on Individual's Age

When assessing an individual's need for an assistive mobility device, consideration must be given to age and future needs. For example, young children quickly outgrow walkers and wheelchairs. Both children and adults with an acquired disability resulting from accident or illness sometimes make rapid recovery, which decreases their need for high-level technology as they regain skills and function. The opposite holds true for persons with progressive or degenerating conditions; they require increasing support and a higher level of technology to maintain mobility. This also is true for persons whose mobility is affected by the aging process. For example, an individual who has used a cane for many years may find, because of failing eyesight and increasing joint stiffness, that a walker provides a more stable means of assisted mobility.

CHOICE: FUNCTION VERSUS IMAGE

As discussed previously, the assessment process for determining an appropriate assistive mobility device has included looking at the following: the individual's physical ability, daily and less frequent activities that the person wants to participate in, the accessibility of the environment, and the potential for needing a different level of technology. An equally important piece of information to be considered in the assessment process is whether the device is to be obtained solely for its function, or whether it is more important that the device fit with the image that the person has about his or her self and his or her disability. Although a person's physical and cognitive capabilities are important factors to consider, it is also essential that the assistive device fits into the individual's environment and the family's lifestyle ("Wheeled mobility. . . ," 1994).

Example of Function versus Image

Tom is a 10-year-old boy with Duchenne-type muscular dystrophy. From the time he was 3 years old, when his family first noticed that he could not keep up with his friends on the playground, Tom has been losing strength and coordination, especially in his trunk and leg muscles. After discussion with his physicians and physical therapist, Tom's parents agreed to purchase a wheelchair so that he could keep up with his peers at school. His physical therapist recommended a youth-sized manual wheelchair that could be made larger as he grew older. This chair was identified as the most easily transportable and least expensive option.

After trying out a "loaner" chair, Tom and his parents came to the conclusion that a manual wheelchair was not the right choice. Tom tired quickly from pushing the chair with his arms and found it difficult to maneuver on the grass. Although it was functional in a school setting, Tom had to ask for assistance to go from one end of the school to the other, or else he took extra time to travel that distance, thereby missing valuable classroom time. However, the most important decision-making factor was that Tom hated the wheelchair.

Tom's parents were well aware of the psychological impact that a wheelchair would have on their lives. Tom was losing his ability to walk and someday would be totally dependent on a wheelchair for mobility. His family realistically looked toward the future and realized that Tom might need a motorized wheelchair within the next few years if he continued to lose strength in his arms. Taking this into consideration, they rented a motorized wheelchair for 2 weeks to see if it provided any greater mobility for their son.

Unfortunately, the motorized wheelchair was heavy and difficult to disassemble and transport in the family car. However, Tom was not tired from using the power wheelchair, and he was able to use the chair outside on the playground and in the park. But despite the ease of this chair, he continued to say that he hated the chair.

During this period, Tom and his family visited many medical equipment vendors and collected several brochures and information pamphlets on various wheelchairs. One day they came across a brochure advertising an assistive technology expo in which a variety of equipment vendors would be showcasing their latest assistive devices. Tom's family took him to the expo, and he became very excited when he saw a video at one of the booths that showed a three-wheel motorized scooter. The scooter was being driven by a child who appeared to be his same age. The scooter was also on display at the booth, and Tom was able to try it. He successfully maneuvered the scooter up and down the aisles, went onto the parking lot outside, drove over grassy banks and onto a gravel drive, and was thrilled at being able to go where he wanted to go at a faster pace than if he were walking. In addition, his parents realized that the scooter could be taken apart easily, picked up, and stored in the trunk of the family car.

Although 80% of the cost of the manual wheelchair could have been funded by the family's insurance, Tom's parents chose to purchase a motorized scooter for their son to use at school, at home, and in the community. They were able to obtain a low-interest loan for the scooter and believed that it was a wise investment for Tom now, as well as for the future.

Tom can still walk for short distances at school, but the scooter has provided him with greater independence. He can keep up with his friends as they travel in the halls at school, and the scooter has even allowed him to participate in soccer games on the playground. Tom has found that his scooter is great for blocking goal attempts! Most important, the scooter has provided Tom with a way to transition into using a mobility device. The scooter is seen by everyone, including Tom, as something that he wants rather than something that he has to use.

Using the assessment criteria listed in The First "Step" section of this chapter, we evaluate whether Tom's motorized scooter meets his needs. First, the scooter is a good match for Tom's muscle strength, ambulation capabilities, stamina, and energy level. Second, it helps Tom to participate in daily activities as well as in activities that he could not take part in previously (i.e., soccer). Third, Tom can use the scooter inside the school and outside on the playground, in his yard, and in the community. It is not practical at home or in places in which there are narrow doorways, but he can still walk for short distances and does not yet need a mobility device to move about in his family home. Finally, Tom is at an age at which he has shown that he can responsibly and safely drive the scooter. He and his family are aware that motorized mobility devices, such as the scooter, are likely to be a permanent part of Tom's future.

Often, an assistive walking device or wheelchair is ordered purely for how it can increase an individual's functional ability rather than what it looks like or how it will fit into that person's lifestyle. Professionals tend to look at what the device will do, not at how the person who uses it feels about the image that it portrays to the general public. Users of assistive devices are changing this scenario by demanding choice. It may only be a choice in color, but having a choice provides a degree of personalization and, perhaps, more acceptance toward the assistive device. Manufacturers, especially wheelchair manufacturers, are providing more choices, by offering more than one line of equipment and by marketing their products using words like "sleek," "fast," and "sexy." Eventually, many persons with disabilities may view their mobility devices, which focus on their abilities to get around rather than on their limitations, as extensions of their own positive self-image.

ASSISTIVE TECHNOLOGY THAT SUPPORTS MOBILITY

Assistive devices that support an individual, which in turn facilitate and enhance mobility, can be divided into two groups. The first group is those devices that support an individual during ambulation, such as canes, walking poles or sticks, crutches, and walkers. The other group of devices that is discussed is assisted seating devices, which provide support so that a person can be in a position that allows him or her to use whatever movement is necessary to propel, manually or with a switch, a wheeled mobility device.

Ambulation Devices

Canes

People with visual and physical disabilities use canes for mobility. The types of canes these two groups of people use are quite different. Individuals with very low vision or blindness use their canes as external sensory devices. (See Chapter 6 on devices used for sensory disabilities.)

Canes are used by persons with physical disabilities when there is weakness in one or both of their lower extremities. Although canes do not provide as fast a means of locomotion as crutches (Ragnarsson, 1993), the use of one or two canes can improve the balance of an individual walking on level and uneven surfaces. Canes can be wooden or metal, with curved, rounded, or grip handles, and can be single, triple, or quad footed. Metal quad canes provide the most stable base of support of any cane available (Ragnarsson, 1993). For many people, it is much easier to use a cane than crutches to go up and down stairs.

Walking Poles

Individuals with abnormal muscle tone, such as that caused by cerebral palsy, will sometimes find that by using straight walking poles (or sticks) they have better upper extremity control and more stability. Thus, better balance is achieved than if crutches or a cane were used. Grasping the poles in a "thumbs-up" vertical position and using the poles in front, the individual can move about on all terrains. Poles are made in various diameters and heights, but are usually put together using well-sanded hardwood that is rounded at the top and has a wide, rubber crutch tip at the bottom. Some people use straight, solid tree limbs because they find them less stigmatizing than a device that comes from a medical equipment manufacturer.

Crutches

There are basically three types of crutches—axillary, platform, or forearm. These are made primarily of either wood or metal. Parts of these crutches also can be made of leather, plastic, or rubber. People who use crutches use them for weight bearing and propulsion rather than as sensory aids (Ragnarsson, 1993).

The most widely available and least expensive crutch is the standard *wooden axillary crutch*, the type that people use when they break a leg or ankle. Usually wooden crutches are adjustable and have rubber axillary pads and handgrips. *Metal axillary crutches* are slightly different; they consist of a single, contoured, tubular structure with a telescoping push-button feature used for adjustment. Axillary crutches provide maximum support when used correctly but require the user to have good strength in his or her arms (Ragnarsson, 1993). A common problem that persons who use crutches have when their upper extremities are not strong is that they lean on the crutches as they get tired, thus putting pressure on the underarm area. This can cause tingling and eventual numbness in arms and hands. Also, their hands often become sore and blistered from squeezing the handgrip too tightly. Both problems are preventable with proper training in using the crutches to walk.

Similar in design to the metal axillary crutch is the *platform, or forearm support, crutch* (Ragnarsson, 1993). This type of crutch is used by individuals who cannot put pressure or bear weight on their wrists or hands. The bottom part of the crutch comes up to the elbow, and then a trough, or platform, for the forearm is attached at a 90-degree angle. A Velcro cuff wraps around the forearm to hold it in place and a handgrip is attached at the end of the platform.

Forearm crutches, also called *Lofstrand crutches*, reach from the floor to just below an individual's elbow. The top of the crutch is called the cuff and can either completely encircle the arm or mold around the back of the forearm. The cuff can be made of leather, metal, or molded plastic and can be hinged or solid. If it is hinged, the person may find it is easier to perform activities with his or her hands without having to put down the crutches (Toms, 1989). A handgrip is positioned at a 90-degree angle from the bottom, or barrel, of the crutch. Metal forearm crutches have two interlocking metal cylinders that are adjustable for height below the handgrip. Some forearm crutches are also adjustable above the handgrip. Forearm crutches are more expensive than wooden axillary crutches and require the user to have strong upper extremities and good balance. Many people find them to be easier to use on stairs without railings (Toms, 1989). They are less bulky and thus easier to slide under a seat. Also, when using forearm crutches, there is no pressure under the arms as when using axillary crutches.

Canadian elbow extension crutches are not widely used, but sometimes are recommended for people who have weakness in their triceps muscles, which keep the elbow extended (Ragnarsson, 1993). This type of crutch, usually made of metal, has a single shaft attached to bilateral uprights, which extend to above the elbow and serve to keep the elbow straight. They have two half cuffs, one above and one below the elbow, and a handle (Ragnarsson, 1993).

Walkers

After an injury or illness that has affected a person's ability to walk, the first assistive walking device that he or she uses is often some type of walker. Although walkers come in many sizes and shapes and have many different features, they all have four points of contact with the floor or ground, thus providing a stable and wide base of support (Ragnarsson, 1993). There are even walkers available for people who only have the use of one arm. Sometimes, two or even all four of the points of contact are wheels, which decreases the stability but increases the speed of movement. Wheeled walkers can even have brakes that are similar to those used on 10-speed bicycles. Usually, walkers are made of metal and can be solid framed or collapsible for easy storage and transporting.

Young children with motor disabilities can be equipped with walkers when they begin to stand. A sling or a trunk stabilizer sometimes is used as added support to prevent the child from falling down. There are also walkers with removable seats and with adjustable handgrips that have been created to best meet the needs of the user. One advantage of walkers, especially for children, is that they can be equipped with baskets to carry toys, schoolwork, or other objects. The biggest drawbacks to walkers are their size and inappropriateness for use on stairs unless they are designed specifically as stair walkers (see Figure 5.1). Stair walkers have feet that adjust to steps, becoming shorter in front and longer in back when the person ascends stairs and longer in front and shorter in back when the person descends stairs (Ragnarsson, 1993).

Importance of Postural Support

To be able to use a mobility device, the person must be in a position to operate it (Trefler & Taylor, 1991). For many wheelchair users, positioning in the chair is of utmost importance because it provides the necessary postural support and balance that allows for the utilization of other assistive devices (Letts, 1991). What this means is that for a person to move his or her wheelchair forward, if it is a manual wheelchair, he or she has to be able to reach the wheels and propel the chair with his or her arms and hands, or if it is a motorized wheelchair,

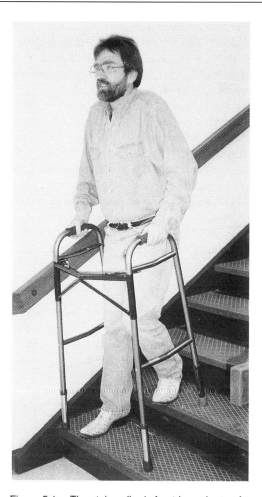

Figure 5.1.   The stair walker's front legs shorten for
ascending stairs and lengthen for descending stairs.

he or she has to be able to engage the control device with some part of his or her body. To accomplish this, a person needs to maintain a symmetrical, upright posture.

Seating systems, or other postural supports, are commonly placed in wheelchairs, but may also be used with regular furniture (e.g., office chairs), in automobiles, or with recreational equipment. For the purposes of this text, the focus is on those seating devices used in wheelchairs. Indications of need for a supported seating system include when:

- The person is unable to independently maintain an upright posture.
- Maintaining upright posture causes excessive fatigue.
- Contractures or other anatomic deformities cause asymmetrical positioning.
- There is too much pressure on any single area of skin.
- The sitting position affects breathing and swallowing capabilities.
- The person is experiencing pain caused by his or her unsupported posture.

Conducting a seating assessment requires the input from a team of professionals, including physicians, rehabilitation engineers, physical and occupational therapists, the equipment vendor, the individual, and his or her family and caregivers. The team first needs to identify all the problems that the person is experiencing related to seating. Next, the team needs to identify and prioritize the goals to be achieved with the seating system. Allowing a period of time for trial use of the proposed device is also important in order to make adjustments before fabrication and/or purchase. Finally, equipment is selected, purchased, and fitted based on meeting the higher priority goals (Currie, Hardwick, Marburger, & Britell, 1993). For example, one goal of the seating device may be to allow the person to have his or her head held in a midline position. Yet it may be more important for the seating design to allow the person to move his or her head to operate a control switch. As a result, the seating device would have to allow for the needed head movement.

Numerous off-the-shelf and customized products are available to use in the development of seating solutions. These products fall into three general categories: linear, contoured, and molded (Currie et al., 1993). There are several products in each category, with both advantages and disadvantages. Combinations of the three seating systems can be used to meet the needs of each individual user. Available products are frequently being changed and upgraded, and new products are continuously being introduced into the market for assistive technology users.

Linear Seating Systems

These are flat, firm surfaces (i.e., boards) that are covered with foam padding for comfort (see Figure 5.2). They are relatively inexpensive and provide for more movement, especially during transfers, and can easily accommodate for the growth of a child or adolescent. A wheelchair with taut seat and back upholstery that is appropriately sized to the individual is considered a linear seating system.

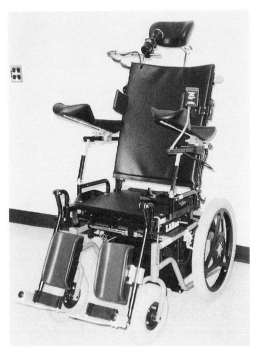

Figure 5.2.   An example of linear seating in a powered wheelchair.

Contoured Seating System

Contoured systems are those seats in which shaped surfaces are used to replicate and interface with the contours of the user's body. They are generic, one-size-fits-all devices usually available in 1-inch increments of width and depth or height. Contoured seating allows for better surface contact than linear systems, which means that the person is allowed less movement but more support with this system.

Molded Seating Systems

Molded systems are customized options that provide for intimate fit with an individual's body (see Figure 5.3). They are made from a direct or an indirect mold of the individual. These systems work well for persons with severe, fixed physical deformities by providing them with maximum support for the best postural alignment possible. Molded seats are generally very restrictive and hard for an individual to use without the aid of another person. Proper assessment, fitting, and regular follow-up are essential.

WHEELED MOBILITY

When a person is unable to walk, some form of wheeled mobility is usually the best option. Throughout the years, persons with disabilities have been creative in using already existing pieces of equipment, many being children's toys that have been adapted as inexpensive devices to assist with mobility. An example of this is the scooter board, similar in appearance and design to the device used by mechanics when they are working underneath a car. A young child with paralyzed lower extremities can lay or sit on a scooter board and use it to get

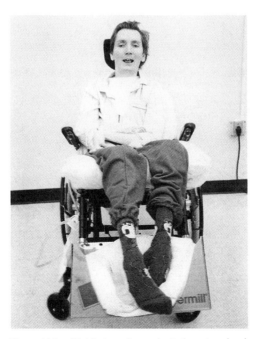

Figure 5.3. Molded seating adaptations to wheelchairs allow individuals with joint contractures and postural problems to maintain an upright, aligned position.

around inside his or her home, preschool, or child-care setting. Scooter boards, sometimes called knuckle boards, were used previously as an alternative to wheelchairs by people who had both legs amputated and who were unable to, or chose not to, use artificial limbs or crutches. The board was propelled either by short poles (similar to short ski poles) or by the knuckles of a person's gloved hands.

A more common means of moving about on wheels is through the use of a bicycle. There are myriad adapted bicycles and tricycles available for use by individuals who have various levels of physical abilities (Figure 5.4). There are upper-extremity–powered bikes, reclining bikes, tandem bikes, bikes with a seat in front for persons unable to assist with pedaling, side-by-side bikes, and motorized bikes (Landers, 1993). Bicycles and tricycles that are advertised as being specially adapted for persons with physical disabilities are usually expensive. Therefore, it is always best to look first at the equipment made for the general public to see if a similar model is available or if there is a model that can be modified for less than the cost of an already "adapted" bicycle.

Consideration must also be given to the strollers and buggies that are available for transporting young children or children who are unable to propel a wheelchair independently ("Wheeled mobility. . . ," 1994). Lightweight and collapsible, strollers and buggies are often the devices of choice because of their ease when traveling. Certain models of strollers can be specially adapted with head, trunk, and leg supports to meet the specific needs of each youngster. These adaptations are especially helpful for children who have poor head control and muscle weakness in their trunk. One drawback of strollers is that the child is always in a semireclining tilted position, which limits his or her field of vision (i.e., it is difficult to see the ground) and promotes a slouched posture. Perhaps the most important drawback that should be considered is that a stroller does not allow an individual to have independent mobility. The individual can only go where he or she is pushed.

Manual Wheelchairs

Although there are other wheeled mobility devices, the device most widely used by persons with disabilities who have difficulty walking or who are unable to use their lower extremities

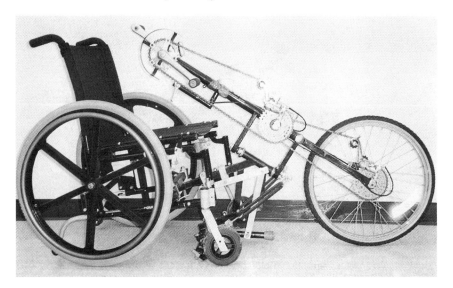

Figure 5.4.   An adapted bicycle can be used by someone who needs the trunk support of a wheelchair but is interested in the exercise benefits of a bicycle.

is the wheelchair. Great advances have been made in the performance of both manual and power wheelchairs through the use of better materials and through changes in configurations and components. The basic wheelchair design, however, has remained unchanged and still consists of a seat, a back, and a legrest/footrest on four wheels. High-performance athletic chairs are an exception in that some of them have a single front caster rather than the conventional two front casters (i.e., the two smaller wheels). The differences among various types of wheelchairs are becoming less defined as companies attempt to incorporate some of the more desirable features of higher cost wheelchairs into their more basic models.

A *standard manual wheelchair* is a basic mobility device. It is usually heavy and allows only minimal adjustment for comfort and no adjustment to enhance performance, but it is the least expensive wheelchair model available. Many have armrests and legrests that are not removable, which interfere with function for transfers and maneuvering under tables and desks or close to bathtubs and toilets. These chairs are typically difficult to propel and handle best when another person pushes them. Manual wheelchairs are often used to transport persons who cannot walk for long distances; thus, they are frequently available as a courtesy in malls, hospitals, and recreational areas.

As the name suggests, the *lightweight high-strength wheelchair* is made of a lighter weight material than the standard chair. Caster and rear wheel positions can be changed to create a tilt in the chair that will improve the user's posture. Also, the seat can be lowered to allow the user to use his or her lower extremities to help propel the wheelchair.

The *adjustable ultralight wheelchair* (Figure 5.5) allows for appropriate positioning of the back of the chair to provide postural support, but allows it to be low enough for free arm movement. Adjustments in the rear axle position and front casters change the tilt and better approximate the user's center of gravity. These adjustments increase the ease of propulsion of the wheelchair and allow for increased speed. Multiple options that will meet the needs of individual users are available for the various components of ultralight wheelchairs. Component options include: frame style (rigid versus folding); type of material from which the frame is made; type of upholstery; push handles; types of back posts; armrest styles; side guards; footrest hangers and angles of those hangers; front rigging; leg straps; heel loops; footplate sizes, materials, and adjustability; caster materials; size of release mechanisms; adjustment and mounting options; rear wheel sizes, materials, and

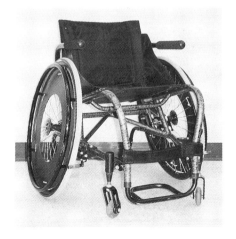 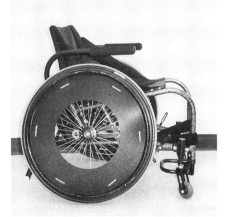

Figure 5.5.   Ultralight manual wheelchairs are easy to assemble and disassemble for transport and are a bonus for users who are active and have good arm strength.

mounting options; types of spokes and push rim variations; and brake mounts, styles, and lengths (Finkbeiner & Russo, 1990). Depending on the number of options, ultralight manual wheelchairs can cost more than $4,000, but average cost is usually between $1,800 and $2,800 ("Wheeled mobility. . . ," 1994).

Power Wheelchairs

In the past, a person's physical and cognitive limitations may have precluded his or her use of a power, or motorized, wheelchair. With current advances in the technology related to adjustments in control parameters and switch options, the degree of disability often is no longer a limiting factor. The cost, however, is sometimes limiting. The price of a power wheelchair is rarely less than $3,500 and can exceed $12,000 for chairs with specialized adaptations ("Wheeled mobility. . . ," 1994).

Power systems can often be added to manual wheelchairs to assist individuals who can no longer independently use the chair due to a change in their physical abilities. With a converted manual-to-power wheelchair, the motors turn against the rear tires or the rear tires are replaced with smaller tires that are attached to the motors. A joystick (Figure 5.6), which serves as the control lever, is attached to the armrest and a control module is mounted on the back of the wheelchair or underneath the seat. Batteries also are mounted underneath the seat. This wheelchair works well indoors and on moderate outdoor terrain. With the addition of the motors, it is difficult to propel the chair manually because of the increased weight and the joystick's interference with arm movement.

A standard power wheelchair is a viable option for the person who can operate a joystick with control and does not have weakness, tremors, or spasticity in his or her upper extremities. It has the familiar design of two front casters and two rear tires with the control module behind the backrest or underneath the chair and with the batteries underneath the chair as well. The joystick is mounted on the armrest. Control module settings are usually preset at

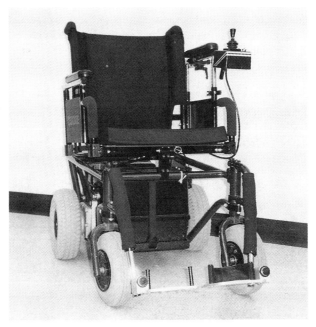

Figure 5.6. A "standard" powered wheelchair with a hand-operated joystick.

the factory and are not adjustable, with the exception of the option of a range of speeds. However, such options are limited. Interestingly, some standard power wheelchairs can be disassembled to allow the chair to be folded and transported easily in a car.

Wheelchair manufacturers have responded to the need for users of power chairs to make control module adjustments based on individual needs (Figure 5.7). A programmable control module allows individualization of the wheelchair to match the user's capabilities. The adjustment features vary and the number of options increase with expense. Some common adjustments are those that influence acceleration and deceleration rates, allowing the user to be more stable in the chair when he or she is starting and stopping. A tremor dampening adjustment, which is useful for persons with certain types of cerebral palsy, blocks extraneous upper extremity movements, thus avoiding erratic chair movements. The short throw adjustment allows persons with weaknesses or with limited ranges of motion to have decreased exertion requirements for full joystick control.

Control devices range from the traditional joystick mounted on the armrest for hand control or near the face for chin control to noncontact switches that respond proportionally to changes in the user's head position. The chair can be operated through these single control options or with multiple switches that control a single movement, such as forward, right, or left. These switches are mounted in positions that optimize the user's available motor control.

Tilt and recline features, which are available in both manual and power chairs, can be incorporated into a wheelchair to allow the user pressure relief or rest without having to get out of the wheelchair. A tilt feature maintains a static seat, back, and knee angle, while tilting the seat backward over the frame of the chair. A recline system opens up the seat, back, and knee angle to bring the person into a stretched-out position. Also available in both manual and power wheelchairs are options that will bring the person from a sitting position to a standing position while in the chair (Health Care Financing Administration, 1992).

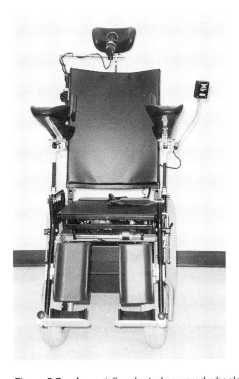 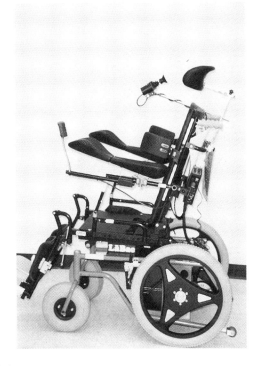

Figure 5.7. A specially adapted powered wheelchair.

Power-Operated Scooters

The power-operated vehicle, or scooter (Figure 5.8), as it is more commonly known, is a viable option for power-wheeled mobility. Some people are more willing to accept the use of a scooter than a traditional wheelchair, as the previous example with Tom illustrates. Scooters are typically configured with a tiller turning mechanism and have thumb-operated acceleration and braking. They are also available with a scooter-like base, with a joystick mounted on the armrest rather than a tiller control. Options are available for seats that pivot and elevate, as well as dual-wheel drive. The greatest advantage of power-operated scooters is that they allow the user to travel over terrain not accessible by wheelchairs. Some models can even be used to travel over sand and through shallow water (Wisniewski & Sedlak, 1992).

Vans and Automobiles

Getting in or out of an automobile is a problem for many individuals with disabilities who use wheelchairs or other seated mobility devices. "Adaptive modifications may be needed for opening the door, entering the vehicle, getting into the seat or driver's location, attaching safety restraints, and stowing mobility aids such as crutches and wheelchairs" (Enders & Hall, 1990, p. 337). Many adaptations require more room than is available in a typical mid-sized automobile. For this reason, many individuals with disabilities or their families choose minivans or full-sized vans as their personal vehicles. Adapted vans can be built to specifics at the factory or retrofitted after being purchased. Certain van models are more easily adapted for the type of lift or ramp that will be needed to enter the van, as well as for the type and position of seating that the wheelchair user will need to drive or ride in the van. Therefore, before purchasing a van, there are several basic factors that should be taken into consideration.

Will the person with the disability be a driver or a passenger? If the person is a first-time driver, he or she should be evaluated at a qualified Adaptive Driving Institute. Whether or not

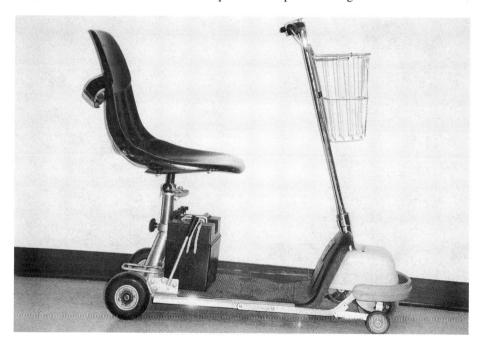

Figure 5.8. A motorized scooter can be used both outdoors and indoors.

the person with a disability is a driver or a passenger, make sure the width of the wheelchair is such that it will fit on the lift available for the type of vehicle being purchased. Also, know the height of the person when he or she is sitting in the wheelchair to determine if there will be adequate headroom inside the vehicle, as well as when getting on or off the lift or ramp. It is also important that the automobile dealer be familiar with the types of adaptive equipment available for the vehicle that he or she sells. The adaptive equipment dealer should also be certified by the manufacturer to install the chosen equipment (PARAdapt Services, n.d.).

ASSISTED DRIVING DEVICES

In the past, having a mobility disability during childhood often meant being denied one of the great American "rites of passage" into adulthood—driving an automobile. Many adults who acquire a disability that affects arm and/or leg movement have also been denied this privilege. Today, with the advent of such "standard" vehicle options as power steering, brakes, seats, and windows; cruise control; and tilt wheel (Enders & Hall, 1990), along with the adaptations that are available such as horizontal, foot, lever and zero-effort steering; zero-effort brakes; vacuum brake and gas systems; and power steering backup (Enders & Hall, 1990), many persons with disabilities are able to drive independently. For many persons, the assistive technology that makes it possible to drive a vehicle defines independence: It is the ability to get to work and perform the many functions associated with daily living (Enders & Hall, 1990).

Hand controls and steering devices can be used with most vehicles, but must be designed to meet the needs of each individual driver. There are products available that will completely operate the vehicle (i.e., gas pedal, brakes, horn, light dimmer switch) by using the hand control with one upper extremity. Some devices are mechanical, while other more sophisticated devices rely on computerized controls that operate with a joystick and a series of levers.

The General Motors Mobility Program for Persons with Disabilities has developed recommendations for drivers needing assistive devices in order to operate a personal vehicle. These include: 1) obtaining an evaluation, 2) contacting the state driver's license agency, 3) selecting the proper vehicle, 4) selecting a qualified equipment installer, and 5) obtaining proper training. (The following information is adapted with permission from General Motors Corporation, 1995.)

Obtain an Evaluation   Contact a local driver assessment facility to arrange for a complete evaluation. An evaluation should include an assessment of the person's sensory (including vision) and motor functions, cognitive processing, general knowledge, and an on-road performance evaluation in an appropriately modified vehicle. The evaluation should also include a review of the person's medical and driving history and his or her driver's license status. The assessment report should include recommendations regarding driving and a complete list of vehicle modification recommendations.

Contact the State Driver's License Agency   There are several conditions that may affect a person's ability to operate a motor vehicle and produce a potentially dangerous situation, both for the person and for the general public. By reporting a condition to the driver's license agency, a medical review can be conducted and, in many cases, driving privileges may be retained with restrictions. Failure to report a change in condition may put a person's driver's license status in jeopardy.

Select the Proper Vehicle   Do not purchase a vehicle, or any adapted device for the vehicle, before consulting with a professional. Although there is a broad range of vehicles and adaptive equipment available, finding the appropriate match is sometimes difficult. Space limitations in vehicles, vehicle use, family size, and the type of equipment required are all factors that must be considered.

Select a Qualified Equipment Installer When selecting a mobility equipment dealer, shop around and inquire about the qualifications, warranty, service practices, and capabilities of the dealer. Consider more than just initial cost, and ask the company for a list of references. Driver evaluation facilities and state rehabilitation services agencies are good sources of information on local mobility equipment installers.

Obtain Proper Training The equipment installer and/or driver evaluator should provide training in the proper use, care, and maintenance of the adaptive equipment and vehicle control system. In addition, the vehicle should be driven under the supervision of a qualified driving instructor until adequate driving skills are demonstrated.

ADAPTED EQUIPMENT USED FOR RECREATIONAL PURPOSES

Until now, this chapter did not address the assistive mobility devices used for recreational purposes. Assistive technology plays a major role in allowing an individual with a disability to get down a ski slope, across the surface of a lake or river, underneath the rim of a basketball hoop, or deep into the woods on the first day of hunting season. Recreational mobility devices are clearly not limited to just adapted bicycles or sports wheelchairs. There are sailboats that can be operated from a seated position, requiring a person to only use his or her upper extremities. Water skis are available for persons unable to stand. There are monoskis and biskis that allow a person to move down a ski slope with as much independence as possible, while remaining in a seated position. Devices that allow persons to snow ski in an upright position with the assistance of another skier are also available for individuals with visual disabilities and with limited mobility. It is important to remember that, with assistive technology, persons of all ages and with all types of disabilities can obtain mobility, which will enable them to get to places that they have been denied access to in the past.

CONCLUSION

Mobility is the process of moving from one place to another. Although this definition seems simplistic, the process can be quite complicated, especially for persons with physical disabilities. If a person is unable to stand, walk outside, and climb into a car or onto a bus to get where he or she wants to go, assistive technology is needed.

In this chapter, various types of assistive devices used for mobility are described. Factors that should be considered when assessing the need for a device are discussed, as well as who it is that decides what type of assistive technology is needed. Personal preference, environments, and lifestyle factors are just as important as functional considerations.

REFERENCES

Currie, D. M., Hardwick, K., Marburger, R. A., & Britell, C. W. (1993). Wheelchair prescription and adaptive seating. In J. A. DeLisa (Ed.), *Rehabilitation medicine principles and practice* (pp. 563–585). Philadelphia: J.B. Lippincott.
Enders, A., & Hall, M. (Eds.). (1990). *Assistive technology sourcebook.* Washington, DC: RESNA Press.
Finkbeiner, K., & Russo, S. (Eds.). (1990). *Physical therapy management of spinal cord injury: accent on independence.* Fishersville, VA: Woodrow Wilson Rehabilitation Center.
General Motors Corporation. (1995). *GM mobility program for persons with disabilities: Helping you meet your transportation needs* (pamphlet). Detroit, MI: Author.

Health Care Financing Administration. (1992). Clinical indications and other patient characteristics in selecting the appropriate wheelchair and accessories: A few suggested guidelines for wheelchair claim review. In *Draft new HCPCS codes for wheelchair accessories/replacement parts.* Baltimore: Author.

Holder-Brown, L., & Parette, H. P. (1992). Children with disabilities who use assistive technology: Ethical considerations. *Young Children, 47*(6), 73–77.

Landers, A. (1993). *Cycling: ABLEDATA database of assistive technology: Adaptive sports and recreation equipment* (ABLEDATA Fact Sheet No. 19). Silver Spring, MD: KRA Corporation and Macro International, Inc.

Letts, R. M. (1991). General principles of seating. In R. M. Letts (Ed.), *Principles of seating the disabled* (pp. 1–24). Boca Raton: CRC Press.

National Institutes of Health. (1990). *Draft V: Report and plan for medical rehabilitation research.* (Report of the Task Force on Medical Rehabilitation Research). Bethesda, MD: National Institutes of Health.

PARAdapt Services. (n.d.). (Brochure). Available from PARAdapt Services, 232 E. Belt Blvd., Richmond, VA 23224; (804) 233-8267.

Ragnarsson, K. T. (1993). Lower extremity orthotics, shoes, and gait aids. In J. A. DeLisa (Ed.), *Rehabilitation medicine principles and practice* (pp. 492–506). Philadelphia: J.B. Lippincott.

Toms, J. (1989). Mobility and ambulation aids. In R. M. Scully & M. R. Barnes (Eds.), *Physical therapy* (pp. 1052–1072). Philadelphia: J.B. Lippincott.

Trefler, E., & Taylor, S. J. (1991). Prescription and positioning: Evaluating the physically disabled individual for wheelchair seating. *Prosthetics and Orthotics International, 15*(3), 217–224.

Wheeled mobility selection: A guide for parents. (1994, March). *Exceptional Parent,* 23–30.

Wisniewski, L., & Sedlak, R. (1992). Assistive devices for students with disabilities. *The Elementary School Journal, 92*(3), 297–314.

6

Assistive Technology for Individuals with Sensory Impairments

Rustie Rothstein
Jane M. Everson

Most persons gather information from the environment, interacting with it and other humans through their senses of vision, hearing, touch, taste, and smell. Many practices and tools that people use in everyday life require the use of vision and/or hearing and depend to a lesser extent on the other three senses. Thus, persons rely most heavily on their senses of vision and hearing (ERIC Clearinghouse on Handicapped and Gifted Children, 1981). If one of these two vital senses is impaired, a person must learn to compensate by depending more heavily on his or her other vital sense (Kinney, 1972). If both vision and hearing become impaired, a person must learn to most effectively use his or her residual vision and/or hearing and to depend more heavily on one or more of his or her remaining three senses (Kinney, 1972). Vision and/or hearing impairments can have an impact on all aspects of a person's life—from expressive and receptive communication and mobility to competitive employment, recreation, and other everyday tasks.

Before the advent of technology in the twentieth century, individuals with sensory impairments used relatively low-tech strategies for dealing with their environment and with other persons. With society's increasing reliance on technology, including use of radio, telephone, mass transportation, television, and computers, the need for, as well as opportunities for, assistance have become more high tech. However, low-tech solutions must not be entirely disregarded; they remain some of the most effective and least expensive supports available to individuals with sensory impairments. Presently, an infinite array of homemade low-tech and commercially available high-tech assistive aids and devices enables individuals with sensory disabilities to live, work, and play more competently and safely.

This chapter describes some of the characteristics and technology support needs of individuals with sensory disabilities. Because commercially available technology changes so often and homemade technology is limited only to our understanding of an individual's sensory

The development of this chapter was supported in part by funds from the U.S. Department of Education (Cooperative Agreement #H025E20001). The opinions expressed are entirely those of the authors. No official endorsement by the U.S. Department of Education is intended or should be inferred.

The authors wish to thank Sr. Bernie Wynne and John Mascia of the Helen Keller National Center, Sands Point, New York, for their contributions to this chapter. Additional thanks are extended to Sandra Rosen, Ph.D., of San Francisco State University, San Francisco, California, and Jennifer Meadows of the ITRIAD Project, Indiana State University, Terre Haute, Indiana, for their assistance in completing this chapter.

impairments, the resources provided in this chapter should serve only as examples and not as definitive, person-specific solutions. Guidelines are included at the close of the chapter to assist service providers in identifying, selecting, creating, and evaluating assistive technology with persons who have sensory impairments.

INDIVIDUALS WITH SENSORY IMPAIRMENTS: DEFINING AND QUANTIFYING THE POPULATIONS

Defining individuals and groups with sensory impairments and quantifying their numbers would seem to be a relatively easy task. A sensory disability is physiologically defined by the degree and type of impairment, as well as by functional use of any remaining senses and the impact that the sensory losses have on everyday life. Actually labeling a person as having a sensory impairment, however, can be an individualized process. Two persons may have the same type and level of sensory impairment, yet only one person may consider him- or herself to have a disability and seek assistive technology to address the sensory loss. Thus, individuals experience disabilities only when the sensory impairments adversely affect their daily lives. Furthermore, the terminology and labels that individuals and groups use to refer to themselves vary along several parameters, including age of onset of the sensory losses, degree and type of sensory losses, and perhaps most importantly, educational and cultural experiences.

Individuals Who Are Visually Impaired or Blind

Definitions of visual impairment, legal blindness, and blindness were initially developed to delineate eligibility criteria for social security, rehabilitation, and special education services. Currently, definitions vary across legislation, as well as state and local agency and programmatic eligibility. Physiological tests, functional usage tests, and medical and educational histories are generally used by service providers to assign one or more of these labels to a person.

Vision is tested along two parameters: *acuity* (clarity of vision) and *fields* (peripheral vision). Normal acuity is the range between 20/20 and 20/40. A person with 20/20 vision can see what the perfect eye is defined as being able to see at 20 feet. A normal field of vision is defined as 160–180 degrees on the horizontal plane and 120 degrees on the vertical plane. A person whose vision proves to be lower than these standards is considered to have a visual impairment. A person is considered to be legally blind if his or her visual acuity is 20/200 or poorer in the better eye with best correction, or if a person's horizontal field of vision is 20 degrees or less.

A person who is legally blind may still have substantial residual vision, but functional use of the remaining vision depends on many factors (type of visual loss, age of onset of visual loss as well as availability of appropriate lighting and reduction of glare). Furthermore, there is much usable vision between legal blindness and total blindness. The term *low vision* refers to vision that is less than perfect, but better than total blindness. However, low vision is defined variably across programs and groups. Dr. August Colenbrander, an ophthalmologist specializing in low vision, defines it "as having a significant visual handicap but also having significant usable residual vision. [This definition is] deliberately broad and non-specific . . . because the determination of what is significant usable vision and what is not depends, in large, on the circumstances of an individual's life" (Faye, 1976, p. 4).

In addition to recognizing the variations in these definitions, the several differing philosophies among consumers and service providers regarding use of terminology and labels must also be understood. Some persons believe that adults with severe visual impairments, as part of the disability acceptance process, must be willing to label themselves as "blind." For these individuals, blindness becomes an all-encompassing, self-defining label. Still other persons (not wanting to "give up" and call themselves blind) believe that a person is only "visually impaired" even if he or she can only differentiate between light and dark or read very magnified print. Because terminology and labels go in and out of style and are based at least in part on the politics of consumer and professional groups, functional, consumer-responsive vision assessments—and not labels—should be used to determine an individual's need for and desire to use assistive technology.

Different types of visual impairments also have different effects on how an individual uses his or her residual vision. Mobility tends to be largely a function of peripheral vision, whereas reading tends to be mostly a function of central vision. Thus, a person with a central loss (e.g., macular degeneration) may be unable to read visually, but his or her mobility may not be significantly impaired. Conversely, a person with a significant field loss (e.g., retinitis pigmentosa) may have problems with mobility, but may not have a problem reading regular-sized print.

In addition to the type and severity of the visual impairment, age of onset also has an impact on the individual's use of residual vision and resultant level of disability. Children and adults who have sight learn many of their skills incidentally, that is, by watching other people. If an adult experiences an adventitious visual loss, he or she has a significant advantage because of visual memory. A child with a congenital visual impairment often must be taught skills (e.g., handshaking) and concepts (e.g., colors) that are acquired incidentally by children who have sight. This does not mean that adults who are visually impaired cannot reach the same levels of competence as persons who are sighted, it only means that teaching and learning must be attended to specifically (Barraga, 1976). Furthermore, some thinking patterns appear to differ for adults who are visually impaired, such as how space is judged or how to make a sequential orientation to a situation as opposed to a visual overview (Barraga, 1976).

Regardless of the age of onset or the type of severity of a visual impairment, these individuals often need to be taught how to make the best use of their residual vision. This responsibility generally belongs to a low vision specialist, a vision teacher, or a rehabilitation teacher. These service providers can assist individuals with visual impairments in using a large number of aids and devices to enhance residual vision. These aids and devices are explored later in this chapter.

How large is the population we are referring to? According to Nelson and Dimitrova (1993), the estimated number of persons in the United States who have severe visual impairments is 4,293,360. The Health Interview Survey from which the authors based their estimate defined *severe visual impairment* as an inability to read ordinary newspaper print even when wearing glasses or contacts. This survey was limited to a civilian, noninstitutionalized population. The incidence of visual impairments increases with age (Luey, Belsa, & Glass, 1989), thus the population of persons with visual impairments older than 65 years of age is the most rapidly increasing group (Nelson & Dimitrova, 1993).

Individuals Who Are Hard of Hearing or Deaf

Hearing is also tested along two parameters—loudness and frequency. *Loudness* is a measure of the degree of sound and is measured in decibels (dB), and a person's degree of hearing loss is described in terms of how loud a sound must be for the individual to hear it. *Frequency* is the measure of a sound's pitch, either high or low, and is measured in hertz (Hz). A person's hearing loss is measured by seeing how loud a sound must be at a given frequency to be heard by him or her.

Hearing losses are also categorized as either conductive, sensorineural, or mixed (a combination of the two). A *conductive loss* is a loss in which movement of environmental sounds through the outer and middle ear to the inner ear is inhibited, causing a loss of sound sensitivity. A conductive impairment causes an even decibel loss across all frequencies. Hearing aids, assistive listening devices (ALDs), and surgery can often help a conductive hearing loss. A *sensorineural loss* is a loss of sound sensitivity and clarity caused by abnormalities in the inner ear or in the nerve pathways from the ear to the brain. Both the amount of decibel loss and the frequencies at which the loss occurs depend on the site and amount of damage or abnormality to the nerves and/or auditory receptors. A person with a sensorineural loss may have variable losses at different frequencies (e.g., a 35 dB loss at 500 Hz, a 50 dB loss at 1,000 Hz). Sensorineural losses may respond to amplification, such as that provided by a hearing aid, but clarity of sound will not be enhanced (Alpiner & McCarthy, 1993). A person with a sensorineural loss may hear environmental sounds and be able to make functional use of them, but may not be able to hear speech well enough to use it functionally. Just as acuity is important in measuring vision, clarity is important in measuring hearing. It is vital for service providers to know if, at a certain dB level, an individual can hear and identify a sound, or if he or she can understand speech. Therefore, along with testing an individual's ability to hear pure tones, an audiologist will also test for speech discrimination. As with vision, individuals often need to be trained by audiologists to make the most effective use of their residual hearing.

Because infants learn language by imitating what is spoken around them, age of onset of a hearing impairment is vitally important. Spoken language is the foundation on which children learn to read and write. If a hearing loss is congenital or occurs before age 3, it is considered a *prelingual loss*, meaning there have been minimal opportunities to learn spoken language. Prelingually deaf adults generally learn and use American Sign Language (ASL) as their primary, native language. As a result, English becomes a second language and the average adult who is prelingually deaf never acquires more than a fourth- to fifth-grade reading level (Levine, 1981).

A hearing loss between the ages of 3 and 19 is considered a *prevocational loss* and is of concern because it affects both career awareness and career exploration activities, as well as the availability of internships, part-time jobs, and other career experiences. These individuals may use spoken English and/or ASL. Because most essential language elements are learned by the age of 3, a prevocational hearing loss may affect the quality of speech, but not necessarily comprehension of the English language (Schein, 1978). The later in a person's life that the hearing loss occurs, the better his or her spoken language skills will be. Hearing loss after the age of 19 is considered to be postvocational and does not have as much of an impact on adult vocational options. However, if an individual's job relies heavily on hearing, job retraining and/or assistive technology may be necessary if a hearing loss occurs.

Individuals with hearing impairments, similar to those with visual impairments, may or may not consider themselves to be disabled and may express strong preferences regarding the use of labels and terminology. Hearing losses and associated labels and terminology are classified by the amount of decibel loss involved. Over the years, different professional groups have developed several classification systems to describe a person's hearing loss. The labels "mild," "moderate," "severe," and "profound" are used by all groups, but the groups often define the terms differently. One common delineation is 25–40 dB (mild loss), difficulty understanding normal speech; 41–55 dB (moderate loss), difficulty understanding loud speech; 56–80 dB (severe loss), can understand amplified speech only; and 81 dB (more profound loss), difficulty or inability to understand even amplified speech.

There are several ways of differentiating if someone is "hard of hearing" or "deaf." A person who is deaf is one whose hearing is impaired to an extent (usually 70 dB or greater) that precludes the understanding of speech through the ear alone, with or without the use of a hearing aid; while a person who is hard of hearing is one whose hearing is impaired to an extent (usually 35–69 dB) that makes difficult, but does not preclude, the understanding of speech through the ear alone, with or without a hearing aid (Moores, 1987). A second way is through the audiogram, a test of the level of dB loss. According to the American Speech-Language-Hearing Association, a person who has an unaided loss of less than or equal to 90 dB is considered to be hard of hearing, while someone with a loss of more than 90 dB is considered to be deaf. ("Deaf" refers to cultural deafness; "deaf" refers to hearing loss as measured on an audiogram.) A third way of differentiation is self-identification: Does the individual consider him- or herself to be Deaf based on his or her use of ASL as the primary language and on his or her adherence to Deaf culture? Persons who identify themselves as Deaf tend to be more comfortable in environments and situations with other persons who are Deaf in which ASL is the primary language used to communicate. Persons who consider themselves to be hard of hearing consider English as their primary language. Persons who are hard of hearing generally use their residual hearing along with speechreading as a receptive communication mode and speech as an expressive communication mode, and generally are more comfortable with persons who can hear than persons who are Deaf. The distinction here has nothing to do with hearing level. A person who has a 70 dB hearing loss may consider him- or herself to be Deaf, and a person with a 95 dB loss may consider him- or herself to be hard of hearing. Both groups, however, have indicated a preference for being referred to as "deaf" or "hard of hearing" rather than "hearing impaired."

Although age of onset and amount of residual hearing correlate highly with an individual's ability to learn to speak understandably, and competence in the language and residual hearing correlate highly with speechreading, these two skills have no relation to each other (Perry & Silverman, 1978). Speechreading relies on the reader's ability to differentiate between words that look the same on a speaker's lips, thus English language skills are helpful. Even a good speechreader can "read" only 40%–50% of spoken words; the rest requires guesswork (Perry & Silverman, 1978).

Rehabilitation for persons who are hard of hearing or deaf can take the form of corrective surgery, provision of hearing aids or ALDs, other specialized equipment, or specialized support services, including interpreters and/or notetakers. Local departments of rehabilitation can serve any client whose hearing loss substantially inhibits his or her employment. Heavy reliance on spoken and written English and limited knowledge of ASL among the general public makes living in a "hearing" world much easier for persons who are postlingually hard of hearing or deaf than for persons who are prelingually hard of hearing or deaf.

The incidence of hearing impairment in the U.S. population is about 8.5%, or an estimated 23,296,000 (National Association of the Deaf, 1992; National Center for Health Statistics, personal communication, October 13, 1993). It is estimated that between one half and 2 million of these individuals are deaf (National Association of the Deaf, 1992; National Center for Health Statistics, personal communication, October 13, 1993). As with vision impairments, the incidence of hearing impairment also increases as a population ages (Mascia, 1994).

Individuals Who Are Deaf-Blind

The term *deaf-blind* is somewhat of a misnomer, as a person does not need to be totally deaf and blind; that is, any person who has both a hearing and a vision impairment may be considered to be deaf-blind. There is great diversity among the population of persons who are deaf-blind—in amount of residual vision, residual hearing, additional disabling conditions, age of onset and etiology, as well as a host of other educational and cultural parameters. There are at least 80 different syndromes that result in dual vision and hearing losses (Regenbogen & Coscas, 1985). Toxins, trauma, and aging are also significant causes (Wynne, 1987).

Most important, service providers must recognize that being deaf-blind is a disability in and of itself; it is not the sum total of deafness and blindness (Wynne, 1987). Unlike a person with a hearing impairment who can compensate with use of vision or an individual who is visually impaired who can rely more heavily on hearing, a person who is deaf-blind may have some residual use of both hearing and vision, but may not be able to compensate fully with either for the loss of the other. The concomitant nature of the dual losses can cause severe communication, social, emotional, behavioral, medical, educational, and vocational problems. It is the combination of sensory and related disabilities, more than the amount or type of hearing or vision loss, that requires a person who is deaf-blind to be considered in a category by him- or herself.

The population divides into four subgroups, which are based on age of onset and the primary disability, or at least the disability that occurred first (Wynne, 1987). The first subgroup consists of individuals who are congenitally deaf-blind. The largest etiology is congenital rubella syndrome (Orenstein, Bart, Bart, Sirotkin, & Hinman, 1986). Another more recently defined group is those with CHARGE (Coloboma, Heart disease, Artesia choanae, Retarded growth, Genital hypoplasia, Ear anomalies) association (Pagon, Graham, Zonana, & Yong, 1981). The amount of vision and hearing impairment varies tremendously among those labeled congenitally deaf-blind, and there is a high incidence of additional developmental and medical disabilities (Wolff & Harkins, 1986). Service providers should note that labels of mental retardation among individuals who are congenitally deaf-blind may be related more to lack of sensory information and appropriate communication training than lack of cognitive abilities.

The second subgroup consists of individuals who are born deaf or hearing impaired and who later become visually impaired or blind. The most prevalent etiology in this group is Usher syndrome, type I (Wynne, 1987), the combination of prelingual deafness and progressive blindness due to retinitis pigmentosa. Other etiologies include deafness combined with other degenerative vision conditions, such as glaucoma, macular degeneration, or optic atrophy. This group typically identifies with the Deaf community, using ASL as the primary language. If vision becomes so poor that reception of sign language through the visual mode is no longer possible, the individual must switch to tactual signing. (Tactual signing requires the communicator to sign or fingerspell in the receiver's palm so that he or she can feel rather than see communication.)

The third subgroup consists of individuals who are congenitally blind or visually impaired, who later become deaf or hearing impaired. Typically, this group uses speech expressively and braille receptively, and has good mobility skills, having learned to depend on their hearing. When a visual loss occurs, they must develop new communication and mobility coping skills.

The last subgroup consists of individuals who become adventitiously deaf-blind or hearing-vision impaired. The most prevalent etiology in this group is Usher syndrome, type II (Wynne, 1987). Typically, these individuals have had a mild to moderate hearing loss since birth or early childhood, and consider themselves "hard of hearing." As retinitis pigmentosa, the vision impairment associated with Usher syndrome, manifests itself in adulthood, the hearing loss, although not progressive itself, appears more significant because of the loss of vision that had been used in compensation. In some cases, the hearing loss also becomes more severe.

There is a common characteristic among individuals in the third and fourth groups; that is, both groups rely on spoken English (or another language) for basic communication. If their hearing loss becomes too severe, they find themselves unable to receive communication from others. Persons in group three tend to use braille and learn receptive fingerspelling, while those in group four tend to use residual hearing until it is no longer possible. Persons in both groups continue to express themselves through speech even after adopting fingerspelling or other receptive communication modes.

Individuals who are deaf-blind often find rehabilitative services difficult to obtain. Although they are categorized as being severely disabled by most departments of rehabilitation, there are not many rehabilitation professionals who are knowledgeable about persons who are deaf-blind (Watson & Taff-Watson, 1993). Most professionals understand either deafness or blindness, but do not understand dual losses. This lack of knowledge makes it difficult for individuals who are deaf-blind to obtain access to appropriate assistive technology.

It is especially difficult to quantify this population. Some individuals are counted among the population of persons who are blind, deaf, multiply disabled, severely disabled, or developmentally disabled. There are very few agencies that provide services specifically designed for individuals who are deaf-blind; therefore, separate numbers are not generally maintained. In 1991, the Massachusetts Institute of Technology estimated that there were 500,000 persons who were deaf-blind in the United States (Lependorf, 1991). That same year, Rehabilitation Experts, Inc., of Washington, D.C. (Lependorf, 1991), estimated the population to be at 733,000, consisting of 42,000 persons who were deaf-blind; 25,000 persons who were deaf-visually impaired; 357,000 persons who were hearing impaired-blind; and 309,000 persons who were vision-hearing impaired.

APPLICATIONS OF ASSISTIVE TECHNOLOGY RELATED TO VISUAL IMPAIRMENTS AND BLINDNESS

Mobility in the Community

One of the most basic measures of an individual's independence is moving from place to place in his or her environment. Mobility is also a measure of independence for an individual with a vision impairment. The task of mobility can be broken down into two component skills: 1) *orientation*, or the process of establishing one's position and relationship to other significant objects in the environment; and 2) *mobility*, or the ability to navigate safely from one place to another (Jacobson, 1993). The challenge is to create substitute methods for the visual collection of environmental information. For the most part, all the devices described in this section aid only in navigation; a person who is blind must either be oriented to a new environment by a person who has sight, or spend time investigating it him- or herself using these devices and the remaining senses. Assessment of mobility skills and needs, selection of assistive aids and devices, as well as training and evaluation in the use of such devices is the responsibility of specially trained and certified orientation and mobility specialists.

For many years, the only mobility device available was the long, white cane. When used properly, this cane provides information about objects in a person's path, as well as drop-offs, steps, and changes in surface texture. However, information obtained from the cane is limited to what is within the cane's reach. It will not alert a user to objects above waist level that overhang or protrude into the body's path. The mobility cane is available in a variety of models, including rigid canes, folding canes, and telescope canes. Some are made of aluminum tubing, others of carbon fiber. Tips can be nylon, abrasion-resistant plastic, or metal glide tips. Nylon and plastic tips come in straight or marshmallow styles. One cane has a small, high-intensity flashing strobe built in below the grip for additional safety. The strobe can be turned on with a slide switch located on the grip when needed.

Dog guides are used by approximately 2% of persons who are blind (J. Deuschle, personal communication, May 2, 1994). A dog will guide its master around any object in his or her path including overhanging or protruding objects, will stop at curbs and stairs, and can even be trained to find doorways that lead to the outside, an elevator, or stairs. A dog cannot, however, decide where to go or how to get there. The master must be able to decide when it is safe to cross the street or which route to take.

Although they are not frequently used, electronic travel aids (ETAs) have been recently developed to provide some of the orientation information untapped by canes and dog guides. The most widely known ETAs are the Laser Cane (Nurion Industries, Paoli, PA) and the Mowat Sensor (Mobility Services, Inc., Atlanta). Most ETAs send out a signal that is bounced back from objects in the traveler's path. The Laser Cane technology has also been modified and attached to a wheelchair. The Mowat Sensor is a secondary aid, to be used with a dog guide or long cane. A small handheld case emits an ultrasonic signal. When the signal is bounced back by an object, the device vibrates or emits an audible signal. The Polaron (Nurion), a similar ETA, can be handheld or worn on a lanyard around the traveler's neck so that his or her hands are free while walking or using a wheelchair.

Travelers who are blind use either residual hearing or vision to know when it is safe to cross a street. Individuals with low vision may enhance their vision with a monocular, which enables them to see signal lights and street signs at a distance. Audible signals may be used to alert the traveler that a traffic light has changed to green and that there is time to cross the street. Two different sounds are produced, one for the north–south street and one for the east–west street. When no signal is heard, it means that the time to start a safe trip has expired, and the traveler must wait for the next light.

The newest type of ETA is the talking sign. This device consists of a transmitter and a personal receiver for each traveler using the system. The transmitter is attached to a traffic signal and can send out information about streets at an intersection or about the status of a signal (e.g., walk, don't walk). The information is sent out via an infrared or radio-frequency signal. The infrared beam can be set to extend the width of a crosswalk, thus providing additional environmental information. Several different receivers might be available using headphones. These devices could also be used to provide auditory information about the address of a particular building or the correct path of travel in an environment such as an airport or office building.

The Wide Angle Mobility Light (WAML) is one final ETA worth noting. For adults who have difficulty traveling in the dark and who do not wish to use a cane, the WAML provides a wide-angle, high-intensity light beam, similar to a giant flashlight. It is made by modifying a rechargeable scuba dive light with a carrying strap.

The mobility devices discussed in this chapter should be purchased and used only with assistance from a qualified orientation and mobility instructor. This assistance will ensure proper fit and safe usage. Replacement or additional equipment may be purchased from many of the agencies and catalogs listed at the end of this chapter.

Mobility in the Home

There are a variety of specialized devices for persons who are blind or visually impaired that enable them to live more independently at home. Many devices were developed with this population in mind and have become more readily available as the U.S. population ages and as persons desire to live at home longer. Other devices are the result of our increasingly technological society and have unintentionally assisted individuals who have visual impairments.

For many years, books were recorded onto special long-play records called talking books. With cassette tape recording technology, most recordings made for persons who are blind are now on four-track cassette tapes, taped at extremely slow speeds to allow more information to fit onto each tape. Special recorders and playback machines are available for these four-track tapes and offer variable-speed playback and even speech compression. Technology allows even material in record form to be on smaller, inexpensive, floppy records that can be discarded after use. (Now even persons who are blind can receive junk mail!)

Reading and writing are taken for granted by most persons who have sight. It is easy to jot down or read a note. A braillewriter and a slate and stylus take the place of the pen and the typewriter for persons who are blind. *Braille* is a system of embossed dots in a cell that is three dots high and two dots across. Braille is not a language in itself, but rather a system for transcribing print into embossed form. Although a braillewriter is fine for use at home or at a person's desk at the office, it is no more portable than a small typewriter. Thus, a slate and stylus, easily carried in a purse or pocket, is used by many individuals. (See Case Study 6.1.) A slate is a hinged metal device with a front and back (like a book), which is closed with a piece of braille paper in between. It acts as a guide when writing braille manually. The stylus is a hand-held device with a dull point, used to press the dots into the braille paper. The slate

---

Case Study 6.1: Ricardo

Ricardo is a high school teacher who is totally blind. He uses a combination of high and low technology to meet his everyday needs. He is comfortable using a slate and stylus to manually produce braille or a braille notetaking device, which can dump information into his computer. (His computer also has voice output and can be connected to both a braille embosser and a regular printer.) Ricardo likes to use the slate and stylus when he will need to refer back to the information quickly, such as in a class or meeting where he will jot down a question or an item to bring up in the discussion. At home, he keeps his addresses in braille on 3″ × 5″ cards and always has a slate and stylus and a few blank cards near the phone.

To take general notes in a meeting, write correspondence, or prepare notes for lectures, Ricardo uses the notetaking device. He can then get a braille or print copy made any time he needs it. He finds he uses his notetaking device much as his colleagues with sight use a laptop computer and uses the slate and stylus the places a person with sight would jot down a note on a scrap of paper. For correcting student papers and doing other personal business, he employs a reader who has sight. Sometimes the reader works in person and other times she tapes the material.

Ricardo uses a dog guide for most of his travel purposes, but has used a cane in the past and keeps up his cane skills for independence in places it may not be suitable to bring a dog or in the event that the dog becomes ill. Ricardo lives in an area that does not have a good transit system. Luckily, he can walk to work, but he must get a ride to most other places.

At home, Ricardo listens to radio news and to the radio reading service for additional information. He receives the *New York Times* weekly braille edition. He especially enjoys television shows and movies that include descriptive video information.

has indentations across its back piece and the outline of a braille cell across its front to guide the writer. Slates come in a variety of sizes to fit 8 1/2″× 11″ paper, 3″ × 5″ cards, and cassette tape labels.

Clocks and watches are available with braille faces and with large-print, high-contrast faces, both in analog and digital formats. Also, watches and clocks are available that will audibly announce the time and date. Most have audible alarm functions. Several different timers, both analog and digital, are also available.

Telephones are available with large buttons, which are especially helpful for individuals who are used to doing things visually but who now have impaired vision. Other individuals find it easier to use regular push-button or dial phones. One-touch and speed dialing can also be helpful.

Many home chores require the use of appliances with gauges or controls: washers, dryers, stoves, microwave ovens, and thermostats. Many manufacturers make special controls that can either be read tactually or have larger numbers (see Case Study 6.2). Frequently, local gas or electric companies provide free modification so that household appliances are accessible. There are also several products that can mark regular appliances with fluorescent or tactual dots at various settings.

There are many kitchen tools available. Specialized tools include knives with cutting guides, cooking thermometers with tactual gauges, pots with special lids to help drain liquids, spatulas with top and bottom blades to grasp the item to be turned, and liquid level-meters that emit a sound when a cup is near capacity. Braille or large-print label makers are available for canned, packaged, and leftover food. These devices can also be used to make shopping lists. Many cookbooks and appliance manuals are available in large print, in braille, or on cassette tape.

Case Study 6.2: Margarite

Margarite is a psychologist who is totally blind. She lost her vision due to diabetes while she was in college. For making personal notes, she uses a Perkins brailler or a slate and stylus. She also uses a computer with voice output and has recently purchased an optical character reader so she can input print materials and have the computer read them aloud to her. Now she is beginning to feel that she can keep up with the professional journals she could not read in the past.

In the past, Margarite used a dog guide to travel independently, but now she uses a car and driver for independent mobility. At home, many of the appliances she uses have been marked with braille or raised markings. Some of these she has done herself, such as the washer and dryer; she used a combination of labeling tape with braille markings and raised dots made with puff paint to mark the cycles she most often uses. A service technician from the local gas and electric company marked her oven dials, and her thermostat and microwave have special tactual dials from the manufacturer. She also has a talking clock in her bedroom, but she prefers to use a braille watch so she can check the time during therapy sessions and meetings.

To independently control her diabetes, Margarite uses a tactual guide for drawing the right amount of insulin into her syringe. For checking her blood sugar she uses a talking glucose monitor. Margarite is hoping to get an insulin pump implanted to alleviate the need for daily insulin injections.

To assist with personal grooming, there are talking thermometers, talking scales, and talking blood pressure gauges. Braille and large-print labels are easy to make for prescription medicines and other items in a medicine chest. Pill dispensers designed to organize a week's worth of medication usually have braille markings. For individuals with low vision, several mirrors with magnification up to 5× are commercially available. Because diabetes is a major cause of blindness, there is an array of devices that allow an adult who is blind and diabetic to be independent in checking blood sugar levels and measuring insulin dosages. For independent clothing care, there are several different types of labels for marking colors, patterns, and sizes on individual clothing items. Such labeling solves the laundry sorting problem for many adults who are blind. Iron safety guides are also commercially available. For mending, there are several needle threaders or easy-thread needles available. For measuring, there are tape measures and rulers with tactual markings.

In the area of recreation and leisure, many popular games have braille, large-print, or tactual versions. Books are available in braille, large-print, cassette, and talking book formats as well. For "couch potatoes," there are television screen magnifiers and radios that receive VHF and UHF television audio bands, as well as the standard AM and FM. Some television shows, and even some live theaters, have begun including audiodescriptive narration. This takes place between segments of dialogue and describes the setting or action taking place. When this is done in conjunction with a live play, the listener uses special receivers to receive the additional audio information. Some cities have special radio stations that broadcast distinct programs, such as a person reading select parts of the newspaper. At the gym, adults who are visually impaired can use tactual locks on their lockers. For field-type games, there is an array of audible devices (beepers) that can be used either as sound sources or to make balls and other objects project a sound to assist the person in finding their location.

For personal record keeping, there are both large-print and braille calendars and telephone books. Guides are available for writing checks, addressing envelopes, and writing in straight lines. Broad-tipped felt markers make print easier to read than either pen or pencil. Large-print checks and check records are obtainable from many banks or can be mail ordered from some of the companies listed at the end of this chapter. Talking calculators can report how much money is left in an individual's checking account. An assortment of lamps and magnifiers are available to help improve lighting conditions throughout the house for persons with low vision.

Several different light probes are on the market that can be used for a variety of tasks. One probe allows a person who is completely blind to know if there are any lights on in a room, so that they may be turned on or off as appropriate. Some light probes can be used to detect contrast; this is useful for someone putting stationery, letterhead side up, in a typewriter. Probes can also be used with a multiline telephone to know which line needs to be answered and which line is on hold.

Mobility at Work

As workplaces for persons with vision have become more technologically oriented, much of the same technology has assisted employees who are visually impaired or blind. Much equipment originally designed for workplace usage—calculators, computers, fax machines, and complex telephone systems—can now be found at home.

If braille is useful in the home, it is also useful in the workplace. There are specialized codes for mathematics, music, and computer notation. Any text can be transcribed into braille, however, this can prove to be slow and costly. In addition, not every person who is blind can read braille. So how can the print world be made available to all individuals who are blind or severely visually impaired?

Closed circuit television (CCTV) systems combine a video camera with a video monitor in a configuration that allows text from a book or other print medium to be shown on the video screen (see Case Study 6.3). The text can then be magnified for easier reading by an individual with a visual impairment. Polarity on the CCTV can be switched, changing the screen from black text on white background to white text on black background, which is generally more comfortable to read. These devices also can be used in conjunction with typewriters and computers that have either single or split screens. Because computers have become such an important part of everyone's life, an array of software has been developed that enlarges the print on computer screens.

Opticon (TeleSensory) is a device that converts print into tactual form. It uses a small hand-controlled video camera that the user runs across a printed page, one line at a time. Simultaneously, the user places one finger from the other hand in the output device, reading small plastic pins that are raised and vibrate the configuration of the letters and words picked up by the camera. A variety of type styles and media can be read this way, including computer screens.

The same speech technology that allows for all the previously discussed "talking" devices, combined with optical character recognition systems, led the way for several different reading systems. These systems take print materials and read them aloud in computer-simulated speech. For computers to be totally accessible to workers who are blind, a wide array of adaptive equipment and support software is necessary. A variety of braille display devices, speech output devices, and braille embossers (the equivalent of a printer) are commercially available. Because computers are not always practical to tote around, small braille notetakers have been developed that can be used to take personal notes in school or at business meetings. Later, information can be entered into a computer, word processor, printer, or braille embosser. Just as laptop computers have become more accessible to the general population, smaller and more portable braille and speech-output computers have also become more available to individuals who are visually impaired or blind.

Several distinct problems arose when engineers attempted to make computers accessible for users who are blind. One problem was how to alert the user to what information is located where on the screen. Some braille displays solved this problem. For users who prefer speech

---

Case Study 6.3: Ann

Ann works as an administrator for a social service agency. She is partially sighted and uses a variety of technology to assist her in her everyday work tasks. She uses a CCTV system to enlarge brief print materials that she has to read, such as correspondence, invoices, memos, and notes. She is also able to gain access to computer information by way of either a magnified screen or speech output. If she has longer printed materials to read, she will sometimes use an optical character reader to scan the information into the computer. She decides whether she will use speech output or a magnified screen based on the type of material, whether she needs to take notes on it, and her vision that day.

Outside the office, Ann does not find mobility a significant problem, but she does carry a white cane for use at night, in unfamiliar places, and for identification. For most of her transportation needs, Ann uses the local transit system. Luckily, she lives in a city in which the transit system is both adequate and user friendly.

access to their computers, one company (HumanWare) produced a "touch tablet." This works similar to computer touch screens, by reading whatever is on the monitor that corresponds to the place touched on the tablet. The tablet lies flat on the desk next to the computer and has raised ridges that correspond to the lines on the screen. Adaptations within the DOS environment were readily available; then Windows was developed. Recently, several screen-review programs have become available that allow a person to gain access to the Windows environment for both braille and speech output.

There was an additional barrier to overcome with braille and print interface. Braille has two grades or levels. Grade one uses one braille cell to represent each letter or punctuation mark, and as such there is almost a one-to-one correspondence between print and braille. When letters are capitalized, or the print changes to italic, is underlined, or is bold, and when numbers are used, additional cells are used to signal the changes. Also, due to the bulkiness of braille as an embossed system, most published materials are in grade two. Grade two uses a host of abbreviations, short forms, contractions, and single-letter representations for whole words as a means of compressing text and increasing reading speed. Furthermore, in grade two, the same configuration of dots may mean different things when placed differently. To overcome this, several different pieces of hardware and software have been developed. These can be used by a person who is blind using grade two braille on a notetaking device in order to write a report and allow it to be translated into printed English for a computer or printer. This hardware can also be used by a transcriber when he or she is using a computer to transcribe print materials into grade two braille.

Historically, one occupation in which many individuals who are blind and visually impaired have traditionally been employed is vending. For many years, these vendors had to rely on the honesty of their customers when accepting money. With the development of optical character recognition systems, a device that will not only provide voice output for the denomination of a given bill, but also let the vendor know if it is a counterfeit, was developed. Although this device could also be useful in everyday life, its cost and bulkiness have limited the device to the workplace.

Because persons who are blind now enjoy a variety of occupations, new adaptations are continually being developed to accommodate them (see Case Study 6.4). For a person who is blind to be able to run a switchboard, he or she had to be able to know which light was signaling which phone line—the light probe solved this problem. For a worker who is blind to be able to measure the tolerance of manufactured materials before assembly, special micrometers were developed. For a worker who is blind to know the readouts on various digital instruments, speech-output devices have been made available. The list of adapted devices will continue to grow as long as people who are blind and visually impaired are allowed to explore new options in jobs and careers.

APPLICATIONS FOR ASSISTIVE TECHNOLOGY RELATED TO HEARING IMPAIRMENTS AND DEAFNESS

Usefulness of technology for persons who are hard of hearing or deaf depends greatly on the type of communication used as well as the amount and type of residual hearing the adult retains. To simplify the discussion in this section of the chapter, assistive technology will be referred to for persons who are hard of hearing or for persons who are deaf. By looking at technology in this way, we will be separating it into that which is used to enhance auditory reception and that which uses other means to provide access. In everyday life, many people actually use both types of technology, switching according to the situation and personal preference. In addition, much of the technology has application across a variety of settings.

Case Study 6.4: Hans

Hans is the manager of sales for a large hotel; he is in charge of all catering, banquet, and meeting arrangements. Hans is totally blind. Hans originally decided to go into this field because of an experience he had during college. He attended the national conference of a blind consumer organization and was amazed at the amount of planning it took by both the organization and the hotel, and the coordination between the two. Once he decided on the field, nothing could deter him.

In the pre-ADA days of the 1970s, Hans realized that he would need better than average credentials to get a job in an area in which no other blind people worked. He applied and was accepted into a nationally recognized graduate program in hotel/motel management. While there, he had to do an internship at a large New York hotel. This involved a rotation of all the different departments at the hotel, including janitorial (where he had to clean rooms) and behind the bar mixing drinks. Once Hans completed graduate school, finding a job was more difficult than he expected. Today, he works for a large hotel chain in one of its hotels on the West Coast.

At work, Hans uses a computer with synthetic speech, a braille embosser, and a scanner. To take notes during client meetings, he uses either a slate and stylus or a braille notetaker. At the end of the meeting, he can either transfer brief notes manually into the correct file by typing them into the computer, or he can dump more extensive notes directly into the computer from his notetaking device.

When he is out of his office, Hans always carries a slate and stylus and a supply of note cards for jotting down quick notes. In arranging for table and chair setups, he uses a book with all the usual setups pictured. By the customer telling him the code on that page, Hans knows exactly which diagram is being discussed and can take notes on any changes necessary.

Communicating

At any conference in which there are large numbers of persons who are hard of hearing and deaf, inexperienced service providers will be amazed at the number of different ways communication is used simultaneously by different people. Most persons who are deaf prefer that the speaker sign for him- or herself. The audience of persons who are deaf may gain access to signing through a large video screen if the room is too big, or they may seat themselves closer to the speaker. If the speaker does not sign, the audience of persons who are deaf will need to either watch the interpreter or the interpreter's image on the video screen. At the same time, other deaf members of the audience will rely on real-time captioning, which appears at the bottom of the video screen. Still others may watch an oral interpreter.

For people who are hard of hearing, some may use their hearing aids to listen to what is broadcast over the public address (PA) system. Others will listen using receivers from FM or infrared (IR) ALDs. ALDs, in large meetings, will take a line feed from the PA system and broadcast a signal, using either an FM or IR carrier beam. The special receivers will pick up this signal and change it back to sound, which can then be amplified as needed for the listener. Sound is transmitted from the receiver to the listener by way of a headset, an earphone, an induction loop, or direct input into the user's hearing aid.

Even though hearing aid technology has improved over the years, it still has limitations. One problem is that internal microphones bring in sound somewhat indiscriminately, then they amplify everything. This often makes a noisy environment worse instead of better. A second problem is that hearing aids amplify most what is closest or loudest, thus they do not work well over an extended distance. With ALDs, there is the ability to place the microphone close to the sound source and use a more selective microphone so that the sound the listener wants to hear is amplified. The biggest difference between FM and IR systems, when used for group functions, is that FM signals continue to carry through walls. Infrared is a wave band of light that is invisible to the human eye, but does not go through walls. For this reason IR systems are used in places such as courtrooms.

ALDs are also available for individual use. When used on a personal basis, there is more of a difference between FM and IR systems. The personal FM system will use the same type of receiver as a wide area system, but will pair it with a minimicrophone attached to a small transmitter. The transmitter is smaller than a cigarette package and can be easily placed in a pocket. This system can be used in a variety of settings: classrooms, lectures, churches, small meetings, and one-to-one conversations. By handing the microphone and transmitter to another person and placing it near the microphone on a speaker's podium or even taking a line feed from a PA, an individual is able to get a clearer, more direct sound signal than if using a hearing aid alone.

IR systems use a different type of transmitter, one that must be stationary during use. These systems work well for meeting rooms, classrooms, and theaters where they can be set up beforehand or installed permanently. Smaller systems are also available for use at home, such as with a television. As with the FM system, a separate microphone can be used, or a line can be taken from a PA system or television. IR systems cannot be used for one-to-one communication.

A third type of ALD, which is only for personal use, is the hard-wire system. With an FM or IR system, the receiver and transmitter do not have to be in close proximity and are not connected by any wires. With a hard-wire system, the microphone is plugged directly into the amplifier, which then sends the sound to the listener's ear. The microphone can also be connected by cord, increasing the distance from the speaker to the listener up to 10–15 feet. This type of system is good for one-to-one conversations, for small groups, and for use with a television, however, the intervening wire can get in the way in some situations.

One older technology that is sometimes still used is an induction loop. Any time an electric current is sent through a loop of wire, an electromagnetic field is established. By making a loop large enough to fit around a room or a portion thereof, a large field is set up. A line feed can be taken from a PA system and sent through the loop. Persons sitting within this area can receive the sound through their hearing aid if it is equipped with a telecoil. This same technology is used on a smaller scale in induction neck loops attached to ALD receivers and with telephone handsets.

Telecommunication

With the invention of the telephone, persons who previously received information by mail, by telegraph, or by face-to-face speech began to rely heavily on its usage. For persons who are deaf, telephone usage was limited until the late 1960s. This was when a phone modem was first linked with a teletypewriter (TTY), enabling persons who were deaf to converse via phone lines by typing conversations back and forth (see Case Study 6.5). The machines were awkward and required a lot of space; as a result, not many persons who were deaf owned them, and even fewer police departments, fire departments, doctors, stores, government offices, or other services made them available. It was not until the early 1980s that the two

Case Study 6.5: Jeff

Jeff directs services for clients who are deaf for his state's department of rehabilitation. When he needs to use the phone, Jeff uses a TTY to communicate with others who have a TTY or TDD. When he must call to someone who can hear and who does not have a TTY, he uses the relay service. The relay operator works like an interpreter on the phone, reading aloud what Jeff has typed onto the TTY and typing back to him what the other person has spoken. If Jeff needs to be out of the office, he takes a portable TTY with him. Both at home and at work, he uses a flashing light to alert him to the phone ringing. He also has an alpha-numeric pager, so he can get messages away from the office.

When meeting with other persons who do not sign, Jeff uses an interpreter who signs to him everything that is spoken, as well as other auditory information as needed. When he is alone and needs to interact with a person who has hearing, Jeff uses his speech and speechreading skills. That method is sometimes successful; other times it is not. Jeff finds writing notes an alternate method that is almost always successful. When giving presentations, Jeff uses an overhead projector helps him keep eye contact with his audience. If people in the audience do not understand sign language, Jeff uses an interpreter for these presentations. At home and work, Jeff uses a closed caption decoder in order to follow the dialogue.

devices were combined into one new, compact device dubbed the telecommunications device for the deaf (TDD) (Arizona Council for the Hearing Impaired, 1993).

To use a TDD, a person simply puts the handset from the phone in the coupler on the TDD, then dials the phone. When the other person answers and puts his or her handset into the coupler, the conversation is ready to begin. Only one person can type at a time, so when the first party finishes his or her turn, he or she types GA (go ahead) to let the other party know it is his or her turn. To signal the end of a conversation, SK (stop keying) is typed.

Soon most persons who were deaf owned TDDs, but they could only call other persons who were deaf who also had TDDs. So relay services were established with special operators who acted as interpreters over the phone. The relays were set up by agencies for the deaf or by private businesses. With the passage of the Americans with Disabilities Act (ADA) of 1990 (PL 101-336), relays have been established in each state, with no fees for personal usage except for toll or long-distance charges. Because more than just persons who are deaf use the machines, the framers of the ADA changed the device's name to text telephone.

As phones and answering machines have become more sophisticated, so, too, have TDDs. Compact models are available for travel, and there are models that have memory and/or produce paper printouts of a conversation. Some models can converse with computers directly in ASCII. Some models even take the place of the phone and are connected directly to the phone lines. These models come with the extra feature of a built-in answering machine for TDD messages. Several companies market pay phone TDDs, which are being made available in public places. Regular answering machines, modified to accept a TDD signal or both voice and TDD, are available, but are only marginally successful.

With the popularity of personal computers and the use of modems to contact bulletin boards and transfer information, several companies have developed software and hardware to make a computer act like a TDD. IBM has recently developed a program that makes it possible for a computer to interact directly with a touch-tone phone, searching letter combinations to make words on the computer screen as phone keys are depressed at the other end of the line. This same package makes the computer "talk" to the other party in synthesized speech as a message is typed on the computer.

For a long time, it seemed as though telecommunications for persons who were deaf progressed much faster than for persons who were hard of hearing. Currently, an array of telephone amplifiers are available. Some of these raise the total volume of phone output, while others can customize the amplification to better accommodate an individual's degree and type of hearing loss. Amplifiers come in models that attach to the handset, are part of the handset, attach via modular wiring to the phone, or are built into the phone.

There are two other ways that access to phones can be gained by persons who are hard of hearing. If an individual has a hearing aid fitted with a telecoil, it will be compatible with phones that also have a telecoil. When the aid's telecoil (T) switch is in the "on" position, the hearing aid is able to receive a signal sent by the telephone handset. This method provides a better sound signal than if the sound had to travel from the handset through the hearing aid microphone. All new phones must have telecoils that meet federal standards; pay phones that have telecoils are marked with a blue grommet at the spot where the telephone cord enters the handset. In addition, most ALDs have hardware that makes them compatible with the telephone.

Alerting Systems

Doorbells and phones ring, smoke alarms buzz, babies cry—what do these actions all have in common? To know of the need to respond to these actions, one must have hearing. Alerting systems for the deaf and hard of hearing change the auditory signal to a visual or vibrating one. Systems can alert the user to the phone, a doorbell, a crying baby, or any other sound that needs attention. One system includes its own smoke detector. Some systems use lamps or lights in the environment as the signal devices, causing them to flash to alert the user. Another multialerting system has a personal receiver, worn by the user, that vibrates. The user then looks at a multilighted receiver to see which source is being alerted. There is also an array of single-use devices commercially available: smoke detectors with strobe lights, audible devices that are extra loud, and strobe or extra loud sound telephone alerts. Most alerting systems are modular, so one need only purchase those parts that are necessary for a particular situation or environment (see Case Study 6.6).

An everyday device found in most homes is an alarm clock. Clocks are available that are modified so that a lamp, a strobe, or a vibrator may be plugged into them. The vibrator can be placed under a pillow or between the box spring and the mattress. When the alarm goes off, the light or vibrator turns on, waking the user.

Audiovisual Media

For persons who are deaf and hard of hearing, watching a television show or a movie leaves them unaware of the storyline. Captioning for television programs is similar to the subtitles found on foreign films. Some shows are open captioned, but most are closed captioned, necessitating use of a decoder to open the captions. Currently, about 500 hours of programming per week are captioned on television (National Captioning Institute, personal communication, October 13, 1993). Many news and sports shows, as well as special, live programming, are real-time captioned. Some network stations even have secondary video programming, providing an information service in text format.

Originally, decoders were an external addition to the television, connected much like a VCR. Beginning in July 1993, all new televisions produced for market in the United States were required to include internal decoder circuitry. It is estimated that this requirement of the

---

Case Study 6.6: Susan

Susan is an administrator for a large school district and is hard of hearing. Her speech and speechreading skills are both excellent. Most of the time Susan does not use an interpreter because of her facility at using her residual hearing along with her speechreading skills; however, if there happens to be an interpreter in a meeting, she will occasionally check to make sure she has understood something properly. If no interpreter is present, she asks questions to clarify anything she did not understand. She does use an amplifier on her phone, but she finds that hearing aids are "more trouble than they are worth" for her.

At home, Susan can hear the phone ring if she is in the same room. She has a phone in her bedroom and one in the kitchen. Because she lives in a big house, she has installed bells in each additional bedroom, in the living room, and in the garage so that she can hear the phone no matter where she is in the house. These bells plug in to regular modular plugs, the same way an extension phone would be plugged in. Now she never misses a call. Susan finds her closed caption decoder to be a real asset. She watches more television now because most of prime time is captioned. She also waits for movies to come out on videotape to see them captioned rather than seeing them at the theater.

Americans with Disabilities Act (PL 101-336) will cause a $5–$10 increase in the cost of a television set, while bringing this technology to many persons. With the popularity of decoders, the makers of videotapes recognized an untapped market. Many videos now include closed captions—the number of available titles currently is about 3,000 (National Captioning Institute, personal communication, October 13, 1993). Decoders are easy to use with both VCRs and cable boxes.

Assistive technology for persons who are deaf and hard of hearing has wide-ranging applications: at home, in the workplace, and in the community. Many devices discussed in this chapter have multiple uses. An ALD, for example, might be of assistance in a business meeting, while talking to a salesperson at a store, and when conversing with a friend in a noisy restaurant. An alerting device will signal the user of the doorbell at home or the phone at work.

APPLICATIONS OF ASSISTIVE TECHNOLOGY FOR ADULTS WHO ARE DEAF-BLIND

Most technology for adults who are deaf-blind is hybrid from deafness and blindness technology, but some devices have additional uses for individuals with dual sensory impairments. Much of the technology is used "as is," regardless of whether a person has a single or dual sensory impairment.

Telecommunications Device for the Deaf

Several companies have linked their braille computer displays to TDDs from Ultratec (Madison, WI), producing braille TDDs. These devices include all the features of direct connect TDDs (i.e., auto dial, answering machine) and can be interfaced with a computer, printer, or braille embosser. Both can be used in face-to-face communication by disconnecting the braille display from the TDD and placing them side by side.

The Infotouch™ was created by Enabling Technologies (Stuart, FL), joining a TDD with their Romeo™ braille embosser. Although there is no mechanical braille display, one advantage to the Infotouch™ is that there is a braille-embossed copy of the conversation. The TDD keyboard can be used in standard QWERTY typing mode or commanded to work as a six-key brailler. The Infotouch™ does have the capacity to act as a phone answering machine. When not in use with the phone, the system can be used to translate other materials into either grade one or two braille, or the embosser can be coupled with a secondary input source.

For TDD users who are not braille readers, two adapted TDDs are available. Ultratec markets a TDD with a large LED display. This visual display has figures that are both larger and bolder than the regular display. Display color can be changed by changing the cover lens. The large visual display can only be used with a modified Superprint 100 TDD. KRI Communications (Santa Ana, CA) manufactures a TDD with a variable size printout. Type size is about one third larger and bolder than regular TDD type.

Assistive Listening Devices

Because an adult who is hard of hearing and either blind or visually impaired cannot depend as much on speechreading to fill in lost auditory information, the amount of clear auditory information that can be obtained becomes vital. ALDs can cut out most unwanted background noise. In addition, ALDs can be attached to talking book machines, tape players, voice-output computers, and other voice-output devices. (See Case Studies 6.7 and 6.8.)

Case Study 6.7: Mary

Mary is in her last year of law school. She has Usher syndrome type II and does not remember when she did not have both hearing and vision problems, although they have become progressively worse over the years. Before attending law school, Mary worked in the business world. She survived through grade school, college, and in business with her brains and her hearing aid, but the extra effort required a lot of energy.

During law school, she realized that things were becoming more difficult and sought help. An ALD in the classroom helped a lot. The professor wore a small wireless microphone that transmitted a signal to the receiver Mary wore. She also had a second microphone in the receiver so she could hear the other students during class discussion.

Now that she has passed the Bar exam, she is specializing in an area of law that will not bring her into the courtroom but will necessitate her being in many meetings to negotiate contracts. She will continue to use the ALD with a conference microphone, so that she can better hear all the parties around a conference table. If that is not sufficient, she can hook a monitor screen to the court reporters steno machine and read the discussion on the screen as it happens.

As her vision deteriorates, Mary knows she may need to use a CCTV for more and more of her research reading. She already uses a computer and has changed the screen colors to make it easier to read. She has plans to learn braille, so that later she can gain access to the computer in that way.

Case Study 6.8: Carla

Carla is a veterinary dermatologist and an associate professor of veterinary medicine. Until recently, she used no ALDs aside from her hearing aids; however, after using an ALD at a conference, she realized how much easier life would be with one. She now uses an ALD in the classroom, asking her students to either come to the microphone or pass it around when they are talking to her. She also uses it in faculty meetings and when she goes to professional conferences. She said that now she finally can hear what is being said and can actually learn something while earning her continuing education credits. Since having the ALD, she finds it is now easier for her to take more responsibility for creating or changing environments so it is easier for her to hear. This winter she will go skiing in Colorado with her family; she will take her ALD along to use during her ski lessons.

Carla has also started using a CCTV and a screen magnifier program for her computer. She has also found it helpful to change the background and print colors on the computer. Recently she has given up driving and has begun lessons in orientation and mobility. She finds sun shades and a visor help her use her residual vision much better.

Alerting Systems

Several alerting systems are manufactured for individuals who are deaf-blind. Both of them use transmitters wired to the phone, doorbell, smile alarm, or other device that has an audible signal. The user wears a receiver that is roughly the size of a pack of cigarettes. When the phone rings, or another device sends its audible signal, the transmitter sends a signal to the receiver, which vibrates. One systems receiver vibrates in four different patterns to let the user know which device is sending the signal. The other vibrates briefly, then the user pushes four small buttons on the receiver in sequence; the buttons each correlate with one of the audible signaling devices. When the right button is pushed, the receiver vibrates a second time. Although delighted that these devices are available, consumers have not been completely happy with either of them. A third company is currently looking into development of another system. (See Case Study 6.9.)

Clocks

Although any of the clocks with vibrators discussed previously will work as an alarm clock for a person who is deaf-blind, because they all have digital readouts, individuals who are totally blind will not be able to read the time and they will not be able to set it themselves. There are several analog clocks on the market that have been modified so that a vibrator can be attached. A deaf-blind person can then read and set the clock and alarm independently. The vibrator is placed under the pillow, between the mattress and box spring, or attached to the bed frame. In place of the alarm sounding, the vibrator shakes.

Closed Caption Decoders

Many persons who are deaf-blind complain that they do not get news and other information in a timely manner. One solution, developed by Dewtronics, is a braille version of the closed caption decoder. The collection of devices that make this system possible are a television, a VCR, a decoder, a computer with the necessary software, and a TeleBraille (TeleSensory) for use as a braille display. Playback speed can be controlled by the computer. The system can

---

Case Study 6.9:   Abe

Abe is completely deaf-blind, although he grew up deaf and later lost his vision. His primary mode of interpersonal communication is through ASL. When he still had some vision, he received signs visually; as his vision deteriorated, he began to use tactual signing. When he must talk with another person who does not sign, Abe uses an ASL interpreter who signs into his hands. Before he lost all of his vision, Abe used a CCTV and a computer with a text enlargement program. Currently he uses a mechanical braille display to read his computer screen. He can output material through either a braille embosser or a regular printer.

For using the phone, Abe uses a braille display in combination with a TTY. The model he has enables him to use the two devices in tandem or use the braille display as a stand-alone braille notetaking device. In the past, he thought about getting a laptop with a braille display, but now he has similar capability with the notetaking part of his braille TTY.

Abe has an alerting system that lets him know if his phone is ringing, if someone is at his office door, or if the fire alarm is sounding. Transmitters are connected to each piece of equipment, and they send signals to the receiver in his pocket. He can tell what he is being alerted to by the way the receiver vibrates. He also has transmitters wired at home. They are set with the same codes, so one vibrating pattern means the same thing at home as at the office: a continuous – – – – – always means fire, and so on. Having this system has really given Abe a boost. Now he knows when someone is coming into his office before the person touches him on the arm, and he feels safer and more self-reliant at home.

---

also provide captions in large print on a computer monitor and provide braille readout in either grade one or two. The system can also be used with commercially available videotapes that are captioned.

Mobility

Individuals who are blind normally depend quite heavily on their hearing as an important information source for mobility. Hearing is used both to obtain auditory information directly from the environment, as well as to communicate with others when assistance is needed. With limited or no usable hearing, other information gathering and communication methods must be used. Some individuals use the Mowat Sensor (Mobility Services, Inc., Atlanta) or Polaron (Nurion) in conjunction with a dog guide for street crossings or to aid in finding a person to ask for assistance. Others use the Safe-T-Lite™ cane (Safe-T-Lite Enterprises, Victoria, British Columbia, Canada) to provide added safety while traveling. This cane has a small, but powerful, red strobe built into the body of the cane, directly under the handgrip.

When it becomes necessary to seek assistance to cross a street or to board the correct bus, the individual who is completely blind or deaf is at a great disadvantage. The traditional method for getting help has been to hold up a card requesting help, then wait for someone to lend assistance. It has been shown that using a tape player with a loop tape (outgoing message tape from a phone answering machine) with a prerecorded message asking for assistance works much better (Florence & LaGrow, 1989). The Attention Getter™ (Companion Products, Milford, PA) is a small device that can record up to 20 seconds of information and play it back in up to four separate messages. This is done using digital technology and a computer speech chip, so that cassettes tapes are not necessary. Anyone can make the recording, so the playback voice can be male or female, young or old, to match the user. Once someone offers assistance by tapping on the user's shoulder, a card with more specific information can be given to that person.

Other Communication Technology

The Tellatouch (Lighthouse Consumer Products, Long Island City, NY) is a small mechanical device that enables the speaker to type a message to a person who is deaf-blind. The person who is deaf-blind is then able to read it by means of one mechanical braille cell. The machine, which measures $9 \times 10 \times 2 \ 1/2,$ has a typewriter-style keyboard along with a braille keyboard on one side. When turned around, there is one braille cell with small metal pins that pop up in the braille configuration of the letter typed. This device is used by most persons who have been blind for some time, then lose their hearing, so that English or another spoken language is their primary language. Most of the Tellatouch users express themselves verbally. A common conversation would be for a person who has sight or for a speaker with a visual impairment to type a message to the individual who is deaf-blind, the person who is deaf-blind will read the braille, and then that person will respond verbally.

Several other devices are in various stages of development. One is a mechanical hand that could be used to provide fingerspelled output in place of voice or braille output for TDDs, computers, and other devices. Development on several different mechanical hands is being done by different teams in the United States. One issue currently being addressed is fingerspelling speed, which is now about two characters per second. A second device currently in development is called The Talking Glove, which is a glove fitted with sensors that can be used to provide fingerspelled input for a computer. The original idea was to link this glove with a wearable computer module to produce voice output, thereby providing a voice source for persons who cannot speak intelligibly. Currently, the glove technology is being used in connection with sign language research and could even be used in connection with telecommunications for the deaf (Chapin, Kramer, Haas, Leifer, & Macken, 1992). The system would include the glove and a computer at each end, connected by telephone lines. The computer would actually display an active graphic image of an upper torso, showing the hand, arm, and head movement elements of sign language, just as a person wearing the glove is producing them. Such a system may be useful in place of current models of videophones, which do not update the video image fast enough to follow a person signing. The glove could also be connected to the mechanical hand to create a full two-way tactile telecommunication system. Such a system would permit a deaf-blind person to transmit and receive tactile fingerspelling over a telephone line, just as he or she would do in person.

SUGGESTED GUIDELINES FOR SELECTING ASSISTIVE TECHNOLOGY

To choose the appropriate assistive technology for an individual, a three-step assessment must be conducted. It is critical that the user be not only at the center of, but intimately involved in, the process. If this is not the case, there is a greater chance that the technology selected will not satisfy the requirements of either the situation or the individual or that the individual will reject it.

First, it is necessary to conduct a functional assessment of the user's abilities. This should include assessment of both physical and cognitive abilities and limitations. It should be noted if any of the individual's disabilities are progressive in nature and, if so, the prognosis. Special attention should be made to the individual's personal preferences and style.

Second, the user's environment must be evaluated. This evaluation will include an analysis of the tasks the individual wants or needs to perform, along with a discrepancy analysis. What modifications (in the job or the environment) will make it possible for the individual to perform the required task(s)? Note should be made of natural helps in the environment, such as co-workers, the possibility of job sharing, and so forth.

Once the capabilities of the individual and the requirements of the situation are known, the third step is to search for the proper technology to match the circumstance. There are several guidelines to follow in this pursuit:

1. *Look for simple solutions*   Low-tech items are usually less expensive, often easier to use, and more frequently used than some of the more complex solutions. People tend to abandon devices that are too difficult to learn or use. Simple, low-tech equipment breaks down less often and is easier to fix. It also makes people feel more comfortable (normal) if they do not need to use a lot of special equipment.

2. *Consider the learning and work style of the user*   Does he or she enjoy using aids and devices? Does he or she resist equipment that sets him or her apart? What is the best way to compensate for hearing and/or vision impairment?

3. *Consider the long-range implications of the hearing or vision impairment(s)*   Will this product or method be something that will work long term? Will there be the need to repeat this procedure if the individual loses more hearing and/or vision? Are there options that will work for this individual for a longer period of time?

4. *Look at each piece of equipment*   Keep the following considerations in mind:

- How easy is the device to assemble or set up?
- How easy is it to use? to maintain?
- How long will the device last?
- Will it be outdated shortly? Can it be updated easily?
- Will the individual continue to have the same needs over time?
- Is the device easily adaptable to a wide variety of situations and uses?
- If portability is a factor, how portable is the device?
- Does this device have a history of dependability? durability?
- If it breaks, how easy is it to get the device fixed? Is there a service contract?
- Is technical support easily available (i.e., by phone) if there is a problem?

5. *Investigate all options*   Such investigation can be done by talking to other consumers at consumer organizations, support groups, or rehabilitation agencies. Many agencies have technology centers where hands-on trials and lending libraries are available. Many consumer organizations have conferences with exhibits of adaptive and assistive devices. Ask a lot of questions! In addition, catalogs offer a place to view a variety of devices. For the more technical equipment, it is best to see it in person and talk to a salesperson before ordering. For other devices, catalogs are a great way to shop.

6. *Compare similar equipment from different manufacturers*   Look at the following:

- What features and options does each have? What is needed for the task?
- Is the manufacturer or brand dependable? Will the manufacturer stand behind the equipment even if that model is discontinued?
- What are the pros and cons for each device?

It is not always necessary to purchase the most expensive or best-known brand, however, sometimes the phrase "you get what you pay for" is very true.

7. *Purchase some devices only after consulting with a professional in the field*   Some of these professionals may include the following:

- An audiologist for hearing aids and ALDs
- A low vision specialist for magnifiers, monoculars, and other optical aids
- An orientation and mobility specialist (who should be consulted before a consumer uses a mobility cane or purchases an electronic travel aid)

Once again, it is critical that the individual be at the center of and intimately involved in the decision-making process. In addition, depending on the individual's sensory disabilities, there are a variety of service providers who should be members of the team: the audiologist, the low vision specialist, the rehabilitation teacher, the orientation and mobility specialist, and the rehabilitation counselor.

CONCLUSION

Impairments in hearing and/or vision affect different people in different ways. Before we can assist a student or client to become independent and successful in the community, we must first find out what his or her definition of independence and success is—what it is that individual wants to do with his or her life. We may need to help clients to discover hidden talents and broaden their horizons. Most of all, we must treat each person as an individual.

A wide variety of technology is available to assist persons with hearing and/or vision impairments to cope with their surroundings by providing them with information or helping them communicate. Different people will need different types of assistance. It is vital that the right devices and training be matched with students and clients, that Johnny doesn't get a certain device because it worked well for Sherry. At the same time, people need to learn to be flexible, creative, and resourceful when a piece of equipment breaks down. Above all, we need to look to the needs of the individual first, then at ways to meet those needs. The technology we have discussed in this chapter is just one way to meet those needs.

In the past the absence or impairment of vision and/or hearing could severely limit the amount of access blind, deaf, or deaf-blind persons could have to the world around them. There are those who will argue that deaf people had ASL and interpreters long before the TTY and closed captioning were invented, and likewise those who would say that blind people had braille and white canes and could use readers long before speech-output and mechanical braille display technology became available. These "low-tech" methods were useful then and remain so today; they should not be discarded or forgotten. However, no one would argue that the development of these and other technologies hasn't provided the kind of access to the environment only dreamed of in the past. Let us continue to dream and to create new technologies to broaden this horizon and dash all its limits.

REFERENCES

Alpiner, J., & McCarthy, P.A. (1993). *Rehabilitation audiology for children and adults* (2nd ed.). Baltimore: Williams and Wilkins.

Americans with Disabilities Act of 1990 (ADA), PL 101-336. (July 26, 1990). Title 42, U.S.C. 12101 et seq: *U.S. Statutes at Large, 104*, 327-378.

Arizona Council for the Hearing Impaired. (1993, Winter). Telecommunications for the Deaf, Inc. Tenth international convention. *ACHI News Bulletin*, p. 5.

Barraga, N. (1976). *Visual handicaps and learning: A developmental approach.* Belmont, CA: Wadsworth.

Chapin, W., Kramer, J., Haas, C., Leifer, L., & Macken, E. (1992). TeleSign: A sign language telecommunications system. In *Proceedings—Johns Hopkins national search for computing applications to assist persons with disabilities* (pp. 2–4). Baltimore: IEEE Computer Society Press.

ERIC Clearinghouse on Handicapped and Gifted Children. (1981). *Learning related visual problems fact sheet.* Reston, VA: Author.

Faye, E. (1976). *Clinical low vision*. Boston: Little, Brown, and Co.

Florence, I.J., & LaGrow, S.J. (1989). The use of a recorded message for gaining assistance with street crossings for deaf-blind travelers. *Journal of Visual Impairment and Blindness*, *83*(9), 471–472.

Jacobson, W.H. (1993). *The art and science of teaching orientation and mobility to persons with visual impairments*. New York: AFB Press.

Kinney, R. (1972). *Independent living without sight and hearing*. Arlington Heights, IL: Gray Dove.

Lependorf, B. (1991, April). On the loose . . . with Bertt. *DCARA News*. San Leandro, CA: Deaf Counseling, Advocacy and Referral Agency.

Levine, E.S. (1981). *The ecology of early deafness*. New York: Columbia University Press.

Luey, H., Belsa, D., & Glass, L. (1989). *Beyond refuge: Coping with losses of vision and hearing in late life*. Sands Point, NY: Helen Keller National Center.

Mascia, J. (1994). Understanding age-related hearing loss. In S.E. Boone, D. Watson, & M. Bagley (Eds.), *The challenge to independence: Vision and hearing loss among older adults* (pp. 93–98). Little Rock: University of Arkansas Rehabilitation Research and Training Center for Persons Who Are Deaf or Hard of Hearing.

Moores, D.F. (1987). *Educating the deaf: Psychology, principles, and practices*. Boston: Houghton Mifflin.

National Association of the Deaf. (1992, October). Who are people with disabilities? *The NAD Broadcaster*. Silver Spring, MD: Author.

Nelson, K.A., & Dimitrova, E. (1993). Severe visual impairment in the United States and in each state, 1990. *Journal of Visual Impairments and Blindness, 87*(3), 80–89.

Orenstein, W.A.B., Bart, S.W., Bart, K.J., Sirotkin, B., & Hinman, A.R. (1986). Epidemiology of rubella and its complications. In E.M. Gruenberg (Ed.), *Vaccinating against brain syndromes: The campaign against measles and rubella* (pp. 49–69). New York: Oxford University Press.

Pagon, R.A., Graham, J.M., Zonana, J., & Yong, S.L. (1981). Coloboma, congenital heart disease, and choanal artesia with multiple anomalies: CHARGE association. *The Journal of Pediatrics, 99*(2), 223–227.

Perry, A.L., & Silverman, S.R. (1978). Speech reading. In H. Davis & S.R. Silverman (Eds.), *Hearing and deafness* (4th ed.) (pp. 375–387). New York: Holt, Rinehart, and Winston.

Regenbogen, L.S., & Coscas, C.J. (1985). *Occulo-auditory syndromes*. New York: Mason Publishing.

Schein, J. (1978). The deaf community. In H. Davis & S.R. Silverman (Eds.), *Hearing and deafness* (4th ed.) (pp. 511–524). New York: Holt, Rinehart, and Winston.

Watson, D., & Taff-Watson, M. (Eds.). (1993). *A model service delivery system for persons who are deaf-blind: 1993 edition*. Little Rock: University of Arkansas Rehabilitation Research and Training Center for Persons Who Are Deaf or Hard of Hearing.

Wolff, A.B., & Harkins, J.E. (1986). Multihandicapped students. In A.N. Schildroth & M.A. Karchmer (Eds.), *Deaf children in America* (pp. 55–83). San Diego: College-Hill Press.

Wynne, B. (1987). The deaf-blind population: Etiology and implications for rehabilitation. In S. Barrett, T. Carr, & A. Covert (Eds.), *Community-based living options for young adults with deaf-blindness* (pp. 3–23). Sands Point, NY: The Helen Keller National Center-Technical Assistance Center.

Appendix A:
For More Information

Blindness

Espinola, O., & Croft, D. (1992). *Solutions: Access technologies for people who are blind.* Boston: National Braille Press.

This book contains information specifically on computer access technology for persons who are blind. It also contains lists of access technology vendors, newsletters, other blindness-related publications, technology training centers, and so on. Overall, this book is a good source of general information. Contact the National Braille Press, 88 St. Stephen Street, Boston, MA 02115, 617-266-6160.

Deafness

National Information Center on Deafness
Gallaudet University
800 Florida Avenue, NE
Washington, DC 20002-3695
202-651-5051 (voice)
202-651-5052 (TDD)

The center has fact sheets on hearing aids, ALDs, and alerting and communication devices.

Deaf-Blindness

Helen Keller National Center for Deaf-Blind Youths and Adults
111 Middle Neck Road
Sands Point, NY 11050
516-944-8900 (voice)
516-944-8637 (TDD)

The center has specialists at its New York training center, as well as representatives in 10 regional offices who can assist with locating assistive/adaptive devices. They also offer technical assistance to local agencies that are serving deaf-blind clients.

Indiana's Technology-Related Assistance for Individuals with Dual-Sensory Impairments (ITRAID) Project
School of Education–502
Indiana State University
Terre Haute, IN 47809
812-237-4380 (voice)
812-237-3022 (TDD)

The center provides training, information, and technical assistance for individuals with both hearing and vision impairments. A training module and videotape are available.

Appendix B: Resources

The following companies have national mail-order businesses and deal with products for persons with hearing and vision impairments and other disabilities. Specific disabilities covered by each catalog are listed using the following codes:

B/VI blind and visually impaired
D/HH   deaf and hard of hearing
Phys physically disabled
Gen   general use

American Foundation for the Blind (B/VI)

Product Center
100 Enterprise Place
P.O. Box 7044
Dover, DE 19903-7044
1-800-829-0500

Ann Morris Enterprises, Inc. (B/VI)

890 Fams Court
East Meadow, NY 11554
516-292-9232

Compu-TTY, Inc. (D/HH)

3309 Winthrop, Suite 85
Ft. Worth, TX 76117
817-738-2485 (voice)
817-738-8993 (TDD)

Deafworks (D/HH)

P.O. Box 1265
Provo, UT 84603-1265
801-375-3560 (TDD)
Voice—use local relay service
  with TDD number

HARC Mercantile (D/HH)

P.O. Box 3055
Kalamazoo, MI 49003-3005
1-800-445-9968 (voice)
616-381-2219 (TDD)

Harris Communication (D/HH)

6541 City West Parkway
Eden Prairie, MN 55344-3248
1-800-825-6758 (voice)
1-800-825-9187 (TDD)
612-825-5856 (voice)
612-825-8791 (TDD)

Independent Living Aids (B/VI, Gen)

27 East Mall
Plainview, NY 11803
1-800-537-2118

LS & S Group (B/VI)

P.O. Box 673
Northbrook, IL 60065
1-800-468-4789

Maxi-Aids (B/VI, D/HH, Phys, Gen)

P.O. Box 3209
Farmington, NY 11735
1-800-522-6294

Potomac Technology (D/HH)

1 Church Street, Suite 402
Rockville, MD 20850
301-762-4005 (voice)
301-762-0851 (TDD)

Science Products (B/VI)
P.O. Box 888
Southeastern, PA 19399
1-800-888-7400

VisAids (B/VI, Phys)
P.O. Box 26
102-09 Jamaica Avenue
Richmond Hill, NY 11418
1-800-346-9579

7

Assistive Technology Applications and Strategies for School System Personnel

Katherine J. Inge
Jayne Shepherd

In the mid-1970s, students patiently typed term papers using the family's manual typewriter. Hours were spent proofreading to ensure that spelling and typographical errors were corrected by carefully using correction tape and by realigning pages for retyping. Today, students type their term papers on personal computers that quickly correct errors using grammatical and spelling software packages. The computer reads the paper to find misspelled words, highlights them in text, and provides choices for corrections that can be selected with the stroke of a key. A task that once took a great deal of time can now be accomplished in a matter of minutes.

Almost every person's life has been affected by technology. Microwave ovens, automatic teller machines (ATMs), video cameras, compact disc players, fax machines, and cellular telephones are but a few examples of technology that most people take for granted. There are even more simple technology adaptations that make everyday activities easier to accomplish, such as Velcro straps on a child's tennis shoes, the pump on the toothpaste dispenser, or the automatic "off" switch on the coffee pot. In other words, technology has enhanced our ability to live, learn, work, and play in the community. As technology has had an impact on the everyday lives of most people, it also has facilitated inclusion for individuals with disabilities, allowing them to gain greater control over their lives and to become more independent and productive (Church & Glennen, 1992; Franklin, 1991).

DIFFERENT LEVELS OF COMPLEXITY IN TECHNOLOGY

There is a continuum of complexity in technology related to devices themselves and the type of materials or manufacturing techniques used to produce such devices. This low- to high-tech continuum is constantly redefined as users become more comfortable with technology (Anson, 1993). *Low-technology devices* are defined as devices that are passive or simple, with few moving parts (Mann & Lane, 1991). Low-tech devices that students may use everyday are built-up pencils, book holders, reachers, weighted spoons, keyguards, and crutches. Velcro, Dycem, and splinting materials are also low-tech materials that aid students. For instance, a student may have a placemat made from Dycem, a nonslip material, to prevent his or her plate from moving around on the table when eating. In addition, he or she may benefit from a spoon with a handle that has been enlarged using splinting materials.

High-technology devices are devices that have greater complexity and may have an electronic component. Computers, power wheelchairs, computer-based augmentative communication devices, environmental control units, robotics, and electronic spell checkers are examples of high-tech devices. Many lightweight orthotics or wheelchairs that have a titanium frame, specialized wheel bearings, or microswitches are considered to be high-tech devices because they are made using specialized techniques and materials (Anson, 1993).

In the school system, low-tech devices often can be used effectively and efficiently. Many therapists and teachers experiment with low-tech or environmental adaptations prior to even thinking about high-tech devices. Low-tech options may be as simple as taping paper to a desk, using a tablet, or giving the student a clipboard to stabilize a piece of paper during writing. Table 7.1 gives examples of both low- and high-tech solutions that can facilitate student participation in an activity.

LEGISLATION RELATED TO ASSISTIVE TECHNOLOGY

Congress recognized the importance of technology in the lives of individuals with disabilities by passing the Technology-Related Assistance for Individuals with Disabilities Act (Tech Act) (PL 100-407) in the spring of 1988 and the Technology-Related Assistance for Individuals with Disabilities Amendments of 1994 (PL 103-218). The purpose of the Tech Act and its amendments was to provide funds to states to improve assistive technology systems and to develop services to individuals across all age groups.

Congress again recognized the importance of technology when it amended the Education for All Handicapped Children Act of 1975 (PL 94-142) to create the Individuals with Disabilities Education Act of 1990 (IDEA) (PL 101-476, itself amended by the Individuals with Disabilities Education Act Amendments of 1991 [PL 102-119]). IDEA added assistive technology as a new amendment and provided guidelines for developing a student's individualized education program (IEP) to include technology. More important, IDEA adopted the definitions of assistive technology device and service from the Tech Act, creating consistency across two important pieces of legislation. According to IDEA, an assistive technology device and service as included in a student's IEP are defined as follows:

> The term *assistive technology device* means any item, piece of equipment, or product system, whether acquired commercially off the shelf, modified, or customized, that is used to increase, maintain, or improve functional capabilities of individuals with disabilities. (20 U.S.C. §1401[25])

> The term *assistive technology service* means any service that directly assists an individual with a disability in the selection, acquisition, or use of an assistive technology device. (20 U.S.C. §1401[26])

IDEA further defined assistive technology service to include a number of specific supports. First, a student must have access to an evaluation of his or her technology needs, including a functional evaluation, within daily living environments. IDEA also indicated that purchasing, leasing, or otherwise providing for the acquisition of assistive technology devices is the school system's responsibility. Acquisition can include selecting, designing, fitting, customizing, adapting, applying, maintaining, repairing, or replacing the assistive technology device. In addition, a service can consist of coordinating and using therapies, interventions, or services that are associated with the student's education and rehabilitation plans and programs. Finally, the school district is responsible for providing training and technical assistance to the student with a disability and his or her family and "for professionals, employers, or other individuals who provide services to, employ, or otherwise are substantially involved in the major life functions of individuals with disabilities" (20 U.S.C. § 1401[26]).

ASSISTIVE TECHNOLOGY AND THE INDIVIDUALIZED EDUCATION PROGRAM

In August 1990, the Office of Special Education Programs (OSEP) released a policy statement specifying that assistive technology is a part of the process of developing a student's IEP (RESNA Technical Assistance Project, 1992, pp. 34–35). A policy letter to clarify that statement addressed two important questions: 1) Can a school district deny assistive technology to a student with a disability? 2) Should the need for assistive technology be considered on a case-by-case basis when developing a student's IEP? Dr. Schrag, director of OSEP, stated the following in the policy letter:

> In brief, it is impermissible under EHA-B (Education of the Handicapped Act) for public agencies (including school districts) to presumptively deny assistive technology to a child with handicaps before a determination is made as to whether such technology is an element of a free appropriate public education (FAPE) for that child. Thus, consideration for a child's need for assistive technology must occur on a case-by-case basis in connection with development of a child's individualized education program (IEP). (RESNA Technical Assistance Project, 1992, pp. 34–35)

The letter specifies that the IEP must be developed by a team of participants at a meeting that includes both the parents and school system representatives. If the team identifies assistive technology to be in the realm of special education or a related service, the student's IEP must include a statement indicating the nature and amount of services needed.

There are three major places in the IEP where assistive technology can be identified (Meadows, 1992). First, the need for assistive technology may appear in the student's annual goals and short-term objectives. Second, assistive technology may be listed in the section on supplementary aids or services needed to maintain the student in the least restrictive educational environment. Third, assistive technology may be included in the list of related services necessary for the student to benefit from an appropriate education.

The August 1990 OSEP policy letter and the guidelines found in IDEA clearly indicate that school systems are responsible for providing assistive technology within a FAPE. Schools cannot require parents to pay for assistive technology devices and services if they have been identified in the child's IEP as necessary to achieve goals and objectives of the program (RESNA Technical Assistance Project, 1992). The school system can ask parents to use private insurance, but the parents are not required to do so (Button, 1991). In considering whether private insurance should be used, parents must consider the lifetime limit of their policy and how claims will affect future insurability or costs. If assistive technology is purchased using a student's private insurance or Medicaid funds, the device belongs solely to that student and should not be used by others (RESNA Technical Assistance Project, 1992).

In contrast, devices and equipment that are bought by the school system remain the property of the district. Each school can designate a particular assistive technology device for exclusive use by one student or have many devices that are used by various students. The use and distribution of such devices will remain under a district's control so long as each student's IEP goals are being met. School-owned assistive technology devices should be catalogued to include the date of purchase, repairs, the location of the devices, students who are using the devices, where they are being used, and other relevant information (RESNA Technical Assistance Project, 1992). Finally, the school district should cover the assistive technology devices under a liability policy.

Table 7.1. Examples of low- and high-technology solutions

Activity	Low-technology solutions	High-technology solutions
Reading	*Holding book:* Nonslip mat; book holder *Turning pages:* Rubber finger, universal cuff with pencil and eraser; head/mouth stick *Reading words:* Magnifying glass; cardboard "jig" to isolate words; ruler to read line by line	Electric page turner; books on tape; enlarged computer monitor; closed circuit television (CCTV); software that reads "out loud"; language master with books; spell check and dictionary software
Math	*Working math problems:* Abacus; counter; ruler to read problems line by line; visual model of numbers or money *Using functional math skills:* Money card "jig" to count coins for use in a vending machine, to rent bowling shoes, to ride bus, etc.	Calculator; computer software (spreadsheets, home budgets, etc.); handheld computers
Writing	*Holding a pencil:* Built-up pencil (e.g., cylindrical foam padding or foam curler); large marker; pen holder; splint made from low-temperature plastics; keyboard mitt with isolated finger; universal cuff with pencil or dowel; weighted pen/pencil; typing stick; head- or mouthstick to hold instrument *Using paper:* Templates; color-coded or textured-line paper; tape paper to desk; clipboard *Peer support:* Note-taking with carbon paper	Electric typewriter; laptop computer; word processor; orthotics (ball-bearing forearm orthosis); prosthetics; robotics; software with word prediction, grammar check, spell check; tape recorder; augmentative communication devices
Eating	*Holding utensils:* Universal cuff; built-up utensil handles; hand-splint made from low-temperature plastic that positions utensil(s); elongated handle; rocker knife *Drinking:* Sport bottle; cup holder; straw holder; adaptive cups *Positioning:* Dycem; nonslip mat; scoop plate; plate guard	Robotic arm; electric feeder; overhead sling; movable arm and wrist supports; wrist/hand splints

136

Category	Description
Toileting	*Positioning:* Seatbelt; raised commode seat; safety frame around toilet; footrests; grab bars *Toileting:* Long-handled mirror; digital stimulator; reacher; toilet tissue tongs	Specialized toileting chair; lift; pneumatic or electric leg bag clamp
Dressing	*Modifying clothing:* Elastic loops; buttons sewn on with elastic; pullover or front-opening clothing; Velcro closing; elastic laces; larger size clothing *Devices:* Button hook; reacher; sock donner; long-handled shoe horn; dressing stick; zipper pull; universal cuff	Robotics; splints with attachments; electric bed or chair that reclines and sits up
Recreation/leisure	*Positioning:* C-clamps; card holder; Velcro straps; universal cuff	Sports wheelchairs; adapted skiers; adapted bikes; hand controls for cars, boats; electric fishing reel; automatic card shuffler; computer games; electronic switches

Adapted from Kohlmeyer (1993).

137

Home Access to Assistive Technology

In 1991, OSEP issued a second policy statement on assistive technology concerning the right to take devices that have been purchased by the school district home from school (RESNA Technical Assistance Project, 1992, pp. 44–46). Figure 7.1 provides a copy of OSEP's 1991 policy letter. In the letter, Dr. Schrag, director of OSEP, responded to three issues raised by the parent of a student with a disability. The parent's letter read as follows:

- I would like to make the request from the appropriate officials for another CCTV {closed circuit television] for home use to accomplish the same results as is done in school [homework, reading books, school assignments].
- If the committee approves the request, it will go to the school board for approval. I would like to know what happens if the school board doesn't approve the proposal? Is it impartial hearing time?
- Is there a time limit on the implementation of updated IEPs? Every year I have long delays on implementation of board-approved IEPs.

OSEP's position statement on the first issue was that students must be provided home access to assistive technology if the IEP team indicates that a specific assistive technology device is necessary for a student to benefit from a FAPE. "The need for assistive technology is determined on a case-by-case basis, taking into consideration the unique need of each individual child" (RESNA Technical Assistance Project, 1992, pp. 44–46). To obtain a CCTV for home use, the IEP team would need to specify in the student's IEP that the device was needed for the student to read and complete school assignments at home. In addition, the team must include a statement on the nature and amount of the services.

The policy letter also clearly addressed the parent's second issue by saying that a school board cannot "unilaterally change the statement of special education and related services contained in the IEP" (RESNA Technical Assistance Project, 1992, pp. 44–46). The public agency must implement the IEP as developed unless it is changed by reconvening the IEP team. In other words, the school board cannot reject the assistive technology decisions of the IEP team, change them, refuse to pay for devices, or otherwise slow down the implementation process. In addition, it is not valid for a school system to deny home access to technology based on inadequate property insurance coverage (Morris, 1992).

Finally, OSEP's policy letter stated that "an IEP . . . must be implemented as soon as possible following the meetings required to develop, review, or revise a child's IEP" (RESNA Technical Assistance Project, 1992, pp. 44–46). School systems cannot delay implementation after an IEP has been finalized; however, the policy letter indicated that there may be times when a delay is necessary to make arrangements. For instance, the school may need to arrange for purchase of a specific assistive technology device as recommended by the IEP team.

RESNA Technical Assistance Project (1992) recommends several actions that can be taken for ensuring that the intent of IDEA and OSEP policy letters is met. First, information concerning assistive technology and the IEP must be disseminated to parents, therapists, educators, and administrators. Such information is available from a variety of sources (Table 7.2). In addition, each locality should have a process for ensuring that students' assistive technology needs are addressed. This may include 1) developing school standards to determine if a student needs assistive technology devices and services to benefit from a FAPE, 2) determining how parents will be notified of their child's right to assistive technology, 3) identifying who needs to participate on the assessment team to determine the student's technology needs, and 4) establishing a process for settling disagreements regarding assistive

November 27, 1991

Dear _____:

This is in response to your recent letter to the Office of Special Education Programs (OSEP) requesting a copy of any OSEP policy clarifications on assistive technology, as well as asking specific questions concerning the assistive technology needs for your _____. You also asked a question about the time limits for implementation of an individualized education program (IEP).

In response to your request, I am enclosing a copy of OSEP's August 10, 1990 letter to Ms. Susan Goodman concerning the obligations of public agencies under Part B of the Individuals with Disabilities Education Act (Part B), formerly cited as Part B of the Education of the Handicapped Act, to provide assistive technology to children with disabilities, along with some additional information on assistive technology and a copy of the Part B regulations. I would also like to provide you with OSEP's response to each of your specific questions as stated below.

> I would like to make the request to the appropriate officials for another CCTV for home use to accomplish the same results as is done in school (for home-work, reading books, any assignment from school).

The IEP must be developed at a meeting that includes parents and school officials, and must contain, among other things, a statement of the specific special education and related services to be provided to the child. *See* 34 CFR §§ 300.343–300.346. As stated in OSEP's letter to Ms. Goodman, if the IEP team determines that a child with disabilities requires assistive technology in order to receive a free appropriate public education (FAPE), and designates such assistive technology as either special education or a related service, the child's IEP must include a specific statement of such services, including the nature and amount of such services. *See* 34 CFR §300.346(c); App. C to 34 CFR part 300 (Ques. 51). The need for assistive technology is determined on a case-by-case basis, taking into consideration the unique need of each individual child. If the IEP team determines that a particular assistive technology item is required for home use in order for a particular child to be provided FAPE, the technology must be provided to implement the IEP.

> If the committee approves this request, it will go to the School Board for approval. I would like to know what happens if the School Board doesn't approve the proposal? Is it impartial hearing time?

As part of the public agency's Part B obligation to provide FAPE to an eligible child with disabilities, the public agency must ensure that special education and related services are provided in conformity with an IEP that meets the requirements of 34 CFR §§ 300.340–349. One requirement of 34 CFR §300.343(a) is that the public agency conduct a meeting to develop, review, and revise a child's IEP. The Regulations require that certain participants attend the IEP meeting. *See* 34 CFR §300.344. The role of the participants at the IEP meeting is to determine the specific special education and related services that a child needs in order to receive FAPE. Once the determination is made at a meeting convened pursuant to 34 CFR §300.343(a), Part B does not recognize any authority on the part of a local School Board to unilaterally change the statement of special education and related services contained in the IEP. After the IEP is developed

(continued)

Figure 7.1.   1991 policy letter on assistive technology from the Office of Special Education Programs.

Figure 7.1. (*continued*)

---

and the placement decision is made by a group of persons knowledgeable about the child, the meaning of the evaluation data and placement options, the public agency must implement the IEP. *See* 34 CFR §300.533(a)(3). Without reconvening the IEP meeting, the local school board could not change the IEP.

Is there a time limit on implementation of updated IEPs? Every year I have long delays on implementation of Board-approved IEPs.

Part B imposes no specific time limits for the implementation of IEPs. The Part B regulations at 34 CFR §300.342(b) require that an IEP: (1) must be in effect before special education and related services are provided to a child; and (2) must be implemented as soon as possible following the meetings required to develop, review, or revise a child's IEP. The answer to Question 4 in Appendix C to the Part 3 regulations states that no delay is permissible between the time a child's IEP is finalized and when special education and related services is provided. It is expected that the special education and related services set out in the IEP will be provided by the agency beginning immediately after the IEP is finalized. In certain circumstances such as when the IEP meeting occurs during the summer or vacation period or where there are circumstances which require a short delay (e.g., working out transportation arrangements), the implementation may not be immediate. *See Comment* 34 CFR §300.341.

I hope that this information is helpful to you. Please let us know if you have any additional questions or concerns.

Sincerely,

Judy A. Schrag
Director
Office of Special Education Programs

Table 7.2. Sources for information on assistive technology and IEPs

- Obtain the article, "Technology and the Individualized Education Program," by writing to: RESNA Technical Assistance Project, 1101 Connecticut Avenue, N.W., Suite 700, Washington, DC 20036.
- Distribute a copy of the 1991 OSEP policy letter on assistive technology (Figure 7.1) to parents, therapists, educators, administrators, and so forth.
- Request a copy of the Individuals with Disabilities Education Act of 1990 (IDEA) (PL 101-476) from the Superintendent of Documents, U.S. Government Printing Office, Washington, DC.
- Obtain information from NICHCY, such as the *News Digest,* by writing or calling for a list of free publications: NICHCY, P.O. Box 1492, Washington, DC 20013-1492, 1-800-695-0285 (Voice/TT).
- Write to RESNA for copies of the *AT Quarterly* (e.g., Volume 2, No. 5, and Volume 3, No. 2). Request to be on the mailing list for future publications.
- Contact the UCPA and ask about available information such as the UCPA Spring 1991 issues of *Family Support Bulletin.* Also request information such as cost of receiving other UCPA publications: UCPA, Inc., 1522 K Street, N.W., Suite 1112, Washington, DC 20005. 1-800-USA-5UCP, or 202-842-1266.

NICHCY, National Information Center for Children and Youth with Disabilities; OSEP, Office of Special Education Programs; RESNA, Rehabilitation Engineering Society of North America; UCPA, United Cerebral Palsy Association.

technology access (RESNA Technical Assistance Project, 1992). Most important, schools must make decisions regarding assistive technology needs on a case-by-case basis. Assistive technology should not be selected based on group needs or by disability type, nor should it be denied to a student due to availability issues, lack of services, or by cost of the proposed devices and services (Button, 1991; Morris, 1992).

Case Study 7.1 is an illustration of the common assumptions that any assistive technology application will enhance a student's education program. In actuality, assistive technology is only one of many tools that can be used for achieving outcomes. A number of issues should be considered when selecting assistive technology for student instruction. As previously noted, a student's IEP, including the selection of assistive technology devices and services, must be individually designed to meet the needs of each student. The student's IEP should not be developed to fit a school system's pre-existing program or service (Button, 1991). Some of the questions that should be answered when using assistive technology to develop IEP objectives include the following:

1. What is the expected outcome from the application of assistive technology?
2. Is the assistive technology device or service facilitating inclusion in age-appropriate activities and environments?
3. Is the activity important or necessary for the student to participate in current and future environments?
4. Is assistive technology necessary for the student to acquire the targeted skill, and has it been selected based on the student's individual needs?

CASE STUDY 7.1:   IEP ANALYSIS

Betty is an 18-year-old student with severe physical disabilities due to cerebral palsy and moderate mental retardation. She has right-side hemiplegia, ataxia, and a seizure disorder. Betty uses a motorized wheelchair, which she can maneuver independently. During the past school year, she has been attending regular classes at the local high school with her same-age peers. One class that was identified for her was computer programming; the school had recently obtained a computer with a touch screen and several software programs. The new system was set up in the back of the computer lab because it was different from the other models in the class and required special interfaces for operation.

Betty's instruction involves one of the programs that came with the computer system. Her IEP goal states that she will learn to identify common household objects and self-care items by touching the computer screen when prompted. For instance, when two choices such as a line drawing of a chair or bed appear on the screen, the computer prompts Betty (e.g., "touch the chair") while simultaneously showing the written word for the object. The software program, which was designed for preschool students, has a feature that collects data on student responses. Currently, Mr. Jones, Betty's teacher, has observed a steady increase in her correct responses. He is excited about this program because Betty can work on it independently while he assists the other students. Mr. Jones anticipates that Betty will master common household objects and begin learning the program on self-care items within a month.

5. Is the assistive technology device being substituted for instruction or interaction with the teacher and/or the student's peers?

What Is the Expected Outcome from the Application of Assistive Technology?

In Case Study 7.1, it appears that Betty's school system has developed her program around pre-existing computer software that came with the system, rather than considering the specific skills that Betty needs to acquire. When designing an instructional program for a student with a disability, the educational team must determine the *functional relevance* of the activity for each student. In other words, the anticipated outcomes that will enable the student to function in current and future environments need to be considered (Brown, Nietupski, & Hamre-Nietupski, 1976; Brown et al., 1980). Betty's IEP team must determine how learning a preprogrammed list of household objects and self-care items will allow her to function more independently. If the anticipated outcome is acquiring a sight-word vocabulary for communicating, the words in the prepackaged program should be functionally relevant to daily activities, or else an individualized program should be developed that meets her specific daily living needs. Perhaps Betty should be working on a program that allows her to immediately communicate, rather than working on a prerequisite sight-word vocabulary.

Is the Assistive Technology Device or Service Facilitating Inclusion in Age-Appropriate Activities and Environments?

In addition to considering whether an activity has a functional outcome for a student, the IEP team also must select age-appropriate materials, adaptations, and tasks for teaching the identified objectives. Using a computer software program that was designed for preschool students *is not* appropriate for a student of transition age. As Betty's peers are learning word-processing skills, she is engaged in a stigmatizing activity that clearly emphasizes her disabilities rather than her capabilities. Although she is physically in the same room with her peers, by sitting in the back of the room she is not being included in their environment. Similarly, using adaptive switches that activate toys (e.g., barking dogs, fire engines with sirens) should be limited to preschool- and elementary-age students. If in doubt, team members should socially validate that same-age peers without disabilities are engaging in similar practices.

Is the Activity Important or Necessary for the Student to Participate in Current and Future Environments?

Teachers may use training programs, such as the commercially available vocabulary software, with the primary IEP objective being that of teaching the student to use an assistive technology device. The assumption is that the student must learn to use the touch window and computer within the context of the introductory program as a *prerequisite* to learning more advanced skills. However, many students will not be able to generalize the skills from one training situation to another. For instance, Betty may not be able to transfer the ability to use the touch screen for identifying vocabulary words to a vocational task in a community jobsite. This may mean that she will have limited time to learn a job skill, since emphasis was placed on "readiness" programming within the classroom.

Therefore, application of assistive technology should be within the context of an activity that has a functional outcome for community involvement. Because Betty is of transition age (14–22 years), it would be important to determine whether the touch window and computer system are potential tools for facilitating employment. If so, her IEP team must identify objectives that incorporate the use of technology within a work environment. For instance, a survey of Betty's community may uncover several job opportunities that use computer systems for data entry purposes. These specific jobs should be analyzed to determine if components of the job duties could be completed by Betty. If so, learning to gain access to the computer system during community instruction in real work environments would have more functional relevance for her than learning the preprogrammed vocabulary words in the computer classroom (Inge & Wehman, 1993; Sowers & Powers, 1991).

Is Assistive Technology Necessary for the Student to Acquire the Targeted Skill, and Has It Been Selected Based on the Student's Needs?

School personnel and parents should consider if a student has the potential to learn to physically complete a task without assistive technology (Inge, in press; York & Rainforth, 1991). Issues such as how long it will take the student to acquire the physical skill and whether it will be functional for him or her should be discussed. For example, will abnormal movements be facilitated if the person completes the task without assistive technology? In some instances, the use of a specific movement to perform a task without an assistive technology device may ultimately result in more restricted movement and loss of function (York & Rainforth, 1991). Also, it may take a great deal of effort and time for the person to complete the task without an assistive technology device. The goal for using technology is to reduce the physical demands of the task in order for the student to be able to complete the task more easily and effectively. For instance, Betty should be evaluated to determine if she needs the assistance of the touch screen or whether she can learn to gain access to the computer by direct selection on the keyboard or by using a mouse. If learning to direct select would take too much time or physical effort, then assistive technology should be chosen based on Betty's needs rather than on the availability of a particular device within the school system.

In addition, bigger or more complex is not always better (e.g., "If it costs more, it will be more effective and more appropriate") (Garner & Campbell, 1987). Sometimes a low-tech choice is as good or better than an expensive high-tech solution. Again, these choices are made based on the student's needs and desires.

Is the Assistive Technology Device Being Substituted for Instruction or Interaction with the Teacher and/or the Student's Peers?

Garner and Campbell (1987) stated that one of the major obstacles to integrating appropriate use of technology into instructional programs is the practice of using technology to replace teacher–learner interactions. For instance, positioning a student in a sidelyer is not instruction nor is providing a student with an assistive technology device without the development of an instructional program (York & Rainforth, 1991). Initially, it may appear that Betty is included in a classroom with her peers; however, the combined effects of using age-inappropriate materials and the location of her workstation result in isolation and decreased opportunities for instruction and interaction. Technological advances can only enhance the quality of previously valid and appropriate instructional techniques (Campbell, Bricker, & Esposito, 1980). The identification and use of assistive technology must not be viewed as an end in itself, rather it is a means for supporting the development of a student's IEP within a functional curriculum (Garner & Campbell, 1987).

ASSESSMENT PROCESS

Since technological devices are so expansive, expensive, and evolutionary, with changes occurring daily, a systematic assessment procedure for recommending technology is critical. Bain (1989, 1993) describes three interdependent components that should be assessed to include the student, the assistive device, and the environment. Each component needs to be evaluated, selected, and applied based on its relationship to the other. If there is a change in one component, there will be changes in the other two components. For instance, when a student changes grade levels, resulting in a change in the environment, the student and the assistive devices that may be needed will change. Considering these components in isolation, such as conducting an assessment of the student in a clinical setting versus the school environment, usually will result in the purchase of devices that do not meet the student's needs.

Team Approach

No one individual or professional discipline will be familiar with all the information available on assistive technology, which includes software, hardware, and other recent technological developments (Smith, Benge, & Hall, 1994). Similarly, no one individual will possess the expertise to design, fabricate, or modify assistive technology devices for students with severe disabilities (Garner & Campbell, 1987). Therefore, the assessment process begins with a team of persons who knows the student well, including the student and his or her family, as the primary team players. The student and his or her family will have personal preferences and interests related to assistive technology, and only they can determine what will fit into the family's lifestyle and environment (Johnson, 1993). Other team members assist the student and his or her parents in developing goals for the IEP and in selecting the appropriate assistive technology devices and services that are needed to assist the student in benefiting from an appropriate school program.

Team members can include teachers, therapists, construction workers, rehabilitation professionals, social workers, employers, friends, and extended family members (Bain, 1993). For instance, school personnel can provide valuable input to assist families in making appropriate decisions based on the student's educational needs. Teachers know what educational tasks the student will be learning and what assistive technology devices may facilitate participation. The speech therapist can assess and suggest the appropriate software or device for the student's communicative needs. Occupational and physical therapists can determine how the student will gain access to technology and make recommendations for positioning, environmental modifications, and assistive technology devices based on the student's abilities (Smith, 1993). Social workers can identify funding sources, and rehabilitation engineers can devise adaptations based on team recommendations. Carpenters, such as the school's maintenance personnel, may assist in making environmental modifications to the school building in order for a student to participate in various activities. Finally, team members may vary over time as a student's educational goals change; for instance, as the student nears graduation and his or her programming shifts to community employment, an employer may become an invaluable member of the assessment team.

Depending on the age of the student, his or her assistive technology needs, and the family's needs (e.g., home modifications, financial assistance), professionals outside the school system may be involved in the assessment process. These professionals may come from a system or center with assistive technology expertise and have current technology training or experience with a variety of individuals (Uditsky, James, & Joseph, 1994). However, it should be emphasized that professionals from outside the system should function as team players within the student's environment(s) rather than taking the student for an evaluation in an external location, such as a clinic, in which he or she will never function. Assessment that occurs outside of the student's everyday school, home, or work environments will not identify the academic, environmental, functional, social, vocational, or behavioral issues that will have a direct impact on the student's assistive technology needs (Shuster, 1993).

If the team suggests assistive technology, it needs to evaluate the assistive technology device and how it fits with the student and the environment in which it will be used (Bain, 1989; Batavia & Hammer, 1990; Mann & Lane, 1991). Students and their families need to be informed about the purpose of the device, its advantages and disadvantages, and how to use the device (Bain, 1993; Kohlmeyer, 1993). Whenever possible, devices should be borrowed or loaned for trial use prior to ordering. Assessment should be an ongoing process that does not end when the device or equipment is chosen. Students, families, and school personnel must learn how to use it, how to adapt it for different environmental demands, and how to maintain the device so it is available when needed (Smith et al., 1994).

Assessment of Positioning

When assessing the student's assistive technology needs, the team must determine if the student is positioned properly so that he or she can concentrate on the task of using the assistive device. Proper positioning allows the student to have postural stability while moving to complete a motor action (Campbell & Forsyth, 1993); for example, the student can sit upright with his or her arms in a stable position while typing on a computer keyboard. Proper positioning also can correct or minimize orthopedic and neuromuscular influences on the student's movements (e.g., decrease stiffness or spasticity, reduce the influence of obligatory reflexes, and compensate for limited movement and/or muscle weakness) (Campbell, 1993; Inge, in press; Taylor, 1987). Assessment of the student's position needs to be evaluated while he or she is performing various tasks within many environments (Coley & Proctor, 1989).

Environmental/Task Demands

A student of preschool age may be evaluated on the playground, at the art table, in the housekeeping area, or in the bathroom. The adolescent student may need to be evaluated in multiple classrooms such as the choral room, the gym, the industrial arts lab, the bathroom, the cafeteria, the auditorium, or during community-based activities (Smith, 1993). Transition-age students, ages 14–22, will require an assessment of their positioning needs within school environments, as well as within community jobsites (Inge & Wehman, 1993).

When in different environments, students typically change positions frequently—they may sit to write or copy from the board, sit on the floor to do a group project, go to the library, bend or reach to get materials from shelves, reach food and carry it to the table in the cafeteria, or exit the school for a fire drill or a field trip (Smith, 1993). Students may use the same tool or object while in a variety of positions (e.g., using a pen when sitting and taking notes, standing while filling out a checklist or copying an item from a bulletin board, or laying on the floor when doing a crossword puzzle or drawing). Students with disabilities often have difficulty assuming or maintaining these various positions. Therefore, the team considers which positions are most functional for the student in various environments and then evaluates if external support is needed (Proctor, 1989).

Position of the Student

Most students will be seated when using technology in an educational environment. The three key areas of the body that give a student postural stability while seated for task completion are the pelvis and trunk, the head, and the extremities (Jones, Kolar, & Brown, 1993;

Okoye, 1988; Wright & Nomura, 1985). In all of these areas, the team assesses the student's skeletal alignment, symmetry, and ability to maintain the position over a period of time. The best position for a student is the one that gives him or her the most control with the least restrictions (Bergen, Presperin, & Tallman, 1990). Assessment of the student's positioning should occur while he or she is using the assistive device for specific targeted tasks or activities. Table 7.3 provides some guidelines for assessing student positioning. If the answers to the questions in Table 7.3 are "yes," the student is probably positioned ideally. However, the ideal position is not always possible when positioning students with severe disabilities, since there may be skeletal or neuromuscular processes that have made an impact on the physical characteristics of the individual (Swinth, 1994).

School personnel can help a student achieve a functional seated position by providing external support and adaptations. When adapting the seated position of a student, team members must consider all the tasks that the student needs to complete, as well as his or her mobility requirements. For example, it may be necessary to provide a chest strap to give a student additional trunk stability, but the chest strap may interfere with wheelchair propulsion, the locking or unlocking of brakes, or getting items out of the wheelchair backpack. Therefore, modifications to seating must be carefully analyzed and considered. Bergen et al. (1990) and Sylvester (1994) make the following recommendations for providing support when placing a student in an upright seated position. First, give support from underneath and behind (e.g., a firm seat back made of wood or high-density foam). Second, provide support laterally (sides), using hip guides or trunk supports. Third, give support from the front (e.g., harness, lap tray, abductor wedge).

Seated positioning systems are available commercially or may be custom-fabricated and can be categorized as planar, contoured, or custom-molded systems (Jones et al., 1993). Planar systems are usually low tech and use flat pieces or shapes to position the student with minimal needs. Contoured systems are mass produced and use curves and planar surfaces to position the student. Custom-molded systems are shaped to the individual student and can

---

Table 7.3. Assessment of a student's seated position for assistive technology use

1. Is his or her pelvis upright and in a neutral position (e.g., not leaning backward or forward)?
2. Is his or her weight equally distributed on both buttocks?
3. Is there at least 90 degrees of hip flexion?
4. Are his or her upper legs relaxed and symmetrical (e.g., legs not wide apart or tightly pressed together)?
5. Is his or her trunk upright and symmetrical (e.g., not leaning to one side or the other, but slightly forward)?
6. Is his or her head vertical to the floor and the chin tucked (e.g., not tilted or head back with the chin up)?
7. Are his or her head, shoulders, and hips aligned?
8. Are his or her shoulders relaxed and the neck elongated (e.g., shoulders not hunched or one shoulder higher than the other)?
9. Can he or she move the arms forward and toward midline?
10. Are his or her elbows supported and bent to 90 degrees or less?
11. Are his or her wrists straight or supported (e.g., not bent up or down)?
12. Are his or her fingers slightly bent?
13. Are his or her knees bent approximately 90 degrees, and are they lower than the hips?
14. Are his or her feet flat, supported, and bearing weight evenly?
15. Can he or she reach the input device?

accommodate any body shape. The contoured and custom-molded systems are usually considered to be high tech.

Table 7.4 suggests some techniques that school personnel can use to modify the seating of a student who can use existing school chairs. Jones et al. (1993) suggest other adaptations to high-tech seating systems: pelvis seat belts, subasis bar, biangular backs, and flat seats or backs; upper legs/hip pads and abduction pads; trunk/lateral pads, hip pads, anterior support, and biangular back; head/neck lateral support, occipital support, and anterior support; shoulder depressor pads, butterfly or H strap, lap tray, and contoured back; and ankles/feet/instep straps, ankle/foot orthosis, footrests, foot straps, and toe clips. The type and amount of adaptations needed are individually assessed and chosen according to the skills of the students, the assistive device being used, and the environmental demands of the student (Swinth, 1994). Physical and occupational therapists are usually the team members who provide guidelines and assistance in this assessment area.

Position of the Device

When evaluating the student's postural alignment and symmetry, the student's position in relation to the assistive device and the environment also is assessed. For example, when using a computer, the student must be able to reach the keyboard or switch, while maintaining his or

Table 7.4.   Adaptations to standard school furniture—chairs and tables

Height
- Adjust the height of the chair and/or table
- Saw off legs of the chair and/or table
- Extend legs of the chair and/or table
- Insert wooden blocks under each chair or table leg
- Add a platform under the entire chair
- Add a footrest (strap it to the chair with a bungie cord, which allows movement from one environment to another)
- Add armrests to the chair

Seat depth
- Add a foam piece, wedge, or cushion to the chair back
- Add a foam-covered wooden extension to the chair back (use a bungie cord)

Stability
- Use a seat belt, located at the student's pelvis or chest area, on the chair
- Add lateral trunk supports made from wood or high-density foam to the chair
- Add a wedge cushion or wooden seat insert to the chair
- Use lumbar pads (foam or small rolled towel) for back support
- Use lateral hip and thigh pads for buttocks support
- Add a lap tray to the chair
- Provide arm or wrist supports to the chair
- Use a contoured seat back on the chair
- Extend the back height of the chair with wood

Limited mobility
- Add an abductor wedge drilled into the seat of the chair
- Use a wood scapular back support on the chair to bring student's arms forward
- Provide a lap tray placed parallel to the floor or on an incline
- Attach movable wrist or arm supports to the chair

Adapted from Proctor (1989).

her position comfortably. If the student is tilted backward in a wheelchair to assist with head and trunk control, the monitor or device should be positioned so that the student can see it while maintaining the chin in a tucked position (cervical flexion).

An assistive device, such as a microswitch, may be placed at the student's midline, to the left, to the right, at waist level, or at foot level, depending on the student's sensory, neuromuscular, motor, or perceptual skills. The work surface that holds or supports the assistive device, the student, the toy, or the materials of an activity can be changed (e.g., height, size, inclines, additional supports, textures) to improve the student's performance. The team will want to assess the student's performance using the assistive device by varying the position of the device, student, school materials, and so forth to determine the optimal one for task completion. Table 7.5 gives some low-tech solutions for stabilizing devices or objects to facilitate student participation.

Position of Student within the Environment

After adjusting the position of the student, the work surface, and the assistive device, the student and his or her peers should be able to function within the environment. For instance, if the student is seated in the middle of the front row with his or her power wheelchair and augmentative communication device, can the other students see around him or her? Can the student make mistakes comfortably in front of the other students? Can he or she switch positions (lean back) without interrupting others? Is there an outlet to plug in a cord to an electronic device? Does the student have enough room to raise his or her hand? Is he or she positioned so that light does not obscure the monitor screen? Are there architectural barriers that need to be modified? All of these are examples of questions that team members should ask themselves when assessing the student's use of assistive technology within the environment. There needs to be a balance among the best positions for the assistive device, the student, and the environment.

Systematic Process for Selecting Assistive Technology Devices

School personnel need a comprehensive, systematic way to assess the technological needs of students. Lee and Thomas (1989) developed the Control Assessment Protocol to evaluate and select the most appropriate control system for environmental control, mobility, and assistive technology devices. This protocol, in combination with recommendations from Mann and Lane (1991), can be used to evaluate a student's technology needs.

Table 7.5. Low-technology methods for stabilizing items

- Tape (single or doubled sided)
- Nonslip pressure-sensitive matting (Dycem, rug mat)
- Velcro
- Suction cup holders (single or double faced)
- Tacking putty
- C-clamps
- L-brackets
- Soldering clamps
- Wing nuts and bolts
- Bungie cords
- Elastic
- Webbing straps

Adapted from Proctor (1989).

Step 1: Gather Background Information

Background information might be found on a referral form, in the student's IEP or school records, or through informal interviews with teachers, parents, the student, physician, or other professionals already working with the student. First, it is important to collect information about the student's and family's previous experiences with technology and their current and future goals for technology use. Unfortunately, many students may have devices that they do not use due to inappropriate or inadequate assessment of their needs, lack of training, poor equipment maintenance, and so forth. The following questions may be useful when interviewing students and their families concerning technology use.

- Do they believe that assistive technology is necessary?
- What tasks do they want the student to accomplish or participate in with the device(s)?
- Where does the student want to use the device(s)?
- Do they have a "gadget" tolerance?
- Do they understand how to use and maintain the proposed device(s)?
- If the student and family have used assistive technology devices before, what did they like or dislike about them?
- How and where did the student use the device(s)?

When collecting background information, the evaluator needs to know the student's abilities and needs (Baize & O'Brien, 1994). How is he or she performing educationally? What will the student be doing vocationally? Is the student medically stable? Are his or her functional abilities expected to improve or remain stable, or does the student have a progressive disability? For example, if a student has Duchenne muscular dystrophy and is propelling a manual wheelchair, the evaluator needs to think about the child's computer needs (e.g., input devices and programs) and how these needs can interface with equipment that may be needed in the future (e.g., a power wheelchair, a communication device, or an environmental control unit). Or, if the student is older or has difficulty generalizing information, it may be best to work directly with a universal keyboard and forego using, for example, the Muppet Learning Keys™, which have a different keyboard configuration.

Information on the future environmental demands for the student is also critical to collect during the student and family interview process. What are the educational and vocational goals? For example, if the student will be graduating from high school and going to college, it is important to consider the type of campus and parking available at the college. If the terrain of the proposed campus is rough with hills and has minimal parking, a heavy-duty power wheelchair with multiple interface capabilities may be warranted compared to a wheelchair that is suitable for high school. If the student needs to communicate with his or her professors by e-mail or needs to write group projects, the type of computer and software selected could determine the student's future academic success or failure. Finally, choosing equipment that can use integrated controls (e.g., one control that operates the wheelchair, augmentative communication devices, and an environmental control unit) is technologically possible and is being advocated by technology experts (Caves & Furumasu, 1994; Clayton, 1994; Guerrette & Nakai, 1994; Guerrette & Sumi, 1994; Hawley, Cudd, Wells, Wilson, & Judd, 1992).

Step 2: Observe the Student

Observing the student in a variety of environments assists the team in identifying the student's abilities and needs. Prior to even trying high-tech devices, the team must see how the student approaches a task. Information about sensorimotor, cognitive, and social skills can be obtained during these observations. Sensorimotor skills can be evaluated by asking some of the following questions:

- How does the student move into and about a room?
- What body parts does he or she move and how quickly, accurately, and consistently?
- Does he or she seem to react positively or negatively to different sensations (e.g., sounds, touch, light, pressure, temperature)?
- Can he or she see or hear things within the school environment?

Observing the student within the school environment gives team members a general understanding of the student's cognitive abilities. Discussions with the teacher and observations in the classroom obviously are useful in determining the child's abilities, but other environments are also rich in information. For instance, by watching the student in the cafeteria, the team can determine his or her ability to sequence, organize, use money, and follow directions. In the library or music room, memory, reading, or decision-making skills may be easily assessed.

Students interact with many people in the school environment. By observing these social interactions, the team may gain information on how assistive technology can fit within the student's lifestyle. What roles does the student have (e.g., classmate, leader, pep club member, friend)? Does the student like to be with other people? Does the student have a way to communicate with others? Can he or she express his or her emotions appropriately? How does he or she approach new tasks? How does he or she cope with mistakes or frustration?

Step 3: Determine the Student's Abilities and Assistive Technology Needs

This stage is a more in-depth assessment of the student's abilities related to the tasks that the student is or will be performing. During this process, team members are assessing what tasks the student needs to do and how fast (rate)? What capabilities does the student have that will aid or impede his or her ability to function within an environment? Instead of just observing the student, certain team members may be evaluating specific skills, such as visual acuity, ability to perceive touch, or range of motion measurements (e.g., can the student raise his or her arms overhead, reach forward?). These skills should be evaluated within the context of activities that a student performs or will need to perform in current and future environments (Parette, Hourcade, & Van Biervliet, 1993). By assessing the student within environmental contexts, the team members can determine the student's physical capabilities, the tasks in which the student is participating in now, the tasks that he or she will need to do, and how assistive technology devices can facilitate current and future task participation (Hutinger et al., 1990). Table 7.6 provides suggestions on how to organize an assessment for determining a student's abilities within an environmental task context and his or her low- and high-tech needs.

Step 4: Investigate the Ideal Access System

If the team determines that a high-tech solution is needed, team members will review assistive technology systems that could meet the needs of the student during this phase of assessment. It is critical that this investigation incorporate a broad review of what is available, rather than only considering what is owned by the school system. A variety of assistive technology devices should be tried by the student; however, this is probably the most difficult task to accomplish due to limited school system resources and the time required to keep abreast of new devices. Interagency collaboration with other community agencies may provide one solution to this problem such as working with the Department of Rehabilitation

Table 7.6. Assessment of student abilities

I. Assess current and future task requirements

A. Educational

Sample current environment: Classroom

Sample tasks: note taking (e.g., blackboard, overhead projector, books), reading assignments, writing reports; communicating with teachers and peers; mobility within the classroom (e.g., weight shifts, transfers, accessibility); coping with frustrations, willing to persevere, and so on.

Sample future environment: Community college

Sample tasks: completing application; selecting course of study; communicating with teachers and peers; mobility in the classroom and around campus (e.g., wheelchair requirements, accessibility issues, using the college's shuttle bus service); note taking, reading assignments, writing reports, coping with frustrations, persevering on tasks, and so on.

B. Domestic

Sample current environment: School cafeteria

Sample tasks: selecting lunch; communicating with cafeteria workers; socializing with peers; paying for lunch; mobility issues (e.g., maneuvering wheelchair, manipulating lunch tray); eating (e.g., self-feeding, drinking, manipulating utensils); self-management of dietary needs, and so on.

Sample future environment: Group home

Sample tasks: dressing; laundry; making a meal or snack; washing dishes; making bed; cleaning bedroom; communicating with housemates; expressing emotions appropriately; using the telephone; mobility within and around home (e.g., transfers, use of wheelchair); budgeting money; maintaining of assistive technology equipment, and so on.

C. Vocational

Sample current environment: Local bank (nonpaid work experience)

Sample tasks: microfilming checks; data entry; delivering interoffice mail and memos; answering the phone; taking messages; communicating work-related issues with coworkers (e.g., asking for assistance or directions); flexible if changes needed in work routine; socializing during lunch and breaks; caring for personal needs (e.g., toileting, eating, hygiene); maneuvering wheelchair within office and outside of bank, using public transportation, and so on.

Sample future environment: Insurance company

Sample tasks: data entry; answering the phone; taking messages; filing insurance claims; communicating work-related issues with coworkers (e.g., asking for assistance or directions); flexible if changes needed in work routine; socializing during lunch and breaks; caring for personal needs (e.g., toileting, eating, hygiene); maneuvering wheelchair within office and outside of office; using public transportation, and so on.

D. Leisure/recreation

Sample current environment: School gym

Sample tasks: selecting activities; using adaptive sports equipment; following rules of games/sports; taking turns; maintaining self-control; selecting and attending school

(continued)

Table 7.6. (*continued*)

functions (e.g., basketball games, dances); socializing with peers; coping with frustrations, and so on.

Sample future environment: Community recreation center

Sample tasks: self-selecting activities; completing application requirements; paying applicable fees; arranging transportation; monitoring leisure/recreation schedule; socializing with peers, and so on.

E. Community

Sample current environment: Retail store

Sample tasks: arranging transportation (e.g., identifying transportation options, evaluating accessibility issues, following bus schedule, etc.); communicating with sales clerk (e.g., greeting, asking for assistance or directions, etc.); selecting purchases; paying for purchase; mobility within and around the store (e.g., accessibility issues, maneuvers wheelchair)

Sample future environment: Doctor's office

Sample tasks: identifying need for medical attention; using telephone to schedule appointments; arranging for transportation; communicating symptoms to doctor/nurse; advocating for services or prescription for assistive devices; paying bill, and so on.

II. Current sensorimotor functions: Although sensorimotor functioning is identified as a separate category, assessment of these skills occurs within the context of the student's current and future tasks.

A. Sensory awareness

Tactile (touch); auditory; visual (visual fields, acuity); proprioception (knowing where the body is in space); vestibular (balance)

B. Perceptual skills

Perceive movement; identify objects through touch; right-left discrimination; recognize icons or shapes as same and different; find cursor or input device with verbal directions (e.g., up, down, beside); figure ground (e.g., ability to find the cursor on a cluttered screen); depth perception (e.g., can estimate how far to reach to touch the on/off button); directional sense (e.g., forward, backward, right, left, up, down)

C. Neuromuscular skills

Assess range of motion (e.g., flexibility in moving body parts); evaluate strength (e.g., push buttons or switches); determine endurance level (e.g., repetition of movement[s] for gaining access to technology over time); identify obligatory reflexes (e.g., how do they influence student's freedom of movement); evaluate sitting posture (e.g., with and without external support); weight shift; muscle tone (e.g., spasticity or hypotonia that influences movement); skin integrity (e.g., ability to tolerate pressure on skin without breakdown)

D. Motor skills

Identify motor response(s) for turning on computer; access keyboard or peripheral device; evaluate gross-motor coordinator; assess fine motor skills (e.g., does the student have unilateral hand function or bilateral hand function?, what is his or her reaction time?, can he or she bring hands to or cross midline?); observe visual-motor skills (e.g., tracking, fixating, scanning)

(*continued*)

Table 7.6. (*continued*)

III. Cognitive/communication skills: This information can assist the team in matching the student's skill level to the complexity level of the assistive technology device.

A. What level of arousal and/or attention is required to operate the assistive technology device?

B. Does the system use pictures or symbols? Is this appropriate for the targeted student?

C. What are the language concepts required for this task?

D. How complicated is this device to operate? Does it require memory or complicated sequencing of steps? Can the student learn and retain this information?

E. What organizational and problem-solving abilities does this device require?

F. Will the student need to follow complicated directions (more than 1 or 2 directions) to use the device?

G. Can the performance gap between the student's current skills and the characteristics of the assistive technology device be eliminated or minimized by training?

Portions of this table were adapted from AOTA Uniform Terminology (1994), Okoye (1988).

Services or the local Center for Independent Living (CIL). Some states have developed a lending library in which technology users can try assistive technology devices at home before purchasing. In addition, team members can consult a state or national database or center (e.g., Virginia Assistive Technology Information and Referral System, Abledata, CO-NET, Trace Center) to obtain new information about available products or to find vendors or agencies that may loan equipment for assessment purposes (CO-NET, 1991; Enders & Hall, 1990; Smith et al., 1994).

Some students with the most severe disabilities may benefit from a referral to a technology specialist or a center that has numerous devices for assessment purposes. It is critical to remember, however, that these assessments still need to incorporate an evaluation of the student within his or her natural environments. Otherwise, an assessment conducted at a center-based agency could result in the purchase of an assistive technology device that is never used by the student.

There are a variety of solutions available for students with disabilities (Levin & Scherfenberg, 1987). In this stage of assessment, team members must think about the student's capabilities. For example, a student with athetosis may need an enlarged keyboard or a switch due to his or her large range of motion and gross resolution, whereas a student with very little range of motion but good resolution may need a small keyboard. Table 7.7 provides a list of input device examples, and Table 7.8 gives some examples of possible high-tech and low-tech devices or software that could be used for certain functional abilities.

Selecting Control Sites

When selecting the control interface for an assistive technology device, the student's capabilities assessed in the last stage are used to match him or her to an interface. The student should be positioned correctly before assessment of the control sites (motor response) that he or she will use to activate a device. The team may consider some of the following issues. What part of the body can the student use as a control site? Is this the most accurate choice for the student? Will he or she become fatigued before the task is completed?

Table 7.7.   Assistive technology solutions

Input device examples
- Trackball
- Ballpoint mouse
- Minikeyboard
- Split keyboard (two or three splits)
- OCR word scan
- Dragon dictate™
- Expanded keyboard
- Trackball mouse
- Expanded membrane keyboard
- Optical headpointer
- Light pens
- Intellikeys™
- Key Largo™ (light touch) (print custom overlays for K:NEX)
- King keyboard™
- Wand keyboards
- Mouse stick
- Mouth-operated joystick
- Tongue-operated (on roof of mouth) joystick
- Optical scanner with verbal output
- OCR-optical character recognition
- Power pad
- Remote keyboard
- Remote mouse
- Muppet learning keys™
- Koala pad
- Touch window
- Switch-back

Input adaptors
- Adaptive firmware card
- K:NEX™
- AID + ME™
- Multiple switch box
- Power port (for power pad and switches)
- Paddle panel
- Porter (for five input devices)
- Joystick adapter
- Switch interfacer
- Touch window adapter

Usually, the first choice for a control-site selection is the student's hands. If the student can use his or her hands, he or she will be able to see when and how to depress a switch or key to operate an assistive technology device and may have more options for using a standard universal keyboard for operating a computer or augmentative communication system. The head is the next option to consider. Can the student use a head movement (i.e., chin, cheek, back and forth, side to side), tongue movement, or eye movement (e.g., eye gaze, eye blink) to operate the device? Other control-site options may include the student's foot, leg (e.g., knee, thigh, calf), or arm (e.g., shoulder, elbow). Table 7.9 lists some examples of motor responses that students may use to activate assistive technology devices.

Table 7.8.   Interface options for the computer

Student abilities	Possible interface options
Has some fine motor control and accuracy, but limited gross movement	Regular keyboard with arm/wrist supports or keyguards; mini keyboard; paddles; light pen; switches, such as button, lever, tip, pinch, wobble, leaf, grasp/grip, small dual rocker, light activated, light touch, magnetic finger, muscle movement, thumb
Has some gross motor movements, but limited accuracy	Expanded keyboard; King keyboard™; Intellikeys™; Key Largo™; power pad; touch window; arm slot control; koala pad; joystick; switches, such as rocker, plate, pneumatic/air cushion, roller, membrane, wafer, cylindrical grasp, muscle movement pull, ring stack, squeeze, star, treadle, trackball
Has facial muscles, but limited arm or leg movement	Light activated; voice activated; mouth-operated joystick; tongue-operated (on roof of mouth) joystick; switches, such as eye blink, sip and puff, tongue (dual control), eyebrow, mercury tilt
Has auditory sensation, but minimal use of vision	Antiglare screen; braille and speak; screen reader (using speech synthesizer); voice-activated software; enlarger; braille printers; intention switch (plate with music and blinking lights); OCR-optical character recognition

Selecting Control Interfaces

Anson (1993, 1994) has an extremely detailed system to select control devices for computer usage. His diagrams are useful in determining what options to consider (e.g., types and names of devices) and what to evaluate if an option does not work. When matching the device and interface controls with student needs, there are a number of control device characteristics to consider (Brandenburg & Vanderheiden, 1987). This includes such issues as portability, flexibility, availability, and student reaction to the device. A detailed list of questions to consider when selecting a control interface can be found in Table 7.10.

Hierarchy of Interfacing Techniques

There are three main techniques that a student can use to operate an electronic assistive technology device: direct selection, encoding, and scanning. Direct selection is the fastest way to operate technology and is used whenever possible. The input action (e.g., depressing a key) yields the output of a unique character, word, sentence, or symbol. For example, when an "A" is depressed on the keyboard or touch window, an "A" appears on the computer screen (Anson, 1993).

Directed scanning requires the student to perform numerous input actions to yield a single output. For example, using a joystick, a mouse, or a trackball may require proportional movements (i.e., move the device up, down, right, left, or diagonally) to select the desired letter or icon on the computer screen. The joystick may be switch based (i.e., handheld electronic games or Intellikeys™ that have keypad with arrows that move up, down, left, or right)

Table 7.9. Examples of motor responses for activating assistive technology devices

Arm/hand

- Move arm/hand to touch a pressure-sensitive switch (e.g., touch elbow, palm, forearm, fingers to switch) that operates an environmental control unit.
- Push joystick to propel power wheelchair.
- Move arm/hand/finger to interrupt a light beam switch that operates an augmentative communication device.
- Raise arm with a mercury switch cuff to turn on a compact disc.
- Squeeze ball/bulb switch to scan selections on a computer.
- Move elbow to touch skin to a pad switch (no pressure required) that activates a buzzer in parents' bedroom.

Head/face

- Raise/lower eyebrows to activate switch attached to battery-operated toy.
- Nod head to interrupt a light beam to turn on the television.
- Lift head to trigger a mercury switch that is connected to a tape recorder.
- Bite switch to control a power wheelchair.
- Lift chin to operate a joystick for scanning selections on an electronic communication device.
- Use sip-and-puff switch to move an electric scooter.
- Touch forehead, cheek, or chin to a pressure-sensitive switch that operates an electric blender.
- Use voice-activated computer system.

Leg/foot

- Push foot/toes to activate pillow switch to recline electric bed or chair.
- Move toe(s) to activate "splint switch" (molded foot splint with miniature paddle switch mounted near toes), which operates an electric page turner.
- Push joystick with foot/toes to play Nintendo.
- Move leg to touch pressure-sensitive massage cushion.
- Foot/leg moves toward a proximity switch that turns on whirlpool bath (switch is activated when body part is brought within a specific range).

Adapted from Inge (in press).

(Anson, 1992). Using directed scanning usually requires specialized software, and therefore it is not transferable to many types of computer programs.

Scanning is the slowest selection technique where characters are displayed (one at a time or groups of characters) at a certain set rate, and the user activates a switch when the desired character is seen on the screen. The scanning can be in a latch mode where a series of items are presented and then the input device is activated to select the item. Or scanning can be in a momentary mode in which the student must keep his or her hand on the input to keep it going; when the hand is removed, the scanning stops. There are more than 20 different patterns of scanning available and different strategies to speed the scanning process (Anson, 1992).

Encoding is another selection technique that requires input from switches to emulate the keyboard. Encoding can be used where a symbol represents a sentence. For example, using an infrared light, a student can gaze at icons on an augmentative communication device to produce sentences (e.g., a sun represents the sentence, "Good morning, what a sunny day!"). Morse code is another example of using switch encoding (Anson, 1992). A switch is encoded to be a "dash" or a "dot" and then two to five movements produce the desired output. For example, to produce a letter the student may push a left switch to be the "dash" and the right switch to be the "dot." This interface technique is effective with students who have severe physical disabilities and cannot activate a regular keyboard but have a high level of cognition

Table 7.10.   Selecting control interfaces

1. Does the assistive technology device assist the student in doing the task that he or she is trying to complete?
2. Can the student accomplish the task better when using this device than without it?
3. Is the appearance of the device acceptable to the student?
4. What is the device's dimensions? Will it fit the environment in which it will be used (e.g., on the lap tray or with a walker)?
5. If needed, is the device portable?
6. How does the device need to be positioned? Can it be positioned or mounted in order for the student to use his or her best motor response?
7. What operating techniques can be used with the device (i.e., direct select, scanning, encoding)?
8. What type of feedback does the device give (e.g., auditory click, movement when activated, tactile input)?
9. How flexible is the device? Can it be used with the student's augmentative communication device and environmental control unit? Can the configuration of the keyboard be changed?
10. Is the device expandable? (If a kindergarten student is using the device, will he or she be able to use this same device 1–2 years later when doing higher cognitive tasks in school?)
11. Is the student safe using the device? Does he or she have some behavioral, cognitive, or physical characteristics that interfere with using the device? If so, what training strategies need to be in place to facilitate safety?
12. What type of warranty is offered with the device? Is there a toll-free number or way to get service or technical assistance if needed?
13. Is the cost justifiable? Can the school, family, or third-party payer afford the cost of the device? Or is there a less expensive alternative that is just as effective?
14. Is the device available to the student? Is it commercially available, or does it need to be custom fitted? Does the school district have one for the student to use on a trial basis?

and memory to retrieve the codes (Anson, 1992). This is time consuming and is not as efficient as direct selection.

Data Collection

While assessing the ideal access system, it is essential for school personnel to keep accurate records on the student's performance with each assistive technology device and interface technique. The student may be able to use a device proficiently but only for a short amount of time. With practice, the student may be able to improve his or her accuracy in using a device. Figure 7.2 gives an example of how to record data when assessing the student. Issues to consider include the interaction between the position of the student, the type of assistive device, the position of the device, the interface technique, the student's motor response for using the interface, and the environment. Varying combinations of these components will assist the team in identifying the best fit for using the assistive technology device.

Step 5: Propose an Access System

After assessing the student, the interface device, and the selection technique, it is time to propose an access system that will meet the student's environmental demands. This decision can be made by reviewing what the student will be required to do in academic and home environments and by evaluating how this access system will interface with the physical, social, and cultural environment of the student. This is often a stage that requires a lot of trial and error.

Name of student: _____

Date: _____ Assessor: _____

Device:	Device:	Device:
Position: • Student: • Device:	Position: • Student: • Device:	Position: • Student: • Device:
Interface technique:	Interface technique:	Interface technique:
Environment:	Environment:	Environment:
Adaptations:	Adaptations:	Adaptations:
Trial 1: Accuracy/speed/endurance (consider time, rate, quality)	Trial 2: Accuracy/speed/endurance (consider time, rate, quality)	Trial 3: Accuracy/speed/endurance (consider time, rate, quality)
Other observations: (visual, auditory, tactile)	Other observations: (visual, auditory, tactile)	Other observations: (visual, auditory, tactile)

Other suggested equipment or adaptations: _____

Figure 7.2.   Assistive device data collection.

158

Information from the record-keeping form will assist personnel in determining which system is most efficient and effective for the student to use. In addition, student and family feedback is essential. A student may be more accurate using a particular device, but if he or she personally does not accept the appearance or operating technique selected the success with the device will be limited.

Step 6: Personalize and Maximize the Access System

Once the access system is chosen, it can be further modified to meet the individual needs of the student. The student's previously assessed capabilities and needs are matched to the interface and then adapted to increase efficiency and accuracy in using assistive technology.

Modifications to Control Interface

Modifications can be low-tech solutions that are low cost and easy to do, or they can require the expertise of an occupational therapist or a rehabilitation engineer. There are four general ways in which assistive devices can be modified: shape and form, mechanical characteristics, amplification, and transformation (Rein, 1989). Table 7.11 gives examples of how to modify interface devices. Specific examples for adapting a keyboard are provided in Table 7.12.

Choosing Software

Besides choosing the correct hardware, school system personnel often select the software for the student. The type of hardware and input devices (peripherals) that are used by a particular student will determine if a particular software program is appropriate or usable. For example, if the student only can use the power pad as an input device then many other software programs cannot be used, because the power pad requires specialized software. The student's interest in the subject matter or format of the software is essential if it is being used to augment a particular portion of a curriculum. It also needs to be developmentally and age appropriate.

Table 7.11.   Types of adaptations to interface devices

Enlarge or change shape

- Add a handle, knob, or disc.
- Build up the handle (e.g., pipe insulation, foam curler, tape, putty, wood, ball).

Change the mechanical advantage

- Extend handles or headpointers (e.g., tongue depressors, Tinkertoy paddle extensions, dowels).
- Provide gravity assistance.
- Select lightweight or electrical devices.
- Use universal cuff with dowel or pencil of different sizes.

Amplify characteristics

- Enlarge letters or highlight (reflecting tape).
- Use amplifiers or speech synthesizers.
- Add tactile dots or letters.
- Change colors, brightness on monitor, or input device.

Transform the elements

- Change the environment (pair sound with visual or vibratory device or change visual to tactile) (e.g., doorbell, telephone, alarm clock).
- Turn braille into letters.
- Change letter type to vibrating tools (i.e., Opticon™).

Adapted from Rein (1989).

Table 7.12.   Keyboard adaptations

- Arm-support systems (e.g., forearm, wrist supports—foam, plastic, roll, and slide)
- Moisture guards
- Key latch to hold down <shift>, <control>, etc., keys
- Keyguards (made from Plexiglas, plastic lids)
- Key mask (block unused keys with cardboard, plastic lids)
- Disable autorepeat key
- Place keyboard on incline
- Labels—words, symbols, or pictures
- Color code keys (function keys, enter, use stickers)
- Key caps (braille, enlarged letters)
- Tactile cues (glue, embossed letters, high dots)
- Home row key indicators
- Keyboard overlays
- KeyStopper
- Keylocks
- On/off adapter switch
- PC pedal (<control>, <shift>, <alt keys>, or enhanced)
- Dvorak keyboard (one-handed configuration)

When a student is unmotivated and/or he or she is trying to succeed at a difficult motor or cognitive task (i.e., how to use a different input method or learn a new math skill), the outcome of training will be limited if he or she does not find enough or too much challenge within the software program (Buckleitner, 1991).

Software is often chosen according to its purpose. There are many types of software available. Okoye (1988) identifies six main types: tutorials, drill and practice, interactive video or CD-ROM, educational games, motor games, and action-consequence games. Within each of these types, various concepts and reading levels may be required by the student, which determines the suitability of using the software (Okoye, 1988).

Many other factors are considered when evaluating software. For example, how easy is the software to use? User-friendly software is essential; easy-to-read instructions that can be recalled when needed are most helpful to students and school personnel (Buckleitner, 1991). These instructions and the concepts being explored within the software program need to match the grade level of the student so he or she can understand how to use it. Menus that are accessible with clearly defined graphics and sounds are helpful. Error correction that is given in a positive way and is collected as data also aids in training the student and determining his or her success in using the program (Buckleitner, 1991; Okoye, 1993).

Software programs that have a variety of options can be used by one student over a certain period of time or they can be used by many students within the school environment (Okoye, 1993). Programs need to be adaptable to many progressive levels of play. Then the software can be graded to the student's skill level. The program may give options as to the type of input device to use and/or the type of feedback or cues given; the number of players, the size of the print or color contrast; or the difficulty or speed of the program. Software that expands as the student's cognitive and motor skills improve is helpful, because word-processing and spreadsheet programs are expensive. By analyzing the software and the options, school personnel can weigh the costs and benefits of a program for each student and for all students using technology within the school system.

Step 7: Set Goals for Instruction and Training

One of the major obstacles to integrating the use of assistive technology into instructional programs for students with severe disabilities is the identification of an assistive device as an "end in itself," rather than as part of a functional curriculum (Garner & Campbell, 1987). The selection of the assistive technology device is only the beginning of the process, yet the fact that students need training in how to operate and use the device is often overlooked (Vanderheiden, 1987; Vanderheiden & Yoder, 1986). Therefore, team members must allot time to train students to use assistive devices after they have been identified and ordered. Goals may be related to increasing the student's independence in turning on the device or improving accuracy, speed, or efficiency in using the device. For example, an augmentative communication device that uses icons may take more than 200 hours to complete training (S. Cristafuli, personal communication, November 1987). Again, it is essential for school personnel to develop systematic instructional programs and keep records on the student's success in using the assistive device. A daily or weekly record-keeping form can be used to identify the student's progress or lack of progress with achieving the goals. Figure 7.3 provides an example of one instructional program that uses time delay to teach students how to operate technology. (See Snell, 1993, for more detailed information on designing and implementing instructional programs for students with severe disabilities.)

Step 8: Implement the System

Once the system has been received, a team member needs to become the coordinator to show other persons how to show use the system. Decisions about where and when the system will be used need to be made. The student may use the device in numerous environments or only in school. School personnel must think about when the device will be used; for example, during what classes, for what time frame, and with whom. Someone needs to be trained and designated as the troubleshooter if the device becomes inoperable. In addition, another decision needs to be made about who will perform the maintenance on the device (Bain, 1993; Smith et al., 1994).

Step 9: Monitor Programs and Provide Follow Up

This last stage is extremely important and should be ongoing while the student is in the school system. The team needs to determine the outcome of the child using this device, whether he or she can participate in an activity that he or she could not previously be involved in or whether he or she can accomplish a task more efficiently or effectively with the assistive device. The student should also meet the criteria of the assistive technology goal as it was written in the IEP.

When a student uses a device proficiently, the device needs to be systematically monitored to determine whether it is still meeting the student's academic needs. Have the student's capabilities increased or decreased? What changes would be beneficial? What is the student's and his or her family's opinion about the assistive device? Have the student and his or her family had technical difficulties, breakdown, or inconsistency with the manufacturer? What do they like best about the device, and what would they change? How has this device helped the student's interactions within the school and community environment? Such information allows school personnel to learn from their successes and failures when matching the student and an assistive technology device to meet environmental demands. Follow up can help make decisions about purchasing future equipment for the school district and for making recommendations for future students. Service delivery (e.g., assessment and intervention processes and personnel) can be changed according to feedback from former students and their families.

Student's Name: Fred R.

Name of Program: Using a microswitch to play a tape recorder

Setting: Classroom

Program Objective: Fred will independently press a Jelly Bean Switch® attached to a tape recorder within 6 seconds of when it is placed in front of him for three consecutive sessions.

Student Characteristics That:

Assist: Fred's mother reports that he particularly enjoys listening to music at home. She would like for him to be able to turn a tape recorder on and off when he wants to listen to music. At school, Fred always responds to music by smiling, laughing, and vocalizing.

Hinder: Fred has very limited fine-motor skills due to cerebral palsy and severe spasticity. His team believes that the best strategy for gaining access to various leisure/recreation items would be through a switch. Fred has recently moved from a rural community and has not had any exposure to using assistive technology.

Baseline/Probe Procedures: *Baseline:* Prior to the first probe session, demonstrate the operation of the switch. Do not demonstrate or provide reinforcement during all other baseline or probe trials. Place the tape recorder with the switch in front of Fred as specified in his program plan for positioning. Give the cue, "Fred, play the tape." Wait 4 seconds for a response. Record a + for correct or a − for incorrect response within the allotted time period. Take a baseline for 3 days or until student performance is stable. *Probe:* After a stable baseline of performance is established, probe Fred's independent use of the tape recorder for one trial prior to each training session. Use the same procedure as in the baseline assessment.

Instructional Procedure: Prior to placing a tape in the recorder, offer Fred a choice of music by showing him two selections. His mother reports that he likes Barry Manilow and Whitney Houston. Try holding the tape covers or pictures of the artists, one in each hand, and ask Fred to look at his choice. Use whichever tape that Fred looks at first. If he does not appear to make a choice, alternate selections during the training trials. Make notes concerning his musical preferences. For instance, record if he tends to activate the recorder independently when one choice is offered versus no response or always needing prompting when given a specific selection.

Connect the tape recorder and the Jelly Bean Switch® to a control unit. Set the timer for the maximum of 90 seconds. Use a time-delay procedure with a physical prompt for training Fred to use the microswitch.

1. A delay of *0* seconds will be used for the first 25 trials of playing a tape. Place the selected tape in the recorder. Give the cue, "Fred, play the music." Immediately provide a physical prompt to assist him in activating the recorder.

2. Beginning on the 26th trial, begin using a *2*-second delay prior to providing the physical prompt. In other words, once a tape has been selected and placed in the recorder, give the cue, "Fred, play the music." Wait *2* seconds before physically prompting him to press the switch. If Fred does not respond within 2 seconds, provide the physical prompt. If he begins to make an error, interrupt him with the

(continued)

Figure 7.3.   Instructional program using a time-delay strategy.

Figure 7.3. (*continued*)

---

prompt. Continue with this procedure for the next 15 trials. Thereafter, increase the delay levels for each 15 trials to *3, 4, 5, 6* seconds with the maximum delay level set at *6* seconds.

3. *Error correction:* Interrupt errors using a physical prompt if Fred begins to make an incorrect response on any trial. If *3* errors occur in a row on any one delay level, provide *10* trials at *0*-second delay. Return to the previous level.

Reinforcement: Playing music serves as a naturally occurring reinforcement for this program. However, at the beginning of the program during the *0*-second delay trials provide verbal feedback for operating the switch. After providing the verbal cue say, "That's the way you play music!" Once the delay levels have been initiated, provide verbal feedback for independent performance using the same cue. Gradually fade this as independent correct responses increase.

Generalization and Maintenance:

1. When Fred meets the above program objective, begin to generalize the use of the switch to other leisure/recreation items.
2. Consider using two tape recorders with different musical choices that Fred can select from during leisure time.
3. Explore ways to begin using his musical preferences to initiate a communication program using other assistive technology devices.
4. Work with the mother on purchasing switches for home use.

CONCLUSION

No one chapter can address all of the issues that school personnel will encounter when they consider the use of assistive technology within a student's educational program. This chapter has focused on policy and funding issues, assessment procedures, and functional, individualized applications of assistive technology. A team approach has been recommended to identify, design, and select technology with the student and his or her family as the center of the process. This student-focused orientation should facilitate inclusion within school and community settings.

REFERENCES

American Occupational Therapy Association. (1994). Uniform terminology for occupational therapists—3rd edition. *American Journal of Occupational Therapy, 48*(11), 1147–1054.

Anson, D. (1992). *Rehabilitation 492: Technology in rehabilitation and education course syllabus.* Seattle: University of Washington, Department of Rehabilitation Medicine, Division of Occupational Therapy.

Anson, D. (1993). *Rehabilitation 487 course syllabus.* Seattle: University of Washington, Division of Occupational Therapy.

Anson, D. (1994). Finding your way in the maze of computer access technology. *American Journal of Occupational Therapy, 48*(2), 121–129.

Bain, B.K. (1989). Assessment of clients for technological assistive devices. In *Technology review '89: Perspectives on occupational therapy practice* (pp. 55–59). Rockville, MD: American Occupational Therapy Association.

Bain, B. (1993). Section 6A: Assistive technology. In H. Hopkins & H. Smith (Eds.), *Willard and Spackman's occupational therapy* (8th ed.) (pp. 325–340). Philadelphia: J.B. Lippincott.

Baize, C., & O'Brien, D. (1994, March). Seating for children and teenagers, ages 3 to 16 years. *Technology Special Interest Section Newsletter, 4*(1), 3–4.

Batavia, A., & Hammer, G. (1990). Consumer criteria for evaluating assistive devices: Implications for technology transfer. *Proceedings of the 12th annual RESNA conference* (pp. 194-195). Arlington, VA: RESNA Press.

Bergen, A., Presperin, J., & Tallman, T. (1990). *Positioning for function: Wheelchairs and other assistive technologies.* Valhalla, NY: Valhalla Rehabilitation Publications.

Brandenburg, S.A., & Vanderheiden, G.C. (Eds.). (1987). *Resourcebook 2: Switches and environmental controls.* Boston, MA: College Hill Press.

Brown, L., Falvey, M., Vincent, L., Kaye, N., Johnson, F., Ferrara-Parrish, P., & Gruenewald, L. (1980). Strategies for generating comprehensive, longitudinal, and chronological-age-appropriate individualized education programs for adolescent and young adult severely handicapped students. *Journal of Special Education, 14*(2), 199–215.

Brown, L., Nietupski, J., & Hamre-Nietupski, S. (1976). Criterion of ultimate functioning. In M.A. Thomas (Ed.), *Hey, don't forget about me!* (pp. 2–15). Reston, VA: Council for Exceptional Children.

Buckleitner, W. (1991). *Survey of early childhood software.* Ypsilanti, MI: High/Scope Press.

Button, C. (1991). Policy in the making: Fast facts on individualized education programs. *AT Quarterly: RESNA Technical Assistance Project, 2*(5), 5–6.

Campbell, P. (1993). Physical management and handling procedures. In M.E. Snell (Ed.), *Instruction of students with severe disabilities* (4th ed.) (pp. 248–263). New York: Merrill.

Campbell, P.H., Bricker, W.A., & Esposito, L. (1980). Technology in the education of the severely handicapped. In B. Wilcox & R. York (Eds.), *Quality education for the severely handicapped* (pp. 224–246). Washington, DC: U.S. Department of Education, Office of Special Education, Division of Innovation and Development.

Campbell, P.H., & Forsyth, S. (1993). Integrated programming and movement disabilities. In M.E. Snell (Ed.), *Instruction of students with severe disabilities* (4th ed.) (pp. 264–289). New York: Merrill.

Caves, K., & Furumasu, J. (1994). Customized integrated control system. In M. Binion (Ed.), *Proceedings of the RESNA '94 annual conference: Turning into the 21st century through assistive technology—Listen to the music* (pp. 298–300). Arlington, VA: RESNA Press.

Church, G., & Glennen, S. (1992). *The handbook of assistive technology.* San Diego, CA: Singular Publishing Group, Inc.

Clayton, C. (1994). A flexible integrated access system. In M. Binion (Ed.), *Proceedings of the RESNA '94 annual conference: Turning into the 21st century through assistive technology—Listen to the music* (pp. 309–311). Arlington, VA: RESNA Press.

Coley, I.L., & Proctor, S.A. (1989). Self-maintenance activities. In P.N. Pratt & A.S. Allen (Eds.), *Occupational therapy for children* (2nd ed.) (pp. 260–294). St. Louis: C.V. Mosby.

CO-NET (Cooperative Assistive Technology Database Dissemination Network). (1991). *Hyper-ABLE-DATA database, CO-NET CD-ROM version* (3rd ed.) Madison, WI: Trace Research and Development Center.

Education for All Handicapped Children Act of 1975, PL 94-142. (August 23, 1977). Title 20, U.S.C. 1401 et seq: *U.S. Statutes at Large, 89,* 773–796.

Education of the Handicapped Act of 1970, PL 91-230. (April 13, 1970). Title 20, U.S.C. 1400 et seq: *U.S. Statutes at Large, 84,* 121–195.

Enders, A., & Hall, M. (Eds.). (1990). *Assistive technology sourcebook.* Washington, DC: RESNA Press.

Franklin, K. (1991). Assistive technology: Where are we? Where are we going? *Journal of Vocational Rehabilitation, 1*(2), 6–7.

Garner, J.B., & Campbell, P. (1987). Technology for persons with severe disabilities: Practical and ethical considerations. *Journal of Special Education, 21*(3), 122–131.

Guerrette, P., & Nakai, R. (1994). Case studies of performance using integrated and distributed controls. In M. Binion, (Ed.), *Proceedings of the RESNA '94 annual conference: Into the 21st century through assistive technology—Listen to the music* (pp. 298–300). Arlington, VA: RESNA Press.

Guerrette, P., & Sumi, E. (1994). Integrating control of multiple assistive devices: A retrospective review. *Assistive Technology, 6*(1), 67–76.

Hawley, M., Cudd, P., Wells, J., Wilson, A., & Judd, P. (1992). Wheelchair mounted integrated control systems for multiply handicapped people. *Journal of Biomedical Engineering, 14,* 193–198.

Hutinger, P., Clark, L., Flannery, B., Johanson, J., Lawson, K., Perry, L., Robinson, L., Schneider, C., & Whitaker, K. (1990). *Building ACTTive futures: ACTT's curriculum guide for young children and technology: Section III: Preschool curriculum activities.* Macomb, IL: Macomb Projects.

Individuals with Disabilities Education Act of 1990 (IDEA), PL 101-476. (October 30, 1990). Title 20, U.S.C. 1400 et seq: *U.S. Statutes at Large, 104,* 1103–1151.

Individuals with Disabilities Education Act Amendments of 1991, PL 102-119. (October 7, 1991). Title 20; U.S.C. 1400 et seq: *U.S. Statutes at Large, 105,* 587–608.

Inge, K.J. (in press). Cerebral palsy. In P.J. McLaughlin & P. Wehman (Eds.), *Characteristics of mental retardation and developmental disabilities* (2nd ed.). Austin, TX: PRO-ED.

Inge, K.J., & Wehman, P. (1993). *Designing community-based vocational programs for students with severe disabilities.* Richmond: Virginia Commonwealth University, Rehabilitation Research and Training Center on Supported Employment.

Johnson, A. (1993, March). Interface technology: Low-tech as a stepping stone to high-tech. *Technology Special Interest Section Newsletter, 3*(1), 1–2.

Jones, R.M., Kolar, K., & Brown, B. (1993). Technology part I: Mobility and seating in the classroom. In C. Royeen (Ed.), *AOTA self study series: Classroom applications for school-based practice.* Rockville, MD: American Occupational Therapy Association.

Kohlmeyer, K. (1993). Section 5B: Assistive and adaptive equipment. In H. Hopkins & H. Smith (Eds.), *Willard and Spackman's occupational therapy* (8th ed.) (pp. 316–320). Philadelphia: J.B. Lippincott.

Lee, K., & Thomas, D.J. (1989). *Control of computer-based technology for people with physical disabilities: An assessment manual.* Toronto, Ontario, Canada: University of Toronto Press.

Levin, J., & Scherfenberg, L. (1987). *Selection and use of simple technology in home, school, work, and community settings.* Minneapolis, MN: Ablenet.

Mann, W.C., & Lane, J.P. (1991). *Assistive technology for persons with disabilities: The role of occupational therapy.* Rockville, MD: American Occupational Therapy Association.

Meadows, J.E. (1992). Finding independence through assistive technology. *Information Updates, 3*(4), 1–6. Terre Haute, IN: Blumberg Center for Interdisciplinary Studies in Special Education.

Morris, M. (1992). Policy in the making: The right to take assistive technology home from school. *AT Quarterly: RESNA Technical Assistance Project, 3*(2), 5.

Okoye, R. (1988). Section 6B: Computer applications in occupational therapy. In H. Hopkins & H. Smith (Eds.), *Willard and Spackman's occupational therapy* (8th ed.) (pp. 341–353). Philadelphia: J.B. Lippincott.

Okoye, R. (1993). Computer applications in occupational therapy: Assistive technology. In H.L. Hopkins, & H.D. Smith, *Willard and Spackman's occupational therapy* (pp. 341–352). Philadelphia: J.B. Lippincott.

Parette, H., Hourcade, J., & Van Biervliet, A. (1993). Selection of appropriate technology for children with disabilities. *Teaching Exceptional Children, 25,* 18–22.

Proctor, S.A. (1989). Adaptations for independent living. In P.N. Pratt & A.S. Allen (Eds.), *Occupational therapy for children* (2nd ed.) (pp. 335–357). St. Louis: C.V. Mosby.

Rein, J. (1989). *OCT 305 lecture: Computer technology.* Richmond: Virginia Commonwealth University, Department of Occupational Therapy.

RESNA Technical Assistance Project. (1992). *Assistive technology and the individualized education program.* Washington, DC: RESNA Press.

Shuster, N.E. (1993). Addressing assistive technology needs in special education. *The American Journal of Occupational Therapy, 47*(11), 993–997.

Smith, R. (1993). Technology part II: Adaptive equipment and technology. In C.B. Royeen (Ed.), *Classroom applications for school-based practice* (pp. 6–50). Rockville, MD: American Occupational Therapy Association.

Smith, R., Benge, M., & Hall, M. (1994). Technology for self-care. In Christainsen, C. (Ed.), *Ways of living: Self-care strategies for special needs* (pp. 379–422). Rockville, MD: American Occupational Therapy Association.

Snell, M.E. (1993). *Instruction of students with severe disabilities* (4th ed.). New York: Merrill.

Sowers, J., & Powers, L. (1991). *Vocational preparation and employment of students with physical and multiple disabilities.* Baltimore: Paul H. Brookes Publishing Co.

Swinth, Y. (March, 1994). Seating issues of the young child. *Technology Special Interest Section Newsletter, 4*(1), 1–3.

Sylvester, L. (1994). *Infusing positioning and mobility interventions into the curriculum for occupational and physical therapy students*. Paper presented at RESNA Conference. Nashville, TN.

Taylor, S.J. (1987). Evaluating the client with physical disabilities for wheelchair seating. *American Journal of Occupational Therapy, 41*(2), 6–8.

Technology-Related Assistance for Individuals with Disabilities Act of 1988 (Tech Act), PL 100-407. (August 19, 1988). Title 29, U.S.C. 2201 et seq: *U.S. Statutes at Large, 102,* 1044–1065.

Technology-Related Assistance for Individuals with Disabilities Amendments of 1994, PL 103-218. (March 9, 1994). Title 29, U.S.C. 2201 et seq: *U.S. Statutes at Large, 108,* 50–97.

Uditsky, T., James, K., & Joseph, R. (1994). Collaboration: The key to successful technological integration. *Technology Special Interest Newsletter, 4*(2), 6–8.

Vanderheiden, G.C. (1987). Service delivery mechanisms in rehabilitation technology. *The American Journal of Occupational Therapy, 41*(11), 703–710.

Vanderheiden, G., & Yoder, D. (1986). Overview. In S. Blackstone & D. Bruskin (Eds.), *Augmentative communication: An introduction* (pp. 1–28). Rockville, MD: American Speech-Language-Hearing Association.

Wright, C., & Nomura, M. (1985). *Toys to computers: Access for the physically disabled child.* San Jose, CA: Christine Wright.

York, J., & Rainforth, B. (1991). Developing instructional adaptations. In F.P. Orelove & D. Sobsey, *Educating children with multiple disabilities: A transdisciplinary approach* (2nd ed.) (pp. 259–296). Baltimore: Paul H. Brookes Publishing Co.

8

Adaptive Environments in the Workplace

Jo Ann Sowers

In the 1990s, there is widespread recognition that individuals with disabilities should have the opportunity to lead typical lives. A key hallmark of a typical life is employment. For instance, one of the first questions usually asked when individuals first meet is "What type of work do you do?" American adults often define who they are by the type of work they perform, and the natural flow of their daily lives is organized around their work schedules. By providing the financial resources to support themselves and, thus, be free from the controls and regulations imposed by family or governmental supports, work is the means whereby most individuals can gain independence.

Since the 1970s, growing attention has been given to the improvement of employment opportunities available to persons with disabilities. The advent of supported employment has been an important impetus in increasing employment access for persons with disabilities (Bellamy, Rhodes, Mank, & Albin, 1988; Sowers, Thompson, & Connis, 1979; Wehman & Kregel, 1985; Wehman & Moon, 1988). A report describing the impact of supported employment between 1985 and 1990 showed that almost 75,000 persons with disabilities had obtained employment through supported employment funded programs (West, Revell, & Wehman, 1992). However, relatively few of these individuals experience significant physical disabilities (Kiernan, McGaughey, Cooperman, & McNally 1991; Sowers & Powers, 1991). There are a number of reasons for this, perhaps the most prevalent being that ongoing support services in most states are offered only to individuals who experience a significant cognitive developmental disability (i.e., those persons labeled as mentally retarded). Persons who, in addition to their physical disability, experience a significant cognitive disability pose a great challenge to supported employment agencies. Many supported employment agencies have little experience with or knowledge of the unique strategies that are needed to meet such challenges (Sowers, Hall, & Rainforth, 1991). One important strategy in assisting individuals with physical and/or sensory disabilities to obtain employment is the utilization of technologies and other adaptations (Callahan, 1991; Sowers, 1991). Again, few supported employment agency staff have had the opportunity to gain a working knowledge of adaptation strategies.

Even those individuals with significant physical and sensory disabilities who are not in need of supported employment services have also been limited in their opportunity to gain access to employment. Again, the reasons for this are many, including work disincentives (e.g., loss of benefits), current regulations that limit access to worksite PCA services, lack of transportation options, and the reluctance of businesses to make the accommodations and adaptations. The passage of the Americans with Disabilities Act of 1990 (ADA) (PL 101-336) signaled the beginning of a new era of employment opportunity by requiring that employers make reasonable accommodations for employees with disabilities. The challenge now is for job seekers, businesses, and professionals who are involved in assisting individuals with disabilities to obtain employment to become knowledgeable about technology and workplace adaptation strategies (West et al., 1991).

This chapter provides a description of practical issues that should be considered when assisting employers to hire, train, and support employees who may need adaptations. The chapter also overviews a process that can guide the utilization of workplace adaptations and a description of a number of different types of workplace adaptive strategies. Finally, legal and funding implications of ADA are covered.

BECOMING EMPLOYED—THE ROLE OF TECHNOLOGY

Obtaining employment is a process, involving planning and identifying the type of career and job that the person wants to pursue, looking for a job that fits the person's plan, and doing the tasks necessary to meet the expectations of the person's employment situation (e.g., learning the job, getting to work, getting to know your coworkers). The process of obtaining employment for a person with a disability should be in most respects the same as that used by persons who do not have a disability. In fact, supported employment approaches have in many ways used atypical processes. These approaches have focused on the person's deficits and disabilities as a key to identifying the type of job that will be sought. In addition, the primary responsibility for the identification and implementation of strategies that are used to assist the person to meet the expectations of the business has been assumed by the supported employment agency. These approaches have contributed to many of the shortcomings of supported employment, including high job turnover and high levels of ongoing agency-delivered support in order to maintain employees on jobs. As a result, there is a growing understanding of the need to utilize strategies that more closely approximate the manner in which typical individuals (i.e., those who are not considered to be disabled) obtain employment. These strategies and processes have been generically termed naturally supported employment (Hagner & Dileo, 1993; Nisbet & Hagner, 1988).

In this section, a description of the three major phases of assisting a person who may need workplace adaptations to obtain employment in ways that are typical and natural is provided. Particular emphasis is placed on the manner in which adaptations should be considered, identified, and utilized as part of this process.

Career Planning

Career planning for individuals who may need technology should focus, as it should for all persons, on the individual's abilities and interests. For individuals who experience severe physical disabilities, and in particular individuals with multiple disabilities (e.g., those with physical, visual, communication, and cognitive disabilities), it is often difficult to envision what type of job they can do. For these individuals, it is easy to focus on what they cannot do. In large part, this perspective originates from the general approach to employment assessment and planning for individuals with significant disabilities, which emphasizes disabilities rather than abilities. A "vocational evaluation" commonly is little more than a description of an individual's disabilities and difficulties. This approach to assessment has frequently led to recommendations that individuals are not employable, need "prevocational" training, or should be placed in jobs at the lowest level of challenge, status, and pay.

For persons with physical disabilities, formal and informal assessments often suggest that computer-related work should be pursued, again reflecting the underlying assumption that because of the individual's disability his or her abilities and opportunities are limited. The focus on computer-related occupations also reflects the tendency for technology to drive the career planning process. Many formal and informal assessments attempt to identify the types of technologies that the individual can or could use. The assessments then make recommendations for careers that the person should pursue based on these technologies (e.g., a person can use a voice-activated computer, so a computer job should be sought for him or her). More appropriately, the career plan *should* determine whether technology is needed and, if so, what kind will be needed to enable the individual to obtain the type of job he or she desires. In other words, the career plan should lead to the type of technology used, not vice versa.

In the career planning process, professionals help the individual to identify his or her abilities and interests, they help the individual to determine possible careers and jobs that will use his or her abilities and interests, and they assist the individual in identifying technologies that will permit him or her to successfully work in these careers. An individual who has a severe physical disability may not be able to be a professional athlete, coach, or trainer. However, if this person has an in-depth knowledge of sports and athletics, there are a number of possible careers or jobs he or she might wish to pursue, including working in the sports department of a newspaper or television station, in a sporting goods store or in the sporting goods section of a department store, at a fitness club, or in a college athletic department. For example, at one large fitness club, there are many positions available that have no or few physical demands—manager or assistant manager, secretary, membership director, events coordinator, and front desk clerk.

Rather than using standardized tests, functional skill checklists, and interest inventories, an approach similar to that described in the literature under various titles (e.g., Personal Futures Planning, MAPS) is one that focuses on helping the individual to identify any and all of his or her abilities and interests and to explore possible ways in which they may translate into a career (Callahan, 1990; Mount & Zwernick, 1988; Vandercook, York, & Forest, 1989). A number of different variations of this process have been utilized and described. Sowers (1994) describes a process that includes obtaining information about various topics (Table 8.1). (These are only a small sample of the topics covered.)

This information is obtained over a period of several weeks. The career counselor spends time with the career planner in a variety of informal and comfortable settings; for example, having a conversation with the career planner over a soda at a restaurant or while going for a walk. It should also include a visit with the person at his or her home. There are insights into the individual revealed by a home visit that are not evident in other situations. For example, after visiting a young man at home and seeing the posters of cars on his walls, it was evident to the career counselor facilitating his employment that he was interested in cars. Although cars did not become the focal point of the job search, it did provide a useful piece of information in enhancing the young man's connection with coworkers at his job site. In addition, it is also important for many career planners for the counselor to spend time with their family and friends. Many "vocational assessments" perceive the input of family and, in particular, friends as supplementary information at best. In fact, family and friends usually know the person's abilities and interests better than professionals. Of course, many family members have been influenced by professionals to focus on their relative's deficits and to downplay areas of abilities and interests.

For example, a young man enjoyed drawing a great deal and was acknowledged as having talent. However, professionals had convinced both him and his family that art was not something that should be considered seriously as a career. Recently, he and his family were

Table 8.1.   Examples of career planning information

What works and does not work for you?
What works for you—makes you happy, excited, and feel good?
What does not work for you—makes you feel sad, bored, and unhappy?

Clubs, organizations, and groups
What clubs, organizations, or groups do you belong to? What do you do there?
How often do you attend or do things with them?
Are there any people who belong to them who might be helpful to your career planning?

Fun and interests
What do you like to do for fun?
Do you have special interests or hobbies?
How often do you get to do these things?

Typical day
Describe what a typical weekday is like for you.
Describe what a typical weekend is like for you.

Home responsibilities
What home responsibilities and chores do you have?
Are there any that you really like or dislike?
Are there any that you are really good at doing?

Education
What classes did you really like in high school and college? What did you like about them?
Were there any classes that you did really good in?
What classes did you not like? What did you not like about the class?
Have you taken any classes since high school? How did you do? What did you like and dislike about them?

People
Would you like to work with people your own age, older, or younger? One or two people or a lot of people? With men, women, or both?
Are there some things that people do that bother or upset you?
Are there some things that people do that would make you feel motivated and good about yourself?

Supports
What type of supports may you need getting to work? Getting ready for work? Learning the job? Getting to know coworkers?
What type of physical adaptations do you need to do the job? For personal care?

encouraged to pursue this unique gift. He is now conducting art lessons for children and working as a graphic artist.

After time has been taken to help the career planner to obtain a thorough picture of his or her abilities and interests, the individual can begin to use this information to think about the type of job or career he or she might want to pursue. A number of general job areas or types of work situations in which the person may be interested can be suggested. Then, the individual can begin to explore these areas in terms of gaining greater information about the jobs, including the job prospects, types of specific jobs and tasks performed, and educational and experiential requirements. As part of this exploration, the person should be assisted in identifying aspects of the jobs and tasks that may require adaptations and accommodations. This career exploration can be accomplished by talking with friends, acquaintances, and family members who may have experience in these occupations. One of the best means of obtaining this information is by visiting businesses to talk with and observe employees who are performing related work and owners and managers who may have an understanding of the industry or occupational area.

Again, it is important to note that this process of career planning is not driven by technology, but rather technology is considered within the context of the types of jobs and career in which the individual is interested. However, the availability of possible technology and other workplace adaptations may influence the career or job that the person decides to pursue. For example, if through the analysis of specific occupations and jobs it becomes clear that a person cannot perform a critical job function and there does not appear to be any technology or adaptation strategy that could enable him or her to do it, then the person may determine that the specific job is not feasible. After obtaining and reflecting on the information, the individual should now be, with needed facilitation, input, and support from family, friends, and professionals, in a position to determine at what type of job he or she wants to work.

The career planning exploration phase is the time when technologies that will be needed regardless of the type of job he or she will perform should be identified and purchased. For example, an individual who uses a wheelchair needs to have one that provides him or her with optimal mobility and with a seating arrangement that promotes comfort and movement. The individual's communication needs should also be addressed and provided with augmentative devices that will optimize his or her ability to communicate, regardless of the employment site at which he or she will work. Specific analysis of the individual's needs related to building and bathroom accessibility should also be conducted. This will provide important information during the job search phase in terms of the physical requirements of the business' building. It will also serve as the basis for discussion with potential employers about needed accommodations.

Job Search

A common job search approach utilized by employment assistance programs is to look for job openings for their program "clientele" and then to identify the individual whose skills and abilities best match the job requirements. In essence, the approach emphasizes finding jobs and matching individuals to them. A more useful approach is to begin with the individual who is looking for a job (the job seeker). Assisting him or her to find a job that is the best match to his or her interests and capacities seems more logical. This person-first approach is particularly important for individuals who experience physical and multiple disabilities who may require the use of technology and adaptations in order to work (Cooper & Mank, 1989). For many of these individuals, there will be few jobs available that they will be able to enter without significant modifications and adaptations. In addition, it is often necessary to utilize a job creation or job carving approach (Sowers, 1992; Sowers, Jenkins, & Powers, 1988). Using these approaches, a new job description is created from existing tasks. For example, a job was created at a document storage company for Blaine to check the quality of the microfilm records. This was a task done previously by other employees. However, they could no longer keep up with it given their other job duties. Often, the created job may reflect the company's desire to offer a new service; for example, a job was created for Kelly delivering sandwiches from his wheelchair at a deli. This job was an excellent match for Kelly. He had a strong desire to interact socially with people and had a natural sales ability.

Sowers and Powers (1992) described three major phases in adapting and designing jobs and work tasks: initial design/adaptation, intensive design/adaptation, and design/adaptation refinement. The initial design/adaptation phase takes place prior to the individual beginning work at a job site and as part of the job-seeking and creation process. The first activity in this phase is to analyze the accessibility of the worksite and each of the tasks that the individual may perform, identify those aspects that may cause accessibility or performance difficulties for the individual, and identify possible ways in which the site and tasks could be adapted to overcome these difficulties. Table 8.2 provides an illustration of this process for Dave, who was being considered for a clerical support job. It is critical that the job applicant and the employer, manager, or supervisor play active roles in this process (Callahan, 1993). The employer or a coworker will need to describe the job duties to the job applicant and agency employment facilitator. The applicant and facilitator can then identify the aspects of the job that may be difficult. It is then recommended that the employer, coworkers, new employee, and facilitator meet to brainstorm possible adaptation ideas. This involvement of the employer, coworkers, and employee will serve to give the clear message that they are in control of the employment process (rather than the agency staff) and will assist them in gaining knowledge of how to think about adaptation strategies (Nisbet & Sowers, 1994; Powers & Sowers, 1994). The process will also set the stage for open, honest discussions and negotiations about what accommodations are reasonable given the resources of the company and who (the employer, funding agency, or employee) should and can cover the cost of any adaptations. These issues are discussed in greater detail later in this chapter.

At this point in time, it is critical that the employer agree to make those specific adaptations that are necessary for the person to gain access to the business and perform his or her job. It should be kept in mind that as the person begins to work and to perform the job, the extent and nature of adaptive needs will become more clear. Some aspects of the job that were initially analyzed as possibly being difficult may be able to be done without an adaptation. It is important to not overadapt. Unless it is clear that the person could not learn to perform a job or the component of a job without an adaptation, he or she should first be given the opportunity to learn to do it "unadapted." For example, there is no possibility that Dave could learn to reach the top of the photocopier; thus, it is critical that the copier be lowered or that he obtain a wheelchair that can be raised and lowered hydraulically. However, with training and experience, he may be able to learn to identify the collate button without color coding it. Different or "special" strategies should only be used when it is not possible for the person to learn and perform the job in the same fashion as his or her coworkers.

For literally every difficulty that a person may have in performing a job or task, there is more than one possible adaptive strategy that could be used to ease the difficulty. When thinking about a particular difficulty, it is useful to think about many possible adaptive strategies. Again, the employment agency staff should facilitate the active involvement in this process of the employee, employer, and coworkers. Once a number of possible ideas have been identified, one can be selected. There are three major factors that need to be weighed in making this selection. First, and most important, is the relative extent to which each possibility will be effective in reducing the difficulty the person experiences in performing the job. Second, the impact of the adaptations on the site and coworkers should also be taken into account. Employees at a company naturally have a sense of ownership of their work environment. Any changes to the environment will be noticed, particularly ones that require the coworkers to perform their jobs or how they function at the worksite in a different way. When these changes are associated with a new employee at the company, they may well have an impact on the coworkers' perceptions of the person. As has been suggested, it is critical for coworkers to be involved in identifying the types of adaptations the new employee will need.

Table 8.2. Worksite accessibility analysis

Site: Credit Union
Job Seeker: Dave

Area	Description	Possible adaptations
Entrance	There are no steps at entrance. The door is heavy and hard to open.	One of the other employees coming to work could open the door for him. On the way out, coworker or customer could open the door.
Bathroom	Men's bathroom is large. There are three urinals and two stalls; neither is wheelchair accessible. There are no handrails for transfer. The toilet and sinks are regular height.	Dave uses his own urinal. The stalls are large enough for Dave to fit and to make transfer. He will need to have rails and a raised seat. 1) Install a portable seat that is raised and has rails. 2) Rebuild one stall to accessibility code.
Lunch/break areas	The kitchen is on ground level. The sink is not accessible—too high. The microwave is on counter—not accessible.	Sink. 1) Lower to make accessible for Dave. 2) Get help from coworker. Microwave. 1) Place it on a table that is lower. 2) Get help from coworker.
Other	Water fountain is too high.	1) Install lower fountain. 2) Carry container with water. 3) Carry cup and ask coworker to fill with water.

This will not only serve to ensure that the coworkers perceive themselves as primary agents of responsibility for the employee's success, but also will go a long way to alleviate their perceptions that changes to the workplace are being imposed on them.

By brainstorming and identifying a number of different strategies that could potentially be used to decrease a difficulty, the employer and coworkers will be able to objectively weigh the relative impact that each would have on the worksite and, thus, likely be more comfortable with the selection of the one with the lowest impact. For example, if the employment agency simply suggested that the photocopier table be lowered, the coworkers may view their having to bend over to use the copier in a more negative light than if they chose this solution from a number of other possibilities, including having a ramp in front of the copier that they would have to walk around or move every time they needed to use the machine. The extent to which each adaptation option will accentuate the employee as different from the other employees should also be considered. Dave's coworkers will notice the change in the height of the photocopier, but will probably become accustomed to it quickly and forget that it is lower than it used to be. However, if a ramp was put in front of the copier, it would be a highly visible and cogent reminder of Dave's differences.

Finally, cost must be considered in selecting the adaptation. Certainly, the rule of thumb should be that, after taking all factors into account, the least costly option should be selected.

In most cases, by identifying a number of different options, the option that is the least expensive will in fact also be effective and have a low impact on the site and on the perceptions of the employee's coworkers. However, in some situations, the option that is more expensive than the others should be selected. For example, if the table on which the copier was placed had to be lowered so far that it would be an inconvenience to his coworkers, it might be appropriate to choose the most expensive option—purchasing Dave a wheelchair that he could raise and lower.

Training and Support

The intensive design/adaptation phase begins when the individual actually starts his or her job. This is the time when it would be possible to identify the specific difficulties that the individual will have in performing the tasks, to determine which tasks will need to be adapted, and to try out different adaptive strategies. In most situations, the individual's first month will be the time when the most intensive work is done around jobsite and task- and work-related modifications. The major guiding principles for considering and making adaptations should continue to apply here. First, unless it is definite that the person will require an adaptation to perform a task, he or she should first be given the opportunity to perform it in the same fashion as any other new employee. Second, the employee and his or her coworkers should be actively involved in identifying the need for and type of adaptation (Callahan, 1993; Nisbet & Sowers, 1994). This will occur naturally if the employee is trained and supported by his or her coworkers rather than an agency "job coach." The agency staff should serve as a consultant to the coworkers about how to assist the person to learn and perform the job, including how to adapt it. However, the agency staff should not make the decisions about what adaptations are needed; rather they should encourage the coworkers and the employee to brainstorm and try out different possibilities. When high-tech, specialized equipment needs to be considered, the consultant should describe these to the "team" (i.e., the employee and coworkers). The team can then weigh the different considerations (i.e., effectiveness, site impact, perceptions of the employee by the coworkers, and cost) in deciding whether to utilize the high-tech device or some other solution.

The third design phase, design refinement, acknowledges that the job design and adaptation process will probably need to continue for several months, as adaptations that were identified and implemented during the first few weeks are tried out and their effectiveness evaluated. In many cases, slight changes will be needed to make them more effective for the individual and the site. In other situations, it will be clear that a different adaptive strategy is needed.

TYPES OF WORKPLACE TECHNOLOGIES AND ADAPTATION STRATEGIES

As suggested earlier, for any difficulty that an individual may encounter in performing a job due to a physical, sensory, or cognitive disability, there are usually different ways in which the job can be adapted and accommodated (Table 8.3). In this section, a brief overview of different types of adaptive strategies is described.

Generic and Disability-Specific Commercially Available Devices

Commercially available devices are those that are mass produced and can be purchased "off the shelf" from companies and vendors that specialize in producing and/or selling these devices. The significant advances that have been made in the design and production of technological devices for persons with disabilities have paralleled the growth and sophistication of technology in the workplace. In fact, the technology now available in work settings, particularly in office-based occupations, has enhanced the employment of persons with disabilities to a far greater extent than disability-specific technologies. The need for special adaptations and accommodations has and will continue to decrease as these "generic" technologies continue to gain widespread use in business settings.

Computers

During the late 1990s and the early 2000s, it is estimated that at least 75% of jobs will involve the use of computers (Bender, Richmond, & Pinson-Millburn, 1985). Without question, computers have had more impact on the work world than any other type of technology. In the past, the major barriers that an individual with a disability faced in performing a job were its physical demands. For example, many individuals were well able to "understand how" to perform the essential elements of many professional, technical, and management occupations. However, all these required a large amount of paperwork, which involved writing, paper manipulation, and file storage and retrieval. Extensive and costly accommodations were required to enable a person with a physical disability to perform these skills. Today, computers are making these physical components of jobs obsolete—in many offices, all writing is done on computers and files are stored and manipulated via computer. In many companies, little or no accommodations need to be made to enable a person with a disability to perform a job. Accommodations, if needed, frequently focus on easing the individual's access to the company's existing computer system.

There is currently a growing array of technological innovations available that can enhance the utilization of computers for persons with disabilities. There are simple hardware devices such as a keyguard. A wide array of switches are available including those that can be operated by the individual pushing with his or her hand, finger, head, or chin, and by inhaling and exhaling. Access to computers can be gained through voice activation systems. The individual talks to the computer, which then automatically completes the command given (e.g., opens a file, saves) and types what was said. These voice-activated systems are achieving high levels of technological sophistication, enabling them to accurately respond even to persons who are difficult to understand. Software programs are available that permit voice output—the computer "says" text and material. This technology is particularly useful for individuals with visual disabilities. These individuals can also utilize software that enlarges the text on the computer monitor.

Telephone Technologies

Telephone usage is a critical function of many jobs, especially professional, managerial, and sales occupations. As with computers, the advances in general telephone technology have enhanced the employment of individuals with disabilities. Many businesses utilize multisite teleconferencing as a means to reduce the amount of travel required by employees, thus easing the difficulties that an employee who is unable to drive or who finds it difficult to travel long distances may encounter. Offices today are commonly equipped with speakerphone features that permit talking and listening without the need to hold the receiver. It is not uncommon for business people to use phone headsets to enable them to hold private conversations without holding a receiver, as well as to move around while doing so. Phones can be programmed to automatically dial a large number of frequently dialed numbers by pushing one button. Voice-activated dialing is also becoming a readily available technology for businesses and private phone users. There are a number of devices specifically designed for persons with

Table 8.3.   Job adaptation analysis

| Job/task: Photocopying | | |
| Job seeker: Dave | | |

Major step	Description/difficulty	Possible adaptations
Get original and take to machine.	Jane keeps photocopying basket on her desk. She takes what she will photo-copy to room. Carrying papers and moving chair at same time will be hard.	1) Get him a box for carrying originals. Put Dycem on bottom so it will not slide off his lap. 2) Keep photocopying basket on the table next to the machine. 3) Jane brings originals to Dave that she wants him to do.
Determine number of copies to be made.	Jane writes person's name who wants copying done and instructions on a post-it and puts on original. This will be hard for Dave to read.	1) Jane could tell him what to do before he does each one. 2) Have her neatly print each order on the post-it. 3) Create a simple order form that coworkers would fill out when they put the originals in the copy basket. The form could have numbers typed and they would just need to be circled.
Remove clip/staple.	Most originals have both a clip and a staple. Jane uses a claw staple remover. Dave can remove the clip. He will probably have trouble with the staple.	1) Have coworkers remove staples when they fill out order form—the form could remind them. 2) Have Dave try a straight-type staple remover.
Code machine—number of copies, collate.	Buttons are on front—easy to reach, but hard to see from Dave's chair. He may have trouble distinguishing the collate button.	1) Place copy machine on lower table. 2) Devise a mirror that would reflect panel so that he could see it. 3) Purchase him a chair that can be automatically raised and lowered. 4) Place colored tape on collate button.
Put original in feeder.	Self-feeding machine. He will have to stretch to reach.	1) Purchase new chair. 2) Lower table.
Remove original/copies.	They come out on side bins. It will be a little cumbersome for him to reach the bins—the machine is close to the wall.	1) Move table farther away from the wall.
Staple/put clip on.	Jane does this at copier. Dave will have trouble doing this without a work surface. She uses a manual stapler.	1) He takes copies to his desk. 2) Put work table in copy room. 3) Purchase electric stapler.

disabilities, including large button phones. However, for the most part, the technologies designed for general use have decreased the need for special devices.

Environmental Controls

A third area of technology that has great potential for enhancing the employment opportunities of persons with disabilities is environmental controls. These devices allow an individual to operate a wide array of electronic equipment through a switch device or voice activation. Lights and any other electric devices can easily and inexpensively be hooked up to an environmental control system (i.e., computer, photocopier, radio, air conditioner) that can be turned on and off. In addition, doors, drawers, and cabinets can be rigged to open and close, and table and shelves can be made able to be raised and lowered through a simple switch activation system.

Robotics

The use of robotic devices in industry has grown rapidly and all projections indicate that this growth will continue. In general application, robotics has seen the greatest growth in the manufacturing job sector. Robotics is being used to do such tasks as assembly, welding, and parts transfer. In fact, a robot has even been invented that is able to deliver supplies and medications in large hospitals and to do large-scale cleaning tasks (e.g., cleaning a large office building). Increasing attention has also been given to the development of robotics specifically aimed at the challenges that persons with disabilities encounter. Leung (1988) describes a workstation that includes a robotic arm that is controlled by voice commands. This arm can pick up and move objects, such as books, files, and disks.

Constructed Devices

Frequently, there will be aspects of a job that a person will have difficulty performing for which there is no device, generic or specialized, that is commercially available. In this situation, a device may be able to be designed and constructed to meet the unique needs of the person and the specific difficulty he or she experiences. Often, these devices will be simple and require little or no specialized materials or expertise to design or construct.

For example, Roberta (see Case Study 8.1, p. 180) works at a credit union, where one of her tasks is photocopying and stapling documents. Because she only has the use of one hand, it is difficult for her to hold the copies in place while pushing down on the stapler. Consequently, a simple device was built by an employment consultant that served to keep the papers in place while she stapled them. Of course, there often will be the need for the design of sophisticated devices. In these situations, an individual who has particular expertise and skills in construction, fabrication, electronics, and other areas will probably be needed.

Other Adaptive Strategies

The use of both high and low technology in the form of a device or piece of equipment can greatly enhance the ease with which a person is able to perform a job and to work at a job site as independently as possible. However, there are also "no-tech" strategies that can be used for this purpose, such as redesigning how a task is done. For example, Darcy was hired by a bank as a microfilm specialist. In this capacity, she microfilmed all the checks deposited daily at the bank. As originally designed, the microfilm specialist would routinely go to each of the tellers' stations to get their checks. However, because she uses a wheelchair, Darcy found it difficult and time consuming to move around the tellers' stations. The supervisor and tellers agreed that, to ease this aspect of the job, they would simply bring their checks to her.

Another simple job redesign strategy is to identify an alternative method that an individual could use to get a task done. A man assisted by United Cerebral Palsy to find employment provides a creative example of this strategy (Callahan, personal communication, 1993). He had limited use of his hands, but he figured out that he could enter data as accurately and more quickly using his tongue. The keyboard was positioned close to his face in order to most easily permit this mode of input.

Rearranging the work environment is another and often simple method to ease job performance. For example, one of Tiffany's duties at a hair salon was to refill shampoo bottles for the stylist. The replacement containers were kept on a shelf too high for her to reach easily. The salon simply rearranged the shelves, putting the containers on a lower one that Tiffany could gain access to more easily.

An individual's position in relation to the equipment being used can have a profound impact on task performance. For example, when Mike began his computer data position, the copy holder was positioned to his right. However, because Mike experiences a tonic neck reflex, when he turned to the right to look at the copy holder, the arm that he used to enter data went into extension. When the copy holder was repositioned to his left, he no longer experienced this difficulty and was able to accurately enter data.

Technology and Personal Care Issues

Obviously a major focus of workplace adaptations must be on identifying adaptations that will permit the employee to perform his or her work tasks. However, it is also important to think about how the person will be able to take of his or her personal care issues while at the worksite (Sowers & Powers, 1991; York & Rainforth, 1987).

Mobility

The ability to get to and from work and to move around the worksite is clearly critical to job success. There are, of course, a wide variety of mobility assistance devices available, and many advances have been made in the sophistication of these devices. These advances have been particularly important in the area of seating arrangements and power mobility. The seating arrangement that a person has may have a great impact on his or her employment in numerous ways. First, it may affect his or her comfort and, thus, the number of hours that he or she can work. The position in which a person sits in a chair greatly affects his or her ability to execute the hand, arm, and head movements that may be involved in the job. Today, the technology of power wheelchairs has advanced to permit individuals with the least amount of motor control to be independently mobile. One particular innovation in motor mobility, a wheelchair that can be electronically raised and lowered, has interesting relevance for employment. A person who needs to reach files, cabinets, or a photocopier is able to simply raise this chair to do so.

In order to work at a company, the individual needs to be able to get in or out of the building. In light of the ADA, new companies are taking greater care to avoid steps at entrances by building ramps, and older companies are making the necessary modifications.

Communication

The amount and type of communication that is required at a job will depend on the specific tasks that a person performs. However, all jobs will require their workers to have some ability to communicate with coworkers. In addition, the opportunity to interact socially with coworkers is critical to the person becoming truly integrated and accepted. Major strides have been made in the technology of augmentative communication. There are numerous devices—typewriters, manual switches, and infrared light pointers—that people can use to communicate.

There are low-tech communication devices on the market as well, such as communication boards and books that a person points to or looks at to express him- or herself. There are also no-tech options that include simple gestures (e.g., nodding yes or no, raising or lowering one's eyes to indicate yes or no, waving hello or good-bye, or pointing to an object that is wanted). Communication is a good example of how high-tech devices are not always the best options for an individual to use for all work situations. For example, while working, it is expected that individuals will be able to communicate basic information, such as quick greetings, requests for materials, and simple requests or commands, quickly. Using a simple gesture such as a wave or nod, pointing at an object in the room, or using a communication board with a picture word or simple phrase is often quicker and as communicative as the use of an electronic device.

Eating and Drinking

The need for a person to eat and drink is often not considered in the discussion of technology and work. However, except for employees who work short hours, most employees will need and want to eat and drink at work. There are a number of simple strategies that a person can use to drink at work. One particularly unusual device was made for Karen, an employee who was able to drink using a straw, but was unable to handle a cup. An articulated arm device designed to hold cameras was purchased and attached to her chair. A cup holder was placed on the end where the camera was meant to be held. When she wanted a drink, a coworker simply moved the arm in such a way that the cup was located only several inches from her mouth, which allowed her to drink easily from a straw.

There are also a number of types of eating implements that can assist individuals to eat more independently. It is also helpful to assist the person to identify the types of foods that he or she can eat most independently. For example, a person may be able to eat finger foods without assistance (those that can be cut up into small bite-size pieces and that are fairly firm). A strategy used by some persons is to take a high-protein drink to work in order to get the nutrition needed without "eating" a meal.

Bathroom Use

As with eating and drinking, unless a person works short hours, he or she will need to use the bathroom while at work. Under the ADA, many businesses are modifying their bathrooms to be accessible for both their customers and current or future employees. Other strategies may need to be considered for a person who requires assistance using the bathroom and who may not have access to a personal care assistant or other support assistance. Even with the trend toward the use of coworker supports, many individuals understandably are not comfortable having a coworker assist them to use the bathroom. A condom catheter was used by one employee in order to be able to urinate without the constant presence of a support person at the jobsite. An individual who requires a two-person lift to use the bathroom faces a particular challenge in terms of obtaining the needed resources to provide this assistance at work. To overcome this problem, the state vocational rehabilitation agency purchased a lift for Patty, which was kept in the bathroom at her jobsite. When she needed to use the bathroom, her personal care assistant was able to assist her to transfer to and from the toilet using the lift.

High-Tech and Low-Tech Case Studies

There are numerous adaptive solutions to most difficulties a person may have. These solutions include the use of high-tech specialized equipment and devices (e.g., voice-controlled computer, robotic arm that raises and lowers shelf) or low-tech simple devices, such as an electric stapler or a paper guide built out of a few pieces of scrap wood. Two examples of individuals whose workplace was primarily adapted using low-tech and high-tech strategies are provided in Case Studies 8.1. and 8.2.

AMERICANS WITH DISABILITIES ACT— IMPLICATIONS FOR TECHNOLOGY AND ACCOMMODATIONS

Without question, the passage of the ADA has great implications for the utilization of technology in the workplace. As of July 26, 1992, employers with 25 or more employees, and effective July 26, 1994, for employers with 15–24 employees, must make reasonable accommodations that will permit an applicant or employee with a disability to work at their company and perform a job. A reasonable accommodation includes purchasing equipment or devices and making modifications to the workplace. An employer is not required to make an

---

**Case Study 8.1:   Employment Example
Using Low-Tech Solutions**

Roberta is a young woman in her mid-20s with cerebral palsy and cognitive disabilities. Roberta uses a power wheelchair for traveling distances, but can use a manual chair, which she propels with her one functional hand and her feet, for shorter distances. She can speak, but is somewhat difficult to understand.

During her last year of school, a job was created for Roberta at a credit union by an agency in Oregon called Alternative Work Concepts, which specializes in facilitating the employment of individuals with physical and multiple disabilities. She has been employed by the credit union for almost 6 years. Her task assignments include typing and laminating new membership cards, filing, cleaning up and stocking the customer area, destroying misprinted checks, and collating information packets for new members.

A number of low-tech adaptations are utilized by Roberta at the jobsite. A simple device was built for her that assists her in her card laminating task. Because she uses only one hand, it was difficult for her to align the card on the plastic laminating sleeve and to fold it over for placement into the machine—the card kept slipping. A guide was built from plywood that held the sleeve and the card in place, while she folded the sleeve. A simple paper stabilization was also built out of plywood, which allows her to staple papers with the use of one hand. She places the papers on the wooden guide, slides the stapler in place, and pushes down—all with her "good" hand. To insert the informational papers into envelopes, she puts the envelope between her knees and then inserts the papers. This is a very low-tech strategy a person with the use of only one hand can use to get papers into envelopes, a task which is typically done with two hands.

The total cost of these adaptations was less than $10. The employment consultant and coworkers, with input from Roberta, designed these devices based on a common-sense approach. The employment consultant constructed the devices with the use of a saw and nails. No rehabilitation engineer or other person with special training or knowledge of adaptations was used.

Case Study 8.2: Employment Example Using High-Tech Solutions

Tom, who has cerebral palsy and learning disabilities, completed his school eligibility when he was 21 years of age. One of Tom's gifts is his ability to speak and his excellent communication skills. He has no functional use of his hands and has limited vision. Because of these issues, his manual wheelchair is pushed by an attendant or other person.

During his last year of high school, Tom, with the help of his mother, friends, school, and adult program staff (Alternative Work Concepts in Eugene, Oregon), came up with the idea for a job for himself. Tom served on a number of task forces and committees in his community and recognized that it was often difficult to keep straight the dates, times, and locations of these meetings. The heads of the committees often forgot to remind members to attend the meetings. He proposed to start a meeting reminder business. For a fee (a rate determined by the number of persons on the committee), Tom would call each committee member to remind him or her of the meeting date, time, and location. The challenge for Tom and his team was to assemble the adaptations needed to enable him to perform this job. He needed a means to place the phone calls without the use of his hands (he is not able to hold a receiver or dial a phone) and a method that would help him read printed names and numbers. He also needed a means to keep track of who he had called and whether they would be attending the meeting.

He and his team spent months investigating different devices and brainstorming solutions. A number of individuals with rehabilitation engineering experience were consulted for their input. Finally, it was decided that a CoVox voice-activated device would be purchased and a customized computer software program designed by a computer software design specialist. Using this device and system, along with a telephone headset, Tom is able to independently call several hundred people monthly to remind them of meetings. Each of the committees' roster of names is stored in his computer. The computer scrolls through the roster, and Tom selects the appropriate roster by hitting a head switch. As each member's name comes up individually on the computer (the print is enlarged), Tom tells the computer to "dial phone." It dials the telephone number of the person listed on the computer screen. He talks with the person through the telephone headset, reminding them of the meeting date, time, and place. After the conversation is completed, Tom tells the computer to "write message" and four message statements come on the screen including "no contact," "left message," "will attend," and "will not attend." He again selects the relevant message by hitting his head switch. The computer records the message next to the appropriate person's name. After completing his calls for a committee, he tells the computer to "print" and the list of member names with the corresponding message statements is printed out. The total cost of the devices and computer system, including the design of the software, was approximately $10,000. The Division of Vocational Rehabilitation has covered these costs.

accommodation that would impose an "undue hardship," that is, if it involves significant difficulty or expense. Factors that are considered in making the "undue hardship" determination include the size and dollar amount of resources. In essence, larger companies, both in terms of number of employees and financial resources, are obligated to a greater extent than smaller companies.

The reasonable accommodation component of the ADA leaves much ambiguity with regard to the legal obligation of businesses to purchase devices and make accommodations and the manner in which a person seeking a job or an agency assisting a person to obtain employment should utilize the ADA in advocating for such accommodations. Throughout the 1990s, because of cases covered by the ADA related to the reasonableness of specific accommodations, the boundaries of the law will likely become more clearly defined. Perhaps the most important contribution of the ADA is that businesses are gaining an awareness that when persons with disabilities are provided with accommodations, usually simple and inexpensive ones, they can be productive, valuable employees. It is likely that an employer, who through information and education develops a positive attitude about employing persons with disabilities, will be willing to make reasonable accommodations without the force of the law.

The ADA requires that businesses hire an applicant with a disability whose skills, abilities, education, and experience meet all the requirements of the job. Reasonable accommodations that will enable the person to do this job must then be made. Many businesses have gone beyond the ADA and have hired individuals with disabilities who may not be fully qualified for a position. These employers are willing to do this out of a sincere desire to give these individuals a chance to enter the work world and become productive members of society. When these situations are encountered, it seems appropriate for vocational rehabilitation and other service funding agencies (e.g., mental retardation and developmental disability funds) to pay for all or most of the cost of adaptations and accommodations.

OTHER FUNDING SOURCES

When the expense of a jobsite adaptation is not reasonable for an employer to cover or when the employer is willing to go beyond the ADA and hire an applicant who may not meet the skill, experience, and educational requirements of a job, there are other sources that can be utilized to pay for employment-related technology and adaptation expenses. These sources should be considered when the expenses of the device or adaptation are not reasonable for an employer to cover. Any person who is a client of the state vocational rehabilitation (VR) agency can obtain funding assistance for job-related equipment. However, there has existed a dilemma for many individuals who need this assistance. A VR agency provides employment assistance funding for a limited period of time. This period is flexible, but typically not longer than 18 months. In most situations, the VR agency will pay an employment assistance agency to help the person find employment and to assist the company during the initial job training period. During this time, the VR agency will pay for equipment and adaptations. A person who is deemed by the agency as one who will need ongoing support after the initial training period to maintain his or her job will not be provided with funding for the initial job assistance unless there is an identified source for this ongoing support. To date, the primary source of ongoing support was through a state's developmental disability agency. These agencies provide funding to supported employment agencies for support services to individuals with developmental disabilities. Many individuals whose primary disability is physical, rather than cognitive or developmental, do not qualify for services through the developmental disability agency. A clear catch-22 exists here. A person cannot get assistance from VR agencies unless he or she could get ongoing assistance through the developmental disabilities program. However, because of the nature of his or her disability, the person does not qualify for this program. Fortunately, the amended regulations for the Federal Supported Employment Program (*Federal Register,* 1992) clearly suggest that other forms of support can and should be used other than those funded or provided through funding from the developmental disability agency. One possible alternative source for funding of extended support is through a Plan for Achieving Self-Support (PASS) or an Impairment-Related Work Expense (IRWE). The PASS and IRWE are run through the Social Security Administration. Using a PASS or IRWE, a person with a disability pays for job assistance supports. This money is then excluded from countable income and resources in determining eligibility for Supplemental Security Insurance (SSI) and Social Security Disability Income (SSDI) and for the amount of SSI monthly benefits (O'Mara, 1991). In addition to the fact that using a PASS or IRWE plan could be used as the source for ongoing support to enable the VR agency to fund initial job placement, training assistance, and equipment, an employee can use a PASS or IRWE to directly pay for equipment or jobsite adaptations. One possible approach to paying for a jobsite device or adaptation is for the expenses to be shared among the employer, VR agency, and employee. For example, if a workstation needed to be built that was estimated to cost $3,000, the employer might agree to pay $1,000 of the expense, the VR agency might agree to pay $1,000, with the employee paying the remaining $1,000 through an IRWE. Employees with disabilities should be encouraged to share in these and other costs as opposed to relying completely on VR agencies or other governmental resources. These resources are very limited and the extent to which individuals are willing to contribute to expenses from their earnings will permit other individuals with disabilities to obtain VR agency assistance. It is also likely that businesses will be more able and willing to hire individuals with disabilities and to contribute the funds needed for accommodations if these employees are willing to provide some of their own resources. In addition, the perceptions of the employer of the employee and of the employee him- or herself as an equal partner may also be enhanced.

CONCLUSION

The evolution of attitudes, program service models, and legal mandates are opening up employment opportunities for individuals who experience disabilities. However, there are a number of factors that continue to serve as barriers to the acces of individuals who experience severe physical disabilities to employment. Today there is much technology and many adaptive stategies available to enable these individuals to work, but the gap between available technology and knowledge of these strategies needs to be addressed. Employment consultants working for suported employment and other employment assistance programs clearly need to be trained in this area. These staff in turn must proactively assist individuals with disabilities and employers to learn about these strategies and choose among them.

As important as technology is in opening employment opportunities for individuals with disabilities, caution must be exercised in viewing it as *the* most important factor among many that determine whether a person obtains a job and which one she or he obtains. Many people remain in sheltered programs with the rationale that the technology needed is not available (because of lack of funds or expertise in identifying needed technology). Sufficient numbers of individuals with severe physical disabilities have been placed with low or no technology that this is no longer a viable excuse. The lack of funding for on-going employment support for individuals with severe physical disability is probably the most important barrier to their employment. Finally, and once again, technology should not be the primary determinate of the type of career that a person is advised to pursue, but rather it should be viewed as a means to enable the person to pursue the career in which she or he is interested.

REFERENCES

Americans with Disabilities Act (ADA) of 1990, PL 101-336. (July 26, 1990). Title 42, U.S.C. 12101 et seq: *U.S. Statutes at Large, 104*, 327–378.

Bellamy, G.T., Rhodes, L.E., Mank, D.M., & Albin, J.M. (1988). *Supported employment: A community implementation guide*. Baltimore: Paul H. Brookes Publishing Co.

Bender, M., Richmond, L., & Pinson-Millburn, N. (1985). *Careers, computers and the handicapped*. Austin, TX: PRO-ED.

Callahan, M. (1990). The vocational profile strategy. In M. Callahan (Ed.), *Getting the job done: Supported employment for persons with severe physical disabilities* (pp. 31–35). Washington, DC: United Cerebral Palsy Association.

Callahan, M. (1991). Common sense and quality: Meaningful employment outcomes of persons with severe physical disabilities. *Vocational Rehabilitation, 1*(2), 21–28.

Callahan, M. (1993). Job site training and natural supports. In J. Nisbet (Ed.), *Natural support in school, at work, and in the community for people with severe disabilities* (pp. 257–277). Baltimore: Paul H. Brookes Publishing Co.

Cooper, A., & Mank, D. (1989, Autumn). Integrated employment for people with severe physical disabilities: Case studies and support issues. *American Rehabilitation*, pp. 16–23.

Federal Register. (1992, June 24). Washington, DC: U.S. Government Printing Office.

Hagner, D. & Dileo, D. (1993). *Working together: Workplace culture, supported employment, and persons with disabilities.* Boston: Brookline Books.

Kiernan, W.E., McGaughey, M.J., Cooperman, P.J., & McNally, L.C. (1991). *Supported employment for people with severe physical disabilities: Survey of state vocational rehabilitation agencies.* Boston: Training and Research Institute for People with Disabilities, Children's Hospital.

Leung, P. (1988, October). Robotics in rehabilitation. *Journal of Rehabilitation*, pp. 6–7.

Mount, B., & Zwernick, K. (1988). *It's never too early, it's never too late: A booklet about personal futures planning.* Minneapolis, MN: Governor's Planning Council on Developmental Disabilities.

Nisbet, J., & Hagner, D. (1988). Natural supports in the workplace: A reexamination of supported employment. *Journal of The Association for Persons with Severe Handicaps, 13*(4), 260–267.

Nisbet, J., & Sowers, J. (1994). Employees with disabilities. In R. Ritvo (Ed.), *Managing in the age of change* (pp. 10–15). Alexandria, VA: Irwin Professional Publishing.

O'Mara, S. (1991). Current social security incentives and disincentives. In S. Griffin & G. Revell (Eds.), *Rehabilitation counselor desk top guide to supported employment* (pp. 183–198). Richmond: Virginia Commonwealth University, Rehabilitation Research and Training Center.

Powers, L., & Sowers, J. (1994). Evolving perspectives on transitions to adult living: Promoting self-determination and natural supports. In S. Calculator & C. Jorgenson (Eds.), *Providing communication supports to students with severe disabilities in regular classrooms* (pp. 215–247). San Diego: Singular Press.

Sowers, J. (1989). Critical parent roles in supported employment. In G. Singer & L. Irvin (Eds.), *Support for caregiving families: Enabling positive adaption to disability* (pp. 269-282). Baltimore: Paul H. Brookes Publishing Co.

Sowers, J. (1991). Employment for persons with physical disabilities and related technology. *Journal of Vocational Rehabilitation, 1*(2), 55–64.

Sowers, J. (1992). Transitioning students with physical and multiple disabilities to supported employment. *Journal of Vocational Rehabilitation, 2*(2), 31–39.

Sowers, J. (1994). *Career planning profile.* Concord: New Hampshire Natural Supports Project.

Sowers, J., Hall, S., & Rainforth, B. (1991). Related services personnel in supported employment: Roles and training needs. *Rehabilitation Education, 4*(4), 319–333.

Sowers, J., Jenkins, C., & Powers, L. (1988). The training and employment of persons with physical disabilities. In R. Gaylord-Ross (Ed.), *Vocational education for persons with special needs* (pp. 387–416). Palo Alto, CA: Mayfield Publishing Co.

Sowers, J., & Powers, L. (1991). *Vocational preparation and employment of students with physical and multiple disabilities.* Baltimore: Paul H. Brookes Publishing Co.

Sowers, J., Thompson, L., & Connis, R. (1979). The food service vocational training program: A model for training and placement of the mentally retarded. In G. Bellamy, G. O'Connor, & O. Karan (Eds.), *Vocational rehabilitation of severely handicapped persons: Contemporary strategies.* Baltimore: University Park Press.

Vandercook, T., York, J., & Forest, M. (1989). The McGill Action Planning System (MAPS): A strategy for building the vision. *Journal of The Association for Persons with Severe Handicaps, 14,* 205–215.

Wehman, P., & Kregel, J. (1985). A supported work approach to competitive employment of individuals with moderate and severe handicaps. *Journal of The Association for Persons with Severe Handicaps, 10,* 3–11.

Wehman, P. & Moon, M.S. (Eds.). (1988). *Vocational rehabilitation and supported employment.* Baltimore: Paul H. Brookes Publishing Co.

West, M., Revell, G., & Wehman, P. (1992). Achievement and challenges I: A five-year report on consumer and system outcomes from the supported employment initiative. *Journal of The Association for Persons with Severe Handicaps, 17,* 227–235.

York, J., & Rainforth, B. (1987). Developing instructional adaptations. In F.P. Orelove & D. Sobsey, *Educating children with multiple disabilities: A transdisciplinary approach* (pp. 183–217). Baltimore: Paul H. Brookes Publishing Co.

9

Making Sports and Recreation Activities Accessible

Assistive Technology and Other Accommodation Strategies

M. Sherril Moon
Debra Hart
Cheska Komissar
Robin Friedlander

The passage or reauthorization of federal legislation in the 1980s and 1990s has made participation in typical school and community recreation alternatives—through program inclusion, physical adaptations, and facility accessibility modifications—a reality for both children and adults with disabilities. However, before recent legislative mandates, persons with disabilities themselves had been adapting sports and recreation activities so that they could become fit, develop hobbies, and participate in community or team endeavors, or as components of therapy or rehabilitation programs. In fact, most modern sports and recreation accommodations can be tracked to past efforts to help returning veterans of World War II who were experiencing physical, cognitive, and emotional disabilities (Adams, Daniel, McCubbin, & Pullman, 1982).

Since the 1940s and 1950s, the emphasis has evolved from participation in sports and recreation activities that were primarily done in segregated settings, or only with other participants with disabilities, to participation directly with persons who are not disabled (Reynolds, 1993). This *integration* of recreation programs has been made possible by a number of movements, including deinstitutionalization and normalization, of the 1960s and 1970s; school mainstreaming and inclusion in the 1980s and 1990s; legislative mandates such as the Rehabilitation Act of 1973 (PL 93-112), Individuals with Disabilities Education Act (IDEA) of 1990 (PL 101-476), Americans with Disabilities Act (ADA) of 1990 (PL 101-336), Individuals with Disabilities Education Act Amendments of 1991 (PL 102-119), the Technology-Related Assistance for Individuals with Disabilities Act (the Tech Act) of 1988 (PL 100-407), Technology-Related Assistance for Individuals with Disabilities Amendments of 1994 (PL 103-218); and the explosion of technology as it relates to education and rehabilitation programs for persons with disabilities (Moon, 1994; Schleien, Green, & Heyne, 1993).

This chapter shows how assistive technology fits into the realm of various accommodations that may be considered for persons with disabilities as they pursue recreation or leisure activities. This is by no means a comprehensive guide to selecting, building, or buying devices or equipment, but rather this text serves as a resource for locating more detailed descriptions of accommodation prospects based on a recreator's activity preference or specific disability requirement.

RECREATION AND ACCOMMODATION STRATEGIES

The terms *leisure* and *recreation* are used synonymously throughout this chapter to refer to any activity or program in which a person participates for the purposes of fun, relaxation, diversion, and/or amusement. These kinds of activities can include almost anything and typically fall into one or more of the following classifications: 1) physical, cultural, or social; 2) indoor or outdoor; 3) spectator or participant; 4) formal or informal; 5) independent, cooperative, or competitive; or 6) sports, games, hobbies, or toy play (Moon & Bunker, 1987). An activity cannot ultimately be considered recreational for someone unless the participant enjoys him- or herself and chooses to participate in that activity. Dattilo (1992) refers to leisure as a person's perception of his or her freedom to choose to participate in certain experiences. He writes that the purpose of providing leisure services to persons with disabilities must be to give them skills and supports that enable them to be free to choose activities in which they want to be involved.

Accommodation strategies can include various additions or modifications to a facility, equipment, rules, or program procedures that will enable persons with disabilities to participate more fully. In this chapter, the terms *accommodation, modification,* and *adaptation* are used synonymously to denote environmental, equipment, or program changes. Assistive technology, which generally refers to material or equipment additions or modifications, is only one accommodation strategy that might be considered to enhance recreation program accessibility.

CHOOSING THE RIGHT ACCOMMODATIONS

A recreational activity should be altered only after carefully considering how changes will affect everyone involved in that activity. For example, will a modification segregate the person unnecessarily, or will it drastically change the rules, competition, or cooperation for other participants? Are modifications too expensive, highly technological, or cumbersome to use in other settings? Several experts have provided guidelines for making accommodations that can help ensure their universality and practicality (Kennedy, Smith, & Austin, 1991; Moon, Hart, Komissar, & Sotnik, 1994; Rynders & Schleien, 1991). Table 9.1 lists considerations and suggestions for making such accommodations.

The first accommodation strategy that should be pursued in any setting in which recreation programs are open to the public is the assurance of accessibility standards according to new guidelines set forth in the ADA (PL 101-336). This law establishes standards on physical modifications, removal of barriers, and alternatives to physical alterations for settings providing public accommodations, such as schools, restaurants, hotels, gymnasiums, theaters, retail stores, malls, museums, libraries, parks, and child care centers. ADA accessibility standards should be used to survey a facility hosting recreation programs to make sure that the facility meets the legal requirements. The law mandates provisions for changing the facility or altering the program so that everyone can participate (Epstein, McGovern, & Moon, 1994). The following section on ADA accessibility standards is adapted from the work of Epstein et al. (1994).

Table 9.1. Considerations for making accommodations

---
1. Understand the concept of universal design and employ optimal standards of accessibility to reduce costs and accidents and to increase participation.

2. Know accessibility requirements established by ADA.

3. Use resources outside your agency to ensure best practices.

4. Adapt or change only when necessary and make sure participants are comfortable with changes.

5. Always try to choose adaptations that do not segregate the person needing the change and that make the least amount of changes to the normal outcome of the activity.

6. Use accommodations that are "generalizable" across settings or activities and that are as inexpensive as possible.

7. Encourage the person needing an alteration and the other activity participants to design possible accommodations and to make the ultimate choice.

8. Do not initially invest too much time or money into a single adaptation, because the need for specific accommodations can change as the level of participation develops.

ADA's Impact on Recreation Programs

Schools, YMCAs and YWCAs, parks and recreation departments, and other organizations that provide recreation programs may not exclude potential program participants from their services, programs, and activities on the basis of disability. A "potential program participant" is any qualified individual with a disability who meets the essential eligibility requirements for program participation. Essential eligibility requirements may include residency, ability to pay program fees, willingness to abide by the program's rules of conduct, and compliance with registration procedures. Other factors may consist of age requirements and level of skill for competitive programs. However, ADA guidelines require that eligibility standards be the same for all participants, including those individuals with and without disabilities. ADA further specifies three types of accommodations that should be made when an individual with a disability meets a program's essential eligibility requirements. These accommodations are as follows (Epstein et al., 1994):

1. The agency should modify rules, policies, or practices to enable an individual's participation. Many park and recreation departments require in-person registration for popular programs such as day camps, sports leagues, child care programs, and swimming lessons. A reasonable modification under ADA might be to change the procedure to include phone-in or mail-in registration. Another example would be changing the game rules in a particular sport (e.g., tennis players who use wheelchairs are allowed two bounces before returning the ball). A final example may be permitting animals in a recreation center where they are typically not allowed so that an individual who is physically challenged can be assisted or a person who is blind can use his or her guide dog.

2. The agency should remove architectural, transportation, or communication barriers to enable an individual's participation. ADA requires that physical barriers be removed if readily achievable (e.g., a health club may widen doorways for persons who use wheelchairs, a recreation center may install grab bars in the restrooms and ramps). ADA does not require immediate removal of all architectural barriers in existing facilities; however, it does require that all programs within the facility be made accessible. For example, a girl or boy scout troop meeting may be relocated from the third floor to the first floor in a building without an elevator so that a child who uses a wheelchair can attend. If the program is unique (e.g., the only ice skating rink or the only indoor swimming pool), architectural barriers must be removed. Furthermore, all new facilities or areas must be constructed free of architectural barriers under ADA regulations.

Vehicles purchased or leased for use in the transportation of recreation program participants must be "readily accessible." This means, at the minimum, wheelchair lifts, interior passenger securing systems, and other similar modifications must be provided. In certain circumstances, recreation agencies will be required to transport program participants with disabilities to and from programs at the agency's expense.

All agency communications, including flyers and program brochures, should be available in a format that is accessible to persons with hearing and/or vision impairments. Agencies also should acquire telecommunication devices for the deaf (TDDs) or text telephones or have access to a telecommunication relay system that will enable telephone communication with individuals who use TDDs.

3. *The agency should provide auxiliary aids or services to enable an individual's participation.* For example, if a participant with a hearing impairment registers for an arts and crafts program and requires instructional assistance, a reasonable accommodation may be the provision of a sign language interpreter. For individuals with cognitive impairments, the agency may consider furnishing additional staff members or volunteers who can serve as instructors, facilitators, partners, or peer advisors.

Program Requirements

Programs, services, and activities of community recreation agencies must be available in the most integrated setting—the setting in which interaction among persons with and without disabilities is maximally available. Ideally, this means that persons with disabilities would participate side-by-side with persons without disabilities in the same program. Accommodations must be available to enable leisure participation that is as effective for the person with a disability as it is for others.

Community recreation agencies can still offer separate, specialized recreation programs for individuals with disabilities; however, an individual with a disability has the right to choose to participate in a regular recreation program. For example, the YMCA can offer recreation programs for children with mental retardation, but it would be a violation if the YMCA refused to allow children with mental retardation or other disabilities to participate in its other recreation programs.

ADA regulations outline other acceptable accommodations, such as making home visits for an individual who cannot attend activities outside of his or her home because of a disability and providing additional staff. Often, additional staff supervision can make a difference for a person with a cognitive impairment who can learn a skill or enjoy an activity with some additional assistance. Accommodations also include the use of adaptive equipment and auxiliary aids. Adaptive equipment may be a bowling ball with a handle, a computer for games, or other similar devices. Examples of auxiliary aids include sign language interpreters, assistive learning devices, readers, taped texts, braille materials, and large-print materials. Community recreation agencies may not pass on the cost of ADA compliance or of providing accommodations to a participant with a disability. Costs associated with accessibility must be absorbed by all participants or by the agency. Appendix A provides a partial listing of ADA accessibility standards and general accommodations that are particularly crucial to recreational programs.

Once it has been determined whether a facility is or is not physically accessible, any number of environmental modifications may be needed—from structural changes and the addition of ramps to simple rearrangements of furniture and the replacement of doorknobs. Some typical and relatively inexpensive environmental accommodations that facilities must consider include paving, barrier-free hallways, proper handrails, enlarged doorways with automatic doors or doorbells, lever doorknobs, controlled noise levels, use of contrasting colors, and pictorial signs. Table 9.2 provides illustrations of how accommodations in these areas can improve accessibility to recreation programs for everyone.

Programmatic Adaptations

Often a leisure program, especially a sport or fitness activity, can be made more accessible by altering how the activity is done rather than changing the facility or materials. This type of

Table 9.2. General adaptations to consider for any recreation program

Improve mobility and ambulation.	• Paving should be smooth and free of debris. • Curbcuts should be free of snow/water. • Pathways and halls should be barrier free. • Handrails should be securely fastened. • Doorways should be wide.
Improve handling of materials.	• Use lever doorknobs rather than round knobs. • Use gripping gloves and straps. These can be purchased from catalogs or created from Velcro, Dycem, and/or Scoot Guard. • Make built-up handles using tape, wood, or other materials. • Use Dycem/Scoot Guard to assist in holding items in place. • Use Velcro to hold items to items or hands to items.
Improve visibility and participation by persons with vision losses.	• Pathways and halls should be barrier free. • Noise levels should be controlled. Use dampening materials in large, noisy areas. • Use contrasting colors. The best is yellow on black. • Use large-print (14 point or greater) or braille materials or cassette tapes. • Use sighted guides.
Improve communication and participation by persons with hearing losses.	• Use TDDs. • Use FM units/loop systems. • Know which type of communication (ASL, signed English, or oral) is necessary before hiring an interpreter. • Whenever possible, provide voice materials in a written format.
Improve understanding and increase participation levels.	• Use verbal instruction and demonstration. • Use pictorial signs. • Adapt the rules when necessary. • Modify entrance criteria so that a less advanced individual can participate in a more advanced group to remain with his or her peers. • Utilize natural supports.

ASL, American Sign Language; TDD, Telecommunication device for the deaf.

accommodation may also be cheaper and less intrusive to other participants, and the participants themselves can help design the programmatic change that best suits the entire group. A sampling of the kinds of programmatic adaptations that may be considered are included here. More detailed descriptions of a variety of programmatic modifications are provided in other sources (Adams & McCubbin, 1991; Kennedy et al., 1991; Rynders & Schleien, 1991; Wehman & Schleien, 1981; Winnick, 1990).

Rule or Procedural Modifications

Complicated rules or procedures can often prohibit persons with disabilities from playing games and sports or enjoying certain hobbies. These procedures sometimes can be altered without changing the flow or outcome of the activities. For example, in a game of kickball, hitting or throwing the ball can be substituted for kicking for a player who is using a wheelchair. In basketball, two-handed dribbling or deleting the 3-second lane violation can enable players with cognitive or severe motor difficulties to participate. During card or board games, a player who cannot discriminate cards or follow rules can have a silent partner, or all players can participate in pairs. The main "rule of thumb" should always be to have the activity participants design changes so that everyone is comfortable with the changes.

Partial Participation

This concept implies that, even though a person with a disability may not be able to function independently in a situation, he or she should still be able to take part with assistance when and where needed (Baumgart et al., 1982). Partial participation is central to recreation involvement for persons with disabilities because it is the one life domain in which having fun is the outcome, rather than independence, completing an activity, or producing a product (Moon, 1994).

A person with a disability can probably best partially participate in recreation activities by having other participants assist when necessary. Using partners or teams to play, build, or create is a natural way to get an end product without highlighting individual differences. In some cases, extra assistance from a leader or instructor on parts of an activity can help. Yet in most situations, the group can figure out several partial participation accommodations. For example, someone can pick up a bowling ball and give it to the bowler who has a physical disability; someone in a photography class can hold the camera or push the button to photograph a shot that is set up by the photographer with a disability; or partners can be used during a cooking class to jointly measure, pour, mix, or chop. The use of partners for athletes who are blind or who have developmental disabilities can enable them to run, swim, dance, or play team sports. The use of activity participants to provide assistance to a person with a disability may be referred to as the use of "natural supports."

Equipment or Material Adaptations

Modified or special pieces of equipment that are bought or homemade are probably the most frequently used accommodations in leisure activities (Moon et al., 1994). Such material adaptations or assistive devices can involve a simple piece of velcro, an entire environmental control unit, a hardware system that controls appliances throughout a home, or wheelchair runners that enable a person using a chair to ski or skate. This chapter does not attempt to describe the entire array of assistive devices, but there are a number of excellent resources that do provide more detail (Adams et al., 1982; Adams & McCubbin, 1991; Burkhart, 1980, 1982; Glennen & Church, 1992). The organizations and materials listed in Appendix B, particularly the *Assistive Technology Sourcebook* (Enders & Hall, 1990), can also assist persons in building or purchasing assistive devices for particular sports or games.

Several specific assistive devices related to particular activities are shown in Table 9.3. Other general, relatively low-tech, inexpensive types of material modifications are described as follows. In considering any assistive devices, it is important to remember the suggestions in Table 9.1. For some individuals, material adaptations may not be as effective as programmatic alterations, such as changing procedures or using a partner.

Switches

Switches that can be operated by fist, foot, head, cheek, finger, or even breath can be bought or made inexpensively. These switches can be connected to almost any electronic device, such as a toy, television, or CD player, and can be adjusted to assist persons with all types of physical disabilities. Burkhart (1980, 1982) and Glennen and Church (1992) are excellent sources to refer to when selecting or building inexpensive switches.

Velcro

Velcro is a common material that can be helpful to persons having difficulty holding recreational equipment. A piece of velcro attached to a golf glove and a club can help a person play golf. The same principle would apply to holding paddles, bats, or gardening tools.

Dycem and Scoot Guard

These products are available in hardware and crafts outlets and can be used to hold stationary items in place. For example, Dycem or Scoot Guard can hold paints, other liquids, or containers of beads or glass on a table during arts and crafts activities.

Gripping Gloves, Handles, and Straps

A variety of gloves or special straps are commercially available from sports and occupational therapy vendors, such as Access to Recreation, Inc. (1993), that allow people to bat, paddle, play racquet sports, or garden. Special handles or controls can also be purchased or built for persons having problems grasping or gripping. Hot glue, rubber triangles for brushes, pens and pencils, pipe insulation, and a variety of tapes are all appropriate for various activities. Occupational therapists, adapted physical education specialists, or therapeutic recreation specialists can recommend which of these alterations to try.

Large Print and Braille Materials and Cassette Tapes

All materials pertaining to a leisure activity such as directions, descriptions, or lyrics should be available in large print or braille, or on cassette tapes for persons with visual impairments. Often, the state or local office on visual impairments (associated with the department of rehabilitation services) can assist in preparing these materials.

ACCOMMODATIONS FOR PARTICULAR DISABILITIES

An adaptation is not solely dictated by the type of disability but rather by the type of recreation activity and the needs and wishes of the participant in that activity. However, some general types of modifications can usually be considered for recreators who have cognitive, sensory, behavioral, or physical challenges. For example, persons with cognitive disabilities, such as mental retardation, can usually benefit from extra instruction or demonstration, pictorial directions, rule adaptations, and extra peer support. Persons with hearing impairments should have access to interpreters and extra written materials. Participants who use wheelchairs need accessible facilities that meet new ADA standards. An example of accommodation is provided in Case Study 9.1. As mentioned earlier, although these categories of adapta-

Table 9.3.   Assistive technology applications in recreation activities

Fishing
- "Hemicast" adapted reel
- Fishing pier adapted to include 5-foot-wide access walk, 36-inch-high handrail, and kick plate at bottom of pier
- Electronic reels
- Rod holders, such as Free Handerson Recreation Belt
- Pole lock, Batick bracket, Van's EZ Cast, AmpoFisher I, and Handi-Gear

Television, stereo systems, and electronic toys or games
- Homemade switches, such as the Nickel switch, flipper switch, cheek switch, pull switch, puzzle switch, and canning lid switch with light
- Commercially available switches, such as Zygo's Tread Switch, Prentke Romich's Wobble Switch, and Able Net's Big Red Switch
- Environmental control units using infrared, radio, ultrasound, or AC power line control

Frisbee
- Auditory frisbee (small buzzer attached to center)

Twister
- Change visual/colored sections to tactually different materials of four varieties

Backgammon
- Adapted board with tactually distinguishable triangles

Solitaire
- Use of card holder (styrofoam board with strips of elastic) to keep cards in position

Guitar
- Adapted pick that remains in stable position and shapes hand in desired position for strumming

Pull-push toys
- Adapted handle for use by children who use a wheelchair

Downhill skiing
- Ski bra, outriggers, canting wedges, sit skis

Table tennis
- Ball-bearing feeder, bihandled paddle, strap-on paddle, table tennis cuff

Shooting
- Lapboard, forearm adapter, shoulder harness, tripod

Archery
- Bowsling, wheelchair bowstringer, adapted bow, elbow brace

Fitness training
- Equalizer 1005 5 Station, Power Trainer, Paragym, Saratoga Cycle

Bowling
- Bowling ball holder-ring, cradle bowling stick, bowling cues, handle grip bowling ball, bowling frame unit

(continued)

Table 9.3.   *(continued)*

Golf
- Putter finger, miniputter

Horseback riding
- Adapted reins, Humes Rein, safety belts, Peacock stirrup, Devonshire boot

Ice skating
- Outrigger skate aid, ankle-foot orthotic, UCB insert, Hein-A-Ken Skate aid, wheelchair runners

Pool (pocket billiards)
- Adapted bridge, swivel cue holder, wheeled cue rest, control cuff billiard cue, Uni-que

Swimming
- Body Buoy, swim rings, Delta Swim System, sectional raft, stabilizer bar, head float

Sources for these assistive devices include Access to Recreation, Inc. (1993), Adams and McCubbin (1991), Burkhart (1980), Glennen and Church (1992), Rynders and Schleien (1991), and Winnick (1990). Readers should refer to these references for specific instructions on building or purchasing these devices.

tions may be most helpful to someone with a particular disability, these accommodations would also improve accessibility for anyone.

Universal Design

Universal design is a simple concept that calls for buildings, equipment, and products to be designed so that they can be used by everyone. This approach makes recreation, employment, and residential options viable not only for persons with specific disabilities, but for everyone who at different times experiences some sort of temporary physical, mental, or emotional disability (*The Disability Rag,* 1992). The passage of ADA should enhance the incorporation of universal design as new facilities, programs, and transportation and communication networks strive to meet accessibility standards. The fact that employing optional standards of accessibility lowers accommodation costs and reduces accidents should also help (Brown & Vargo, 1993). The references listed in Appendix B, as well as the standards provided in Appendix A, will assist consumers and program providers interested in accommodating through universal design.

CONCLUSION

A single agency could not possibly comprehend all the accessibility requirements and possible adaptations available to leisure and recreation activity providers and to individuals with disabilities. The passage and reauthorization of laws such as ADA, IDEA, and the Tech Act have created a multitude of new products, training programs, and information networks that are constantly growing and changing. Therefore, it is crucial to know of a variety of sources that can help keep up with the ever-changing technology, standards, and available products. The organizations and publications provided in Appendix B can provide information and assistance to persons concerned with making sport and recreation activities accessible to all persons.

Case Study 9.1: A Leisure Recreation Example

Betty is a 14-year-old with severe multiple disabilities. She uses a wheelchair for mobility, because she is paralyzed from the waist down. In addition, Betty has muscle weakness in her arms and hands, making it difficult for her to grasp and manipulate objects. However, she can wheel her chair for short distances using extensions on the rims of the wheels.

Betty lives with her parents in a planned community subdivision. She is an only child but does have several friends in her neighborhood. One of Betty's dreams has always been to have her own dog; however, her mother has always been against the idea. First, her mother does not want the responsibility of the pet to fall on her. She believes that Betty is physically unable to care for a dog. Second, the subdivision has a lease law, as well as a community covenant, that prohibits fences in the neighborhood.

Recently, Betty mentioned her dream of owning a pet during a person-centered planning meeting, and her group of supporters began to brainstorm ways that her dream could become a reality. The team realized that a variety of low- and high-tech devices could assist Betty with her goal. The following ideas were suggested:

1. Purchase an invisible fence system to train the dog to remain within a specified territory. This system would eliminate the need for Betty to walk her dog as well as address the issue of the neighborhood fence covenant.

2. Install a swinging dog door in the family's kitchen, providing the pet with access to the backyard.

3. Identify friends in the neighborhood who also own pets. Establish times during the week that Betty could walk her dog by using a lead attached to her chair. Walking with her pet may increase her physical stamina, be socially rewarding, and serve as a powerful motivator for increasing Betty's independent mobility skills.

4. Build up the handle on a pet brush in order for Betty to groom her pet. Perhaps purchase a grooming glove with nylon teeth on the palm side that grooms the pet as the owner rubs the animal's fur.

5. Purchase an automatic dog feeder and water bowl that would reduce the number of times that Betty needs to fill the containers. Place the item off the floor on a stool or platform that both Betty and the dog can reach. Use Dycem on the top of the stool to prevent the items from sliding around.

6. Enroll Betty and her pet in the YMCA's dog obedience classes. Explore the possibility of identifying a peer buddy who could accompany her to these classes.

The process of identifying technology and support solutions to the barriers that were preventing Betty from owning a pet was useful to her and her family. Plans were made at the meeting that would make Betty's dream a reality within a 3-month time period.

REFERENCES

Access to Recreation, Inc. (1993, Fall). *Don Kreb's Access to Recreation: Adaptive recreation equipment for the physically challenged.* Thousand Oaks, CA: Author.

Adams, R., Daniel, A., McCubbin, J., & Pullman, L. (1982). *Games, sports, and exercises for the physically disabled.* Philadelphia: Lea & Febiger.

Adams, R., & McCubbin, J. (1991). *Games, sports, and exercises for the physically disabled.* Philadelphia: Lea & Febiger.

Americans with Disabilities Act (ADA) of 1990, PL 101-336. (July 26, 1990). Title 42, U.S.C. 12101 et seq: *U.S. Statutes at Large, 104,* 327–378.

Baumgart, D., Brown, L., Pumpian, I., Nisbet, J., Ford, A., Sweet, M., Messina, R., & Schroeder, J. (1982). The principle of partial participation and individualized adaptations in educational programs for severely handicapped students. *Journal of The Association for the Severely Handicapped, 1*(2), 17–27.

Brown, D., & Vargo, J. (1993). Bibliography of resources on universal design. *Journal of Rehabilitation, 59*(3), 8–11.

Burkhart, L. (1980). *Homemade battery operated toys and educational devices for severely handicapped children.* College Park, MD: Author.

Burkhart, L. (1982). *More homemade battery devices for severely handicapped children with suggested activities.* College Park, MD: Author.

Dattilo, J. (1992). Recreation and leisure: A review of the literature and recommendations for future directions. In L. Meyer, C. Peck, & L. Brown (Eds.), *Critical issues in the lives of people with severe disabilities* (pp. 171–193). Baltimore: Paul H. Brookes Publishing Co.

The Disability Rag. (March/April, 1992) (pp. 4–5). Louisville, KY: Author.

Enders, A., & Hall, M. (Eds.). (1990). *Assistive technology sourcebook.* Washington, DC: RESNA Press.

Epstein, R., McGovern, J., & Moon, M.S. (1994). The impact of federal legislation on recreation programs. In M.S. Moon (Ed.), *Making school and community recreation fun for everyone: Places and ways to integrate* (pp. 87–96). Baltimore: Paul H. Brookes Publishing Co.

Glennen, S., & Church, G. (1992). Adaptive toys and environmental controls. In G. Church & S. Glennen (Eds.), *The handbook of assistive technology* (pp. 173–205). San Diego: Singular Publishing Group, Inc.

Individuals with Disabilities Education Act (IDEA) of 1990, PL 101-476. (October 30, 1990). Title 20, U.S.C. 1400 et seq: *U.S. Statutes at Large, 104,* 1103–1151.

Individuals with Disabilities Education Act Amendments of 1991, PL 102-119. (October 7, 1991). Title 20, U.S.C. 1400 et seq: *U.S. Statutes at Large, 105,* 587–608.

Kennedy, D., Smith, R., & Austin, D. (1991). *Special recreation opportunities for persons with disabilities.* Dubuque, IA: Wm. C. Brown.

Moon, M.S. (Ed.). (1994). *Making school and community recreation fun for everyone: Places and ways to integrate.* Baltimore: Paul H. Brookes Publishing Co.

Moon, M.S., & Bunker, L. (1987). Recreation and motor skills programming. In M. Snell (Ed.), *Systematic instruction of the moderately and severely handicapped* (pp. 214–244). Columbus, OH: Charles E. Merrill.

Moon, M.S., Hart, D., Komissar, C., & Friedlander, R. (1993). *The community access survey.* Boston: Children's Hospital.

Moon, M.S., Hart, D., Komissar, C., & Sotnik, P. (1994). Recreation accessibility and activity adaptations. In M.S. Moon (Ed.), *Making school and community recreation fun for everyone: Places and ways to integrate* (pp. 97–119). Baltimore: Paul H. Brookes Publishing Co.

Rehabilitation Act of 1973, PL 93-112. (September 26, 1973). Title 29, U.S.C. 701 et seq: *U.S. Statutes at Large, 87,* 355–394.

Reynolds, R. (1993). Recreation and leisure lifestyle changes. In P. Wehman (Ed.), *The ADA mandate for social change* (pp. 217–240). Baltimore: Paul H. Brookes Publishing Co.

Rynders, J., & Schleien, S. (1991). *Together successfully: Creating recreational and educational programs that integrate people with and without disabilities.* Arlington, TX: The Association for Retarded Citizens of the United States.

Schleien, S., Green, F., & Heyne, L. (1993). Integrate community recreation. In M. Snell (Ed.), *Instruction of students with severe disabilities* (pp. 526–555). New York: Merrill.

Technology-Related Assistance for Individuals with Disabilities Act of 1988, PL 100-407. (August 19, 1988). Title 29, U.S.C. 2202 et seq: *U.S. Statutes at Large, 102,* 1044–1065.

Technology-Related Assistance for Individuals with Disabilities Amendments of 1994, PL 103-218. (March 9, 1994). Title 29, U.S.C. 2201 et seq: *U. S. Statutes at Large, 108,* 50–97.

Wehman, P., & Schleien, P. (1981). *Leisure programs for handicapped persons: Adaptations, techniques, and curriculum.* Baltimore: University Park Press.

Winnick, J. (Ed.). (1990). *Adapted physical education and sport.* Champaign, IL: Human Kinetics Books.

Appendix A: Partial Listing of Accessibility Standards and General Accommodations for Recreation Programs

Transportation

- Accessible public transportation to organization/facility
- Transport to front of organization/facility entrance
- Organization/facility-provided accessible transportation

Parking

- Signs at entrance of lot indicating location of accessible parking
- Zoned area designated for drop off/pick up adjacent to or near curbcut and/or accessible entranceway
- Handicap space closest to accessible entrance
- Parking spaces at least 96" wide
- Symbol of accessibility visible at each space

Pathways (Outdoors)

- Pathways—minimum width of 36" for one wheelchair or 60" for two wheelchairs
- Pathway surface evenly paved and without interruption
- Curbcuts located at the corner of each intersection
- Curbcuts—minimum 1"–8" of length
- Signs to areas of building in both words and symbols

General Organizational Structure

- Staff available with training regarding disabilities
- Staff available to assist with accommodations
- Adaptive equipment available on premises
- Integrated programming available
- Specialized programming available

Meeting Spaces

- Spaces on different floors

Adapted from a survey developed according to new ADA criteria by Moon, Hart, Komissar, and Friedlander (1993). For a complete listing of ADA standards or universal design standards, see Appendix B.

- Spaces accessible (e.g., doors, corridors)
- Facility with modified space for accessibility, if requested
- Spaces clean and free of debris
- Spaces brightly lit
- Controlled noise level
- Spaces adjacent to accessible bathroom

Places of Assembly

- Ticket window maximum height of 36"
- Concession stand maximum height of 36"
- Reserved seating for persons who are blind/visually impaired and deaf/hard of hearing
- Reserved seating available for friends who are not disabled in these areas
- Minimum aisle width of 32"
- Turning radius of 60" × 60" at top and bottom of aisles
- Wheelchair accessible spectator seats available and distributed among different areas of facility and at various prices
- Seating available for friends who are not disabled in these areas
- Listening system for persons who are hard of hearing
- Sign language interpreters available

Libraries

- Minimum aisle width of 36"
- Check-out counter with maximum height of 36"
- Card catalogs with maximum height of 54" and minimum height of 18"
- Computer system available for book availability/location system
- Stacks of books/book shelves maximum height of 54"
- Staff available for book retrieval/general assistance
- Accessible quiet space available free of distractions
- Sign language interpreters available

Swimming Pools

- Minimum 48" wide path of travel around pool
- Slip resistant surface around pool
- Wide ramp with handrails to pool
- Lifting device available
- Lifeguards on duty
- Signs for different water levels made clear
- Shower stalls minimum of 36" × 36" with curb maximum 1/2"
- Shower with single lever control operable with closed fist
- Shower head on slide bar with hose
- Shower stall with two grab bars on wall 33"–36" high
- Shower with securely attached, padded, hinged seat
- Top of shower seat 18" high
- Locker rooms with minimum aisle width of 42"

- Locker rooms with accessible bathrooms
- Dressing cubicles 60″ × 72″ with an opening of 32″

Corridors/Lobbies

- Minimum width of 60″ for wheelchairs to pass
- Turning radius of 60″ × 60″ (to allow 360° turn in wheelchair)
- Corridors free of obstructions with 80″ clear headroom
- Permanent fixtures mounted on wall project maximum of 4″
- Directory of building in words and symbols
- Corridors brightly lit
- Signs for accessible bathrooms, phones, and exits
- Carpeted surface securely attached and not wrinkled
- Accessible drinking fountain maximum of 27″ high with knee space underneath; spout no higher than 36″
- Drinking fountain operable with closed fist
- Vending machine controls maximum height of 48″ and minimum of 15″ for forward reach
- Vending machine controls operable with closed fist
- Telephone area maximum height of 48″ and minimum of 15″ for forward reach
- Amplification system identified and available for telephones

Bathrooms

- Accessible bathrooms available
- Signs on outside door and individual stalls in both words and symbols
- All doors minimum width of 32″
- All doors operable with closed fist
- Bathroom area free of obstruction and debris
- Bathroom area with minimum turning space of 60″ × 60″ on the diagonal
- Stall doors that swing out
- Stall doors that open easily
- Stall doors operable with closed fist
- Accessible sink 34″ high with knee space minimum of 30″ wide, 29″ high, and 19″ deep
- Accessible sink operable with closed fist
- Bottom of mirror maximum height of 40″ or tilted
- All dispensers maximum height of 40″
- All dispensers operable with closed fist
- Accessible urinal rim maximum height of 17″
- Accessible toilet stall with a minimum width of 60″ and minimum depth of 56″ (wall of stall to door)
- Top of toilet seat 17″–19″ high

Doors (Public Entrances Are Those that Are Not Loading or Service Entrances)

- At least one accessible public entrance

- Accessible primary entrance width of 32″ with door open 90″
- Distance between entrances no more than 3-minute walk for persons without disabilities
- Automatic opening doors in entranceway, corridors, and rooms
- Automatic operating mechanism for doors
- Slowing closing doors (minimum of 3 seconds)
- Doors to individual areas with minimum width of 32″
- Thresholds not exceeding 3/4″ for exterior sliding doors or 1/2″ for all other doors
- Door hardware mounted no higher than 48″ above floor
- Doors operable with one hand and not requiring tight grasp
- Signs for rooms in both words and symbols

Ramps/Lifts/Stairs (Inside and Out)

- Slip resistant ramps with maximum 12″ incline to 12′ length
- Ramps with handrails on both sides extending 12″ beyond the top and bottom of ramp
- Ramps made of solid material with a minimum width of 36″ measured at handrails
- Ramps reaching same areas as stairs, usable by standard and scooter (three wheel) style wheelchairs
- Ramps with level areas to stop and rest at least every 30′
- Stairs with solid risers and handrails
- Stairs with nosings that project no more than 1 1/2″
- Mechanical lift available
- Lift operable by user
- Facility staff trained to operate lift

Appendix B: Resource List _____

INFORMATION AND RESOURCES ON ADA

Access Board
800-872-2253 (Voice/TDD)
(202) 653-7848 (Voice/TDD)

Disability Rights Education and Defense Fund
800-466-4232 (Voice/TDD)
(510) 644-2555 (Voice)
(510) 644-2629 (TDD)

Equal Employment Opportunity Commission
800-669-3362 (Voice)
800-800-3302 (TDD)

Federal Communications Commission
(202) 632-7260 (Voice)
(202) 632-6999 (TDD)

National Association of the Deaf
(301) 587-1788 (Voice)
(301) 587-1789 (TDD)

National Center for Law and the Deaf
(202) 651-5373 (Voice/TDD)

National Institute on Disability and Rehabilitation Research
(202) 732-1139 (Voice)
(202) 732-5316 (TDD)

President's Commission on Employment of People with Disabilities
(202) 376-6200 (Voice)
(202) 376-6205 (TDD)

Project Action
(202) 347-3066 (Voice)
(202) 347-7385 (TDD)

Rehabilitation Services Administration
(202) 732-1331 (Voice)
(202) 732-4538 (TDD)

U.S. Department of Justice
(202) 514-0301 (Voice)
(202) 514-0381 or 0383 (TDD)

U.S. Department of Transportation
(202) 366-9306 or 4011 (Voice)
(202) 755-7687 or 366-2979 (TDD)

(continued)

RESOURCES ON ACCESSIBILITY AND UNIVERSAL DESIGN*

Accessible design of consumer products: Guidelines for the design of consumer products to increase their accessibility to people with disabilities or who are aging. (1991).

Describes specific barriers to accessibility and outlines four ways to make products more accessible. Available from:

> Trace Research and Development Center
> Reprint Service
> University of Wisconsin
> 1500 Highland Avenue
> Madison, WI 53705-2280
> (608) 263-2309(V)   (608) 263-5406(TDD)

> *Cost:* $25 ($15, plus $10 handling cost)
> *Accessible formats:* Braille, computer disk

Technical paper on accessibility codes and standards. (1989). U.S. Architectural and Transportation Barriers Compliance Board.

Comparison between Uniform Federal Accessibility Standards and Minimum Guidelines and Requirements for Accessible Design. Provides a useful overview of the regulatory environment for accessibility in the 50 states. Available from:

> The United States Access Board
> 1331 F Street, N.W., Suite 1000
> Washington, DC 20004
> (202) 272-5434(V)   (202) 272-5449(TDD)

> *Accessible formats:* Braille, computer disk

Accessible environments: Toward universal design. (1989). Ronald Mace, Graeme Hardie, and Jaime Place.

Definition, history, and analysis of universal design with an analysis of the costs and benefits. Available from:

> North Carolina State University
> Center for Accessible Housing
> Box 8613
> Raleigh, NC 27695-8613
> (919) 515-3082 (V & TDD)—No phone orders please.

> *Cost:* $3.50

Curriculum: Universal design. (1992).

Instruction outline for first semester course in universal design, covering design of handheld and other small items. Focus on three main facets—the design process, the client, and the final product.

Design primer: Universal design. (1992).

One in a series of primers intended for school-age children. Discusses what design is and what designers do. Discusses people, particularly those whom designers often fail to consider when designing products. Concludes with universal design checklist. (Note: Primer is 34 pages in length and measures 8″ × 11″.)

---

*This is a partial listing of resources from a bibliography by Brown and Vargo (1993).

Pratt Institute
Center for Advanced Design
200 Willoughby Avenue
Brooklyn, NY 11205
(718) 636-3690(V)

Cost: Curriculum, $28.00; primer, $18.00

Rehab brief: Design for the life span of all people. (1987).

Reviews adaptable design research, reasons why adaptable design is not popular with architects, and adaptability solutions.

National Rehabilitation Information Center (NARIC)
8455 Colesville Road, Suite 935
Silver Spring, MD 20910-3319
(301) 588-9284 (V & TDD)

Cost: Reprints available free of charge through NARIC.

Alternative media: Available at Library of Blind Services, 420 Platt Street, Daytona Beach, CA 32114. Betty Boyette (904) 254-3824.

Extend their reach. (1992). Electronic Industries Association.

Introduction to the electronic devices available to help people with disabilities overcome impairments of sight, speech, hearing, motion, and other conditions.

Electronic Industries Association
2001 Pennsylvania Avenue
Washington, DC 20006-1813
(202) 457-8705(V)   (202) 955-5836(TDD)

Accessible formats: Section on vision impairments is available on audiocassette.

ORGANIZATIONS, PUBLICATIONS, AND MANUFACTURERS

ABLEDATA
8455 Colesville Road, Suite 935
Silver Spring, MD 20910
800-346-2742 (voice and TDD)

American Alliance for Health, Physical Education, Recreation and Dance (AAHPERD)
1900 Association Drive
Reston, VA 22091
(703) 476-3400

Assistive Devices Information Network
University of Iowa Hospital School
Iowa City, IA 52242
(319) 356-0768

Assistive Technology Sourcebook
RESNA Press
Dept. 4006
Washington, DC 20042-4006
(703) 524-6686

Basketball: National Wheelchair Basketball Association
110 Seaton Building
University of Kentucky
Lexington, KY 40506
(606) 257-1623

Camping: Office of Special Programs and Populations
National Park Service
U.S. Department of the Interior
P.O. Box 371127
Washington, DC 20013
(202) 343-3674

Canoeing: American Canoe Association
Disabled Paddlers Commission
P.O. Box 1190
Newington, VA 22122
(703) 550-7495

Closing the Gap
P.O. Box 68
Henderson, MN 56044
(612) 248-3294

Fishing: Physically Challenged Outdoorsman's Association
3006 Louisiana Avenue
Cleveland, OH 44109

Gardening: American Horticultural Therapy Association
9220 Wightman Road, Suite 300
Gaithersburg, MD 20879
(301) 948-3010

Horseback Riding: North American Riding for the Handicapped Association (NORHA)
P.O. Box 33150
Denver, CO 80233
(303) 452-1212

National Center on Accessibility
Bradford Woods/Indiana University
5040 State Road 67 N
Martinsville, IN 46151
800-424-1877 or (317) 349-9240
  (voice or TDD)

National Handicapped Sports
451 Hungerford Drive, Suite 100
Rockville, MD 20850
(301) 217-0960 (voice)
  (301) 217-0963 (TDD)

National Lekotek Center
2100 Ridge Avenue
Evanston, IL 60204
(708) 328-0001

National Parks Service, Special Programs and Populations Branch Department of the Interior
P.O. Box 37127, Suite 610
Washington, DC 20013-7127
(202) 343-3674

National Recreation and Park Association (NRPA)
2775 S. Quincy Street, Suite 300
Arlington, VA 22206-2204
(703) 820-4940

National Rehabilitation Information Center (NARIC)
8455 Colesville Road, Suite 935
Silver Spring, MD 20910-3319
800-34-NARIC
  (301) 588-9284 (local and TDD)

National Technology Center American Foundation for the Blind
15 West 16th Street
New York, NY 10011
(212) 620-2077

Outdoor Adventure: Wilderness Inquiry
1313 Fifth Street, SE
Box 84
Minneapolis, MN 55414-1546
(612) 379-3858

RESNA (Association for the Advancement of Rehabilitation Technology)
1700 N. Moore St., Suite 1540
Arlington, VA 22209-1903
(703) 524-6686

Travel: Mobility International USA
c/o Mark Hansen
P.O. Box 3551
Eugene, OR 97403
(503) 343-1284

Quad Rugby: U.S. Quad Rugby Association
2418 West Fallcreek Court
Grand Forks, ND 58201
(701) 772-1961

Racquetball: U.S. Wheelchair Racquet Sports Association
1941 Viento Verano Drive
Diamond Bar, CA 91765
(714) 574-1150

Recreation Information Management: U.S. Department of Agriculture, Forest Service
201 14th Street, SW
Washington, DC 20250
(202) 382-9402

Sailing: National Ocean Access Project
Sailing Programs for People with Disabilities
451 Hungerford Drive, Suite 100
Rockville, MD 20850
(301) 217-9843

**Snow Skiing: National Handicapped
  Sports Association**
451 Hungerford Drive, Suite 100
Rockville, MD 20850
800-966-4NHS   (301) 217-0960

Special Olympics, Inc.
1325 G St.
Suite 500
Washington, DC 20005
(202) 628-3630

Special Recreation, Inc.
International Center on Special Recreation
362 Koser Avenue
Iowa City, IA 52246-3038
(319) 337-7578

**Tennis: National Foundation of
  Wheelchair Tennis**
941 Calle Amanecer, Suite B
San Clemente, CA 92672
(714) 361-6811

**U.S. Architectural and Transportation
  Barriers Compliance Board**
1111 18th Street, NW, Suite 501
Washington, DC 20036-3894
800-USA-ABLE (voice/TDD)

**Waterskiing: American Waterski
  Association**
Disabled Ski Committee
681 Bailey Woods Road
Dacula, GA 30211
(404) 995-8528

MAGAZINES/
NEWSLETTERS/CATALOGS

Access to Recreation, Inc.
2509 E. Thousand Oaks
Suite 430
Thousand Oaks, CA 91362
800-634-4351

Disabled Outdoors (quarterly publication)
5223 South Loral Avenue
Chicago, IL 60638
(312) 284-2206 or (708) 366-8526

Disabled Sportsman
33012 Lighthouse Court
San Juan Capistrano, CA 92675
(714) 661-2132

The Exceptional Parent
  (published eight times each year)
Psy-Ed Corporation
1170 Commonwealth Avenue, 3rd Floor
Boston, MA 02134
800-247-8080

**The Journal of Physical Education,
  Recreation & Dance** (published monthly
  American Alliance for Health, Physical
  Education, Recreation and Dance
  (AAHPERD)
1900 Association Drive
Reston, VA 22091
(703) 476-3400

Parks & Recreation (published monthly)
National Recreation and Park Association
  (NRPA)

Recreation . . . Access in the 90's
  (bimonthly newsletter)
National Recreation and Park Association
2775 S. Quincy Street, Suite 300
Arlington, VA 22206-2204

Sports 'N Spokes (bimonthly publication)
Paralyzed Veterans of America
5201 North 19th Avenue, Suite 111
Phoenix, AZ 85015
(602) 246-9426

MANUFACTURERS/
DISTRIBUTORS OF
ADAPTED EQUIPMENT*

Childcraft Education Company
20 Kilmar Road
Edison, NJ 08817
(201) 572-6100

Constructive Playthings
1227 E. 119th Street
Grandview, MO 64030
(815) 761-5900

Crestwood Company
Communication Aids for Children & Adults
6625 N. Sidney Place
Milwaukee, WI 53209-3259
(414) 352-5678

*Readers are encouraged to purchase the *Assistive Technology Sourcebook* (Enders & Hall, 1990) for a comprehensive listing of organizations, manufacturers, and publications.

**Developmental Learning Materials
and Teaching Resources**
P.O. Box 2000
Allen, TX 75002
(214) 727-3346

Discovery Toys
619 Atlantic Hill Drive
Eagan, MN 55123
(612) 454-7326

Fitness Trend/Fitness Systems
P.O. Box 266
Independence, MO 64051
800-821-3126

Flaghouse, Inc.
150 N. Macquesten Parkway
Mt. Vernon, NY 10550
(914) 699-1900

Fred Sammons, Inc.
Box 32
Brookfield, IL 60513
800-323-5547

J.A. Preston Corporation
60 Page Road
Clifton, NJ 07012
800-631-7277

Salco Toys
RR 1, Box 59
Nerstrand, MN 55053
(507) 645-8720

Sammons Pediatric Catalog
145 Tower Drive
Burr Ridge, IL 60521
800-323-5547

**Simplified Technology for the Severely
Handicapped**
Linda J. Burkhart
8503 Rhode Island Avenue
College Park, MD 20740
(301) 345-9152

Skill Development Equipment Co.
P.O. Box 6300
Anaheim, CA 92807
(714) 524-8750

Sportime
2905 E. Amwiler Road
Atlanta, GA 30360
800-241-9884

Theraplay Products
PCA Industries, Inc.
2924 40th Avenue
Long Island City, NY 11101
(718) 784-7070

Toys for Special Children
385 Warburton Avenue
Hastings-on-Hudson, NY 10706
800-832-8697

III

ASSISTIVE TECHNOLOGY ISSUES

10

Assistive Technology Training_____

Michael M. Behrmann

Federal policy and legislation that began in the early 1980s has contributed to the growth of assistive technology use for individuals with disabilities in their living, learning, vocational, and recreational environments. Service providers and individuals with interests and skills in assistive technology have emerged from professions associated with engineering, medicine, rehabilitation, and education. Prior to federal mandates to provide assistive technology services, creative professionals provided some assistive technology for consumers, often in the area of identifying and providing low-technology solutions to barriers. Assistive technology solutions included examples such as audiotaped instructions for nonreaders or homemade switches for gaining access to battery-operated devices. Currently, however, many companies are developing and marketing devices as technology becomes more powerful, cheaper, and smaller and as the market increases as a result of federal legislation such as the Americans with Disabilities Act (ADA) of 1990 (PL 101-336), the Individuals with Disabilities Education Act (IDEA) of 1990 (PL 101-476), the Individuals with Disabilities Education Act Amendments of 1991 (PL 102-119), and the Technology-Related Assistance for Individuals with Disabilities Act of 1988 (PL 100-407) and its 1994 amendments (PL 103-218).

Not only are new devices being developed, but also devices that can be used by persons with disabilities are being built into systems. For example, voice activation of a computer program is now possible using a Macintosh computer that has voice recognition built into the system. High-tech developments combined with other technologies, such as those that incorporate sensor devices, will enable the relatively inexpensive implementation of "smart environments," where lights go on when a person enters a room or the television and stereo can be operated by voice or switch commands. Even young children can use an eye-blink switch or a puff switch to activate a toy or gain access to an instructional computer software program. Highly sensitive pressure switches that require only a minimal amount of movement or even only a touch are also now on the market (Wilds, 1989).

There are many critical elements related to the actual use of assistive technology by persons with disabilities. These include: 1) developing new and useful assistive technology devices; 2) identifying available devices; 3) getting funding for purchasing or renting devices; 4) evaluating needs in order to obtain appropriate devices; 5) effectively learning to use the devices; and 6) repairing, maintaining, and upgrading the devices as needs change. There are numerous ways to address these elements, or barriers to success, including information and referral, assessment centers, demonstration sites, policy development, and implementation. However, there is one area—training—that is common to all of these elements.

REASONS FOR ASSISTIVE TECHNOLOGY TRAINING

Since 1983, policies to encourage assistive and instructional technology use have been addressed at the federal level. The capability of and need for technology have become apparent to policy makers at the federal level and they have created impetus for using assistive technology in serving individuals with disabilities throughout their lives. Chapter 1 is a review of the federal legislative history related to assistive technology. This chapter illustrates the significance that the federal government has placed on assistive technology and highlights the importance of training to achieve legislative goals.

Switzer Memorial Seminar

In May 1989, the Switzer Memorial Seminar focused on issues surrounding technology and employment. Future implications cited during the seminar included the following:

1. Enhancement of assistive technology service delivery
2. A policy of technology-related program development
3. Technology training for professional staff and the general public
4. Needed research in technology-related areas
5. A progressive course of technology-related legislation

Although assistive technology needs transcend both age and service delivery systems, there still exists different service delivery systems for children and adults. Since rehabilitation was the principal focus, the Switzer scholars primarily addressed the needs of adolescent and adult populations.

State Forum—Delivery of Technology-Related Assistance

Similarly, in a seminar related to assistive technology in education, the Center for Special Education Technology at the Council for Exceptional Children (CEC) held the *State Forum: Delivery of Technology-Related Assistance To Meet Student Needs*. Participants identified and discussed 11 questions that need to be addressed in technology training or technical assistance:

1. Who needs technology training or technical assistance?
2. How can technology training or technical assistance needs be determined?
3. What levels of technology training or technical assistance are needed?
4. What content should the technology training or technical assistance include?
5. How can technology training or technical assistance be delivered?
6. Who provides the technology training or technical assistance?
7. How can barriers to technology training be overcome?
8. What have been successful models for providing technology training or technical assistance?
9. How can technology training events be funded?
10. How can technology training be encouraged at the graduate level, and what responsibilities do universities and colleges have related to training programs and technology?
11. Should competencies be mandated by state government? (CEC, 1989)

Although neither the Switzer Memorial Seminar nor the State Forum provided answers for all of these questions, they did identify that teachers, related service personnel, consumers, and parents need training that includes awareness, preservice, and continuing education. They noted that training needs to be done by individuals with substantial technology expertise and that in-service training should be done at the school level when possible. Other delivery mechanisms included conferences, regional training, and individualized assistance. Finally, they stressed that training should be continuous and consistent, with appropriate follow up and support.

FACTORS THAT INFLUENCE TRAINING

The concept of training persons in the area of assistive technology seems to be a relatively simple and straightforward goal to accomplish; unfortunately, it is not. There are a wide array of factors that inhibit the efficient delivery of training in assistive technology. These factors include persons who need to be trained; how, when, and where training should occur; and the knowledge and skills that are needed in assistive technology.

Persons Who Need To Be Trained

It is apparent from federal legislation, as well as from subsequent state and local policy implementation, that assistive technology must be provided to all persons with disabilities, regardless of age or disability, as long as it is either "appropriate" under IDEA or "reasonable" under ADA. It is also apparent from this legislative history that Congress is intent on ensuring that assistive technology training be provided to a vast array of individuals.

Training is needed for consumers (both children and adults) with disabilities and their families on how to identify, acquire, and use appropriate assistive technology in various environments. Service providers for adults and children with disabilities (rehabilitation coun selors and engineers, teachers in regular and special education, administrators in schools and agencies, employers, physicians, and occupational, physical, and speech-language therapists) must be provided with differing levels of training depending on their roles and functions as they relate to individuals with disabilities. Their training may range from simple awareness of assistive technology and/or means to gain access to information on assistive technology devices and services to issues of policy development and implementation, funding, screening and evaluation for assistive technology, training in the use of devices, maintenance and repair, and/or approaches to training consumers to effectively utilize assistive technology.

In summary, there are few, if any, individuals who work or interact with individuals with disabilities, whether in schools, at work, in the community, or in other agencies, who do not need at least some training. Potentially, this includes millions of Americans who need to know about and understand assistive technology. Also, many of these individuals, including service providers, employers, and even families, will need more advanced training, particularly when they are confronted with the assistive technology needs of an individual user with whom they must interact and provide services.

How, When, and Where Training Should Occur

With regard to provision of training, there are two general groups of individuals who have substantially different training needs. The first group includes individuals who need to be aware of, provide access to, or use assistive technology devices. This includes technology users and their families, as well as employers and employees working in businesses, who must provide accommodations for individuals with disabilities. The second group is service providers who are required to incorporate assistive technology at various levels in their jobs working with individuals with disabilities.

Consumer, Family, Employer/Employee Training

The primary focus of training for consumers, families, employers, and employees is on awareness, attitude training, and training on specific implementation of assistive technology devices that they encounter in their interactions with individuals who have disabilities. They do not need the theoretical and program implementation training that many service providers request. Rather they want general training in awareness and information access and focused training and support in the use of specific assistive technology devices.

Awareness Training

Consumers, families, employers, and employees want to understand what assistive technology is and how it can have positive effects on persons with disabilities and the persons with whom they work and live. These individuals want to be shown how assistive technology can be effectively used and how to gain access to resources that will help them obtain information on assistive technology devices and services. Since those who need this type of training may be many, and difficult to identify, approaches to this type of training need to be easily accessible, simple, and widely disseminated.

One effective means of providing this type of awareness training includes the use of public service announcements in the mass media. For example, the radio and television spots developed by the National Cristina Foundation, a nonprofit organization dedicated to recycling obsolete technology from businesses to consumers with disabilities, have reached many diverse audiences. By providing basic information and encouraging individuals to seek further information, the foundation has been able to recycle thousands of old computers to organizations serving persons with disabilities.

Human interest stories presented in video documentaries or by the print media provide access to similar audiences. These stories allow for more in-depth information on the impact that assistive technology has on the lives of individuals and provide access to more resources for assistance. Information and referral (I&R) systems, often supported by computerized databases that can be accessed electronically or by voice, can provide assistance for getting information on assistive technology services or technical specifications and for ordering information on assistive technology devices. Demonstrations by vendors or service providers at seminars, conferences, or technology fairs that are open to the public offer individuals the opportunity to see different devices demonstrated. Such demonstrations also give individuals the opportunity to gain hands-on experience and judge the effectiveness of different assistive technology devices.

Technical Assistance and Consultation

One reason that technology innovations have failed in the past is because of the critical shortage of access to the expertise that will help individuals receive technology-related training (Carlson & Silverman, 1986). Consumers, families, employers, employees, and service providers who are faced with a particular assistive technology device or who are in need of a particular assistive technology–related service, such as assessment, often need the support of a rehabilitation engineer, occupational or physical therapist, or other knowledgeable individual. The process of implementing technology-based interventions requires the intelligent integration of technology into existing activities (Gerber, 1986), whether they be in the school, workplace, or home. Such implementation requires a collaborative effort among all persons who implement assistive technology solutions for individuals with disabilities. Educational, vocational, and living environments must fulfill the needs of the individual, while also complementing other activities involved in scholastic, occupational, and recreational endeavors.

This requires time and expertise in assistive technology applications, which are not readily available from service providers, places of employment, most residences, rehabilitation agencies, or school systems.

Although the potential of assistive technology to improve the lives of many persons with disabilities is enormous, technology alone is not the panacea it may seem to be. Batavia, Dillard, and Phillips (1990) support the belief that there is a common pattern of adoption and abandonment of assistive devices due to a lack of proper training in their uses. The system of selecting assistive devices that is currently in place in schools and other settings is leading to abandonment of expensive technologies. This has been recognized and documented by Batavia et al. (1990) as follows:

- The individual is provided an assistive technology device through a clinically aided selection process.
- The individual uses the device.
- The teacher, service provider, and individual with a disability recognize that the device is inadequate to meet their needs even after modifications.
- The individual either continues to use the device, or he or she abandons it.
- The service provider helps the individual to select another device, yet the device is again abandoned with dissatisfaction.

This pattern is often repeated several times before the appropriate device is prescribed or located. The Rehabilitation Engineering Center of the National Rehabilitation Hospital in Washington, D.C., recognized this problem in a study entitled *The National Survey on the Abandonment of Technology,* which explained the existence of a severe problem within the current system (Philips, no date). There is a strong need for service providers (clinical experts) to be familiar with the available technology and for them to be well trained in the uses, adaptations, and practices of technology for persons with disabilities. Service delivery personnel need ongoing systematic training in all available assistive technology devices, as well as hands-on experience in prescribing technologies to persons with various types of disabilities.

Technical assistance and consultation is one area of training that bridges the needs of service providers, consumers, families, employers, and employees. All these people need assistance from technology specialists with expertise in assistive technology, consultation, and staff development. These specialists can provide the in-service training needed to reduce the amount of personal and/or professional time to make appropriate assistive technology into a reality for individuals.

Service Provider Training

The 1989 Switzer Memorial Seminar on technology and employment suggested that service providers need awareness and technical assistance training, as well as additional forms of training. The recommendations included the following:

1. Develop formal (e.g., degree- or certification-based) and informal (e.g., technical assistance, conferences, in-service workshops) training programs.
2. Provide programs to train both new and currently working professionals.
3. Train technology specialists for localized, on-site problem solving.
4. Expand training to include vocational, daily living, recreation, and other practical areas.

With these recommendations in mind, determining how, when, and where training needs can be addressed depends on two factors—the level of training required and the current role of the individual service provider being trained. The level of training required ranges from basic awareness to expert training. Training is most often delivered through in-service and preservice training of service providers.

In-Service Training

Service providers of the future need to learn how to make appropriate modifications of using both high and low technology to enable their students to communicate, learn, work, and play—to make the impossible possible (Young, 1988). In the short term, the majority of services provided to consumers with disabilities will be provided by the service providers already employed in their respective fields. The vast majority of these individuals will have limited, if any, training and experience with assistive technology. Professionals providing direct services to consumers with disabilities must have expertise in a wide range of content areas, with only one of those areas being assistive technology. A report by the Office of Technology Assessment (OTA) (U.S. Congress, OTA, 1988) indicated that technology can indeed have a powerful impact on consumer outcomes if personnel have the training and skills to use the technology, education that provides vision and understanding of developing technology, support for experimentation and innovation, and time for learning and practice. Investments in technology acquisition cannot be fully effective unless professionals receive appropriate training and support.

Therefore, resources and training must be developed to address these issues. Conferences, workshops, and in-service courses directed toward technology applications can help to do this. In addition, recertification standards for maintaining employment can provide a stimulus for the current workforce to develop and maintain adequate technology-related skills.

Another method that is perhaps more viable is the implementation of regional technical assistance centers, which will have staff who can assist professionals in developing skills that are directly related to the needs of consumers. By providing technology assistance, the skill level of the professional is increased in areas that are directly associated with need. The consumer thus receives immediate technology-related assistance from a skilled professional. However, in order to be effective, the technology assistance must be easily obtainable and cost must not be a factor, either in obtaining the training or receiving the services (Behrmann, 1989).

As Ruff (1985) and Hlebowitsch (1988) caution, if the use of technology is to succeed where earlier technological innovations have failed, the service provider must be actively involved in implementation. This viewpoint is consistent with the literature on adoption of innovation and the promotion of change (Joyce & Showers, 1982). Evidence on adult learning, adoption of innovation, and implementation of new skills underscores the importance of in-service training, technical assistance, and consultation provided to direct service providers in the setting in which the innovation is to occur (Friend & Cook, 1988; Joyce & Showers, 1982). The knowledge base in this area highlights the importance for personnel to receive training that will promote their abilities to provide various kinds of technical assistance and consultation as well as state-of-the-art training.

Preservice Training

Studies indicating the need for teacher training in technology are summarized in a report by OTA (U.S. Congress, OTA, 1988). OTA reports that less than one half of all the in-service teachers in the United States have used a computer and less than one third of these teachers see themselves as qualified to teach with computers. In addition, only 18 states and the District of Columbia require (7 states recommend) that education majors either take a computer course or demonstrate the ability to use computers for instruction. The report emphasizes that technology can indeed have a powerful impact on educational outcomes if personnel have the necessary training.

However, training needs are not unique to the education of persons with disabilities. There is also an increasing need to develop appropriate methods to train other professionals who will serve consumers with disabilities. An Omnibus Survey (Shewan, 1989) conducted by the American Speech-Language-Hearing Association of current members showed that assistive technology was one of the top priorities for continuing education training for speech pathologists and related service personnel. There are also 77 accredited programs in the United States that train rehabilitation counselors. Few, if any, of these programs provide specialized technology-related training. Most rehabilitation technology-related services come from rehabilitation engineers, and currently there are only four degree-granting programs in the United States—the University of Virginia, Louisiana Tech, Sacramento State, and the University of Illinois (Behrmann, 1989).

In a national survey of teacher preparation programs in special education, the need for technology training was confirmed by 92% of the respondents (Kinney & Blackhurst, 1987). According to the CEC's Teacher Education Division, Project RETOOL (1990), there were seven undergraduate, eight master's, three doctoral, two specialist, and one postdoctoral special education technology degree program(s) offered in the nation's approximately 700 special education personnel preparation programs.

Perhaps the most important consideration in addressing preservice-based technology-related training is the need to utilize the training systems that are already in place. That is, we need to focus efforts on training programs that currently exist in colleges and universities, "infusing" the use of technology-related assistance into the programs that train the majority of personnel who provide direct consumer services (Behrmann, 1989).

Unfortunately, educators in institutions of higher education that train service providers often do not have the expertise or resources for appropriate technology training. In order to achieve the appropriate level of training, it may be necessary to incorporate technology training requirements through state and national organizations that set the standards for professional training. For example, the CEC (1994) has published a set of standards for new teachers that includes instructional and assistive technology competencies. Professional standards must also be set for technology-related training, using organizations such as the Council for Rehabilitation Education and the National Council for Accreditation of Teacher Education. If these organizations mandate this training, then it will be necessary for colleges and universities to either retrain existing faculty or hire persons with expertise in assistive technology (Behrmann, 1989).

Another consideration that also needs to be addressed in preservice training is that assistive technology is only one area of skills and knowledge needed by professional service providers. There is, therefore, the need for trained "technology specialists." These are the individuals whose responsibilities are to know the general field of rehabilitation and special education, but who have specialized knowledge and training in technology-related assistance. These persons have a variety of backgrounds (e.g., rehabilitation counselor, rehabilitation engineer, occupational therapist, special education teacher), but are also trained in the application of technology to meet the needs of individuals with disabilities. They are responsible for keeping up with new technologies and methods, providing technical assistance to other professionals and consumers, disseminating information, and developing new approaches to more efficiently use emerging technologies. Many, if not all, of these professionals are "crossovers," in that they have personally assumed the task of training themselves in assistive technology to better serve their respective consumer populations. Yet formal training programs need to be established to continue to train individuals who will provide these services (Behrmann, 1989).

Knowledge and Skills that Are Needed in Assistive Technology

Recently, the Center for Human disAbilities at George Mason University conducted a survey of Virginia schools to determine the assistive technology training needs within the state (Behrmann, Morrissette, & McCallen, 1992). Results of the survey indicated that 84.3% of the school districts believed that it is important to have trained personnel who can identify assistive technology needs. Reflecting the diversity of professionals in assistive technology roles, the responding school systems also indicated that assistive technology services are currently being delivered by special educators, occupational and physical therapists, and speech clinicians. The survey respondents identified the following assistive technology personnel responsibilities as important: assessing and evaluating students for assistive technology devices and services; determining student eligibility for assistive technology services and devices; conducting in-service training on assistive technology; delivering assistive technology to students; and writing assistive technology goals on individualized education programs (IEPs).

This section addresses the major areas of training still needed in assistive technology. It is beyond the scope of this chapter, however, to address training at the level of a comprehensive, systematic competency-based system. First, domains of needed training are addressed as they relate to the general training needs of consumers, families, employers, employees, and service providers currently working in various human services fields. Second, domains of training for assistive technology experts, generally in degree or certificate programs, are addressed.

General Training in Assistive Technology

General training should include four major areas of instruction: awareness, information access, legal requirements, and funding. *Awareness* of assistive technology should generally incorporate opportunities to see individuals using assistive technology as well as hands-on experience with various devices to overcome fears and inhibitions toward using technology. Generally, it is appropriate to begin with low-tech devices, since they apply common sense to problem solving. Examples of low-tech solutions include placing blocks under table legs so a wheelchair can gain access to a workspace or building up a button on a phone so that an individual with a motor impairment can answer the phone. Such low-tech devices illustrate the relatively low costs of assistive technology and the ability to address barriers in a cost-efficient manner. This is often important for the training of managers with limited budgets or cost-conscious consumers not able or willing to make major investments. The relatively low cost of assistive technology is substantiated by research on costs of assistive technology in jobsites by the Job Accommodation Network (JAN). JAN reported that the majority of assistive technology devices are not unreasonably expensive; that is, 69% of devices or accommodations cost less than $500 and 50% cost less than $50.

Hands-on experience with high-tech solutions is also desirable, since many nontechnical persons are fearful of computers or microprocessor-based devices. A variety of devices, including stand-alone devices such as augmentative communication devices or computer-based assistive technology, should be explored. With stand-alone devices, it is often appropriate to demonstrate similar devices that reflect simple to complex capacity and user interfaces. This will enable trainees to get a better conception of the range and complexity of assistive technology devices. With computer-based systems, it is useful to introduce trainees to more powerful systems that have user-friendly interfaces, such as those found on a Macintosh or Windows-based computer. Again, demonstrations can range from simple access features built into operating systems, such as text enlargement for persons with visual impairments, to relatively complex assistive technology, such as screen readers that can identify graphic images and text boxes as well as translate and read text. It is also appropriate to provide an opportunity to demonstrate both stand-alone and computer-based assistive technologies that address needs of persons with a variety of disabilities. It is particularly important to demonstrate ways that assistive technology can address cognitive and perceptual impairments such as those of persons identified as having learning disabilities or mental retardation. Most people, when describing assistive technology, relate only to visible, physical, or sensory impairments and to not understand that instructional technology also falls under the category of assistive technology.

Access to information on assistive technology devices and services is another area in which general training is needed. In particular, regional training is important in order to find agencies and organizations that can assist in providing services or access to assistive technology. Although information and referral databases on assistive technology are available (e.g., Abledata, HyperAbledata, Assistive Device Locator System [ADLS]), regional information is critical in obtaining timely assistance. A number of systems funded under the Technology-Related Assistance for Individuals with Disabilities Act of 1988 (PL 100-407, or Tech Act) and its amendments (the Technology-Related Assistance for Individuals with Disabilities Amendments of 1994; PL 103-218) have expanded these databases to include regional information. For example, the Virginia Assistive Technology System (VATS) I&R database has expanded on Abledata's national database of more than 17,000 assistive technology, making statewide and regional information accessible electronically. HyperAbledata, a multimedia data base of assistive technology devices available from the Trace Center in Madison, Wisconsin, has the ability to add regional information to its large and user-friendly database on assistive technology.

Legal requirements and procedures mandated by federal legislation, such as ADA and IDEA, need to be addressed as well. In Virginia, inclusion of assistive technology in children's IEPs is not common (Behrmann et al., 1992) and has resulted in recommendations to the state Board of Education to develop guidelines and models of assistive technology goals and objectives for IEPs. More than 90% of the schools indicated that less than 10% of their students have assistive technology IEP goals and objectives. Perhaps systems are wary of adding expense when writing assistive technology services and devices into IEPs. It should be noted, however, that although the courts have set precedents that lack of funding cannot be used as a reason for not providing services (*Mills v. Board of Education of District of Columbia*, 1972), they have also stated that the law does not require an "ideal" education (*Rowley v. Board of Education*, 1982). Similarly, the requirements of ADA, which call for reasonable accommodation in employment and businesses having public access, need to be addressed in this type of training. Finally, issues concerning protection and advocacy for individuals with disabilities as they relate to assistive technology need to be addressed. Both ADA and IDEA contain due process procedures that guarantee the rights of individuals to services.

Funding is the final area that must be generally addressed. There are many sources of funding for assistive technology, including federal grants and entitlement, state education funds, other state agency funds, local education funds, private insurers, and private sector and foundation grants. However, if coordinated plans for funding are not established at the state level, then other funding sources (including other state agencies) may withdraw funds currently available for assistive technology as they realize that schools may have to purchase devices and services under IDEA, much as they had to with the implementation of the Education for All Handicapped Children Act of 1975 (PL 94-142). VATS has recently convened representatives from 10 state agencies, including the Virginia Department of Education, to develop a statewide policy on assistive technology. The recommendations suggest that bureaucratic and fiscal barriers be minimized; interagency collaboration and sharing of fiscal responsibility be promoted; and public and private partnerships be developed to improve access to and funding for assistive technology. For funding individual devices, there are also published documents such as "Funding Resources for Assistive Devices in Virginia" (RehabTech Associates, 1992), which describe the funding system and the obstacles that must be overcome to fund assistive technology devices. RehabTech Associates (1992) notes that, in addition to money being tight, funding systems are not set up to pay for assistive technology. Third-party sources are suspicious of expensive equipment requests, and generally people do not know how to apply for funding. RehabTech Associates (1992) also states that there are serious problems with incorrect prescriptions, professionals who do not know how to train the individual to use the device, or devices abandoned because they were too cumbersome or too complex to use. Most of these issues can be addressed through training and assignment of competent personnel to provide assistive technology services.

Technical Training for Specialists

Specialist training is important for service providers who want to develop particular expertise within their profession or who want to "cross over" and obtain general training in assistive technology. An example of specialist training within a profession would be a speech-language therapist who develops expertise in augmentative communication. This same professional could also become more broadly trained in various aspects of assistive technology including mobility, job accommodation, instructional technology, and so on. One major distinction in these two types of training, however, is in the area of assessment and evaluation. Although general specialists are involved in screening and recommending various assistive technology applications, they rarely become involved in the in-depth evaluations that are closely associated with particular professions, unless they are working on a collaborative team. Areas in which specialist training is important are screening and evaluation, consultation and collaboration, and technical skill development and troubleshooting.

Screening and evaluation for assistive technology is an area in which more trained specialists are needed. Few professional training programs have faculty who are skilled in the use of assistive technology and even fewer are able to provide in-depth training in assistive technology evaluation. Recent research (Behrmann & Schepis, 1994) suggests that a video-based screening approach to assistive technology identification may result in more timely and less costly access to appropriate technology than is available through extensive interdisciplinary evaluations done via a medical model. The video-based screening model of assistive technology assessment offers options for training that include little difficulty in observing behaviors in natural environments. This model also reduces scheduling difficulties, allows qualified professionals to view material at their leisure and to meet for short periods of time to discuss findings rather than spend extensive time testing, and allows for developing a library of training tapes for future use in training. Assuming that the team refers specific in-depth evaluations to appropriate professionals, such a model may enable states to develop adequate screening facilities to meet consumer needs for identification of assistive technology devices.

Consultation and collaboration is another area in which specialized training is appropriate. As U.S. society moves toward inclusion of persons with disabilities into schools, communities, and workplaces, there will be much demand to provide assistance to individuals and groups of persons who are actively trying to provide reasonable accommodations. Expert consultation will often be required to evaluate needs and then to provide specific approaches to training consumers to effectively utilize individual assistive technology devices. In addition, collaborative efforts will be necessary to assist agencies and organizations in policy development and implementation to ensure that persons with disabilities are not discriminated against. Here, specific training in conflict resolution and mediation may assist these specialists in effectively working with consumers.

Technical training and troubleshooting is the final general area of training necessary for specialists. In the early 1980s, it was possible for a person specializing in assistive technology to be familiar with nearly every high- and low-tech device on the market. In fact, many specialists were able to construct their own custom devices using supplies from hardware and electronics stores. However, as reflected in the thousands of devices held in national assistive technology databases, this is no longer possible to do. Therefore, technical training must be broader in scope. With high-tech devices such as computers, training must be conducted across different computer platforms (e.g., Macintosh, IBM). Training in the various parameters that software and hardware peripherals may require is also necessary. Although it is not possible to train repair technicians (even though knowledge of how to find and communicate with these technicians is helpful), it is important to provide basic troubleshooting skills for both devices and computers. Overcoming fears of technology and implementing systematic problem-solving approaches is one area in which specialist training is necessary. Furthermore, this training should provide as much hands-on experience as possible with the intent of investigating and becoming familiar with many of the assistive technology devices that will meet the needs of persons with various disabilities.

CONCLUSION

The issues surrounding training in the field of assistive technology are complex. First, the field is new and there are few professional preservice training standards for personnel needing to provide assistive technology services. Second, training needs to be provided across many professions—special education, speech therapy, occupational and physical therapy, rehabilitation counseling, and rehabilitation engineering, among others. Thus, many professions need to establish minimal standards of training. Additionally, since there are so few training programs capable of providing that training and because of the resistance of states to require training, this is not likely to occur soon. Third, and possibly most important, there is relatively little in-service training for personnel already working across many professions nor is there adequate training for consumers.

Training in assistive technology needs to be conducted across many fronts simultaneously. This includes awareness training for all consumers, families, and their service providers. Second, consultation and technical assistance must support working professionals and their clients by assisting in evaluation, identification of devices, training in specific assistive technology applications, and follow-up and maintenance until preservice training programs produce graduates qualified to provide these services generally as part of their professional preparation. Finally, the field needs to continue to train leadership personnel and specialists in assistive technology who can assume the roles of supervision, research and development, consultation, technical assistance, and personnel training to move this field effectively into the 21st century.

REFERENCES

Americans with Disabilities Act of 1990 (ADA), PL 101-336. (July 26, 1990). Title 42, U.S.C. 12101 et seq: *U.S. Statutes at Large, 104,* 327–378.

Batavia, A.I., Dillard, D., & Phillips, B. (1990). How to avoid technology abandonment. In H.J. Murphy (Ed.), *Proceedings of the Fifth Annual Conference "Technology and Persons with Disabilities."* Northridge: California State University, Northridge.

Behrmann, M.M. (1989). *Technology and employment: The need for trained professional personnel* (Switzer monograph, 13th ed.). Alexandria, VA: National Rehabilitation Association.

Behrmann, M.M., Morrissette, S.K., & McCallen, M.H. (1992). *Assistive technology issues for Virginia schools.* Technical report submitted to the Virginia State Special Education Advisory Committee. Fairfax, VA: George Mason University.

Behrmann, M.M., & Schepis, M. (1994). Assistive technology assessment: A multiple case study review of three approaches with students with physical disabilities during the transition from school to work. *Journal of Vocational Rehabilitation, 4*(3), 202–210.

Carlson, S.A., & Silverman, R. (1986). Microcomputers and computer assisted instruction in special classrooms: Do we need the teacher? *Learning Disability Quarterly, 9,* 105–110.

Council for Exceptional Children (CEC). (1989, April). *State forum: Delivery of technology-related asssistance to meet student needs.* Reston, VA: Author.

Council for Exceptional Children (CEC). Project RETOOL. (1990). *Special education technology in the higher education curriculum.* Reston, VA: Author.

Council for Exceptional Children (CEC). (1994). *CEC standards for professional practice in special education.* Reston, VA: Author.

Education for All Handicapped Children Act of 1975, PL 94-142. (August 23, 1977). Title 20, U.S.C. 1401 et seq: *U.S. Statutes at Large, 89,* 773–796.

Friend, M., & Cook, L. (1988). Pragmatic issues in school consultant training. In F. West (Ed.), *School consultation: Interdisciplinary perspectives on theory, research, training, and practice* (pp. 130–152). Austin: The University of Texas.

Gerber, M.M. (1986). Teaching with microcomputers. *Academic Therapy, 22*(2), 117–123.

Hlebowitsch, P. (1988). Technology in the classroom. *The Clearinghouse, 62,* 53–56.

Individuals with Disabilities Education Act of 1990 (IDEA), PL 101-476. (October 30, 1990). Title 20, U.S.C. 1400 et seq: *U.S. Statutes at Large, 104,* 1103–1151.

Individuals with Disabilities Education Act Amendments of 1991, PL 102-119. (October 7, 1991). Title 20, U.S.C. 1400 et seq; *U.S. Statutes at Large, 105,* 587–608.

Joyce, B., & Showers, B. (1982, October). The coaching of teaching. *Educational Leadership, 37,* pp. 4–8.

Kinney, P., & Blackhurst, A.E. (1987). Technology competencies for teachers of young children with severe handicaps. *Topics in Early Childhood Special Education, 7*(3), 105–115.

Mills v. Board of Education of District of Columbia, 348 F.Supp. 866 D.D.C. (1972).

Philips, B. (no date). *The national survey on the abandonment of technology.* Washington, DC: Rehabilitation Engineering Center, National Rehabilitation Hospital.

RehabTech Associates. (1992). *Virginia assistive technology system: Funding resources for assistive devices in Virginia.* Ellicott City, MD: Author.

Rowley v. Board of Education, 458 U.S. 176 (1982).

Ruff, T. (1985). High technology and education. *The Clearinghouse, 58,* 197–198.

Shewan, C.M. (1989). Quality is not a 4 letter word. . . . *Journal of the American Speech-Language-Hearing Association, 31,* 51–55.

Technology-Related Assistance for Individuals with Disabilities Act of 1988, PL 100-407. (August 18, 1988). Title 29, U.S.C. 2201 et seq: *U.S. Statutes at Large, 102,* 1044–1065.

Technology-Related Assistance for Individuals with Disabilities Amendments of 1994, PL 103-218. (March 9, 1994). Title 29, U.S.C. 2201 et seq: *U.S. Statutes at Large, 108,* 50–97.

U.S. Congress, Office of Technology Assessment (OTA). (1988). *Power on! New tools for teaching and learning* (OTA-SET-379). Washington, DC: U.S. Government Printing Office.

Wilds, M. (1989). Effective use of technology with young children. *NICHY News Digest,* 6–7.

Young, E.B. (1988). One university's role in supporting special needs locally. *Electronic Learning, 8*(3), 10–12.

11

Staff Development for Assistive Technology Personnel_____

Katherine J. Inge
Karen F. Flippo
J. Michael Barcus

This chapter focuses on the "nuts and bolts" of designing a personnel preparation program. The educational method proposed is intended for individuals with a personal or professional interest in assistive technology. The method is not meant to create a new type of rehabilitation professional, but rather to provide a greater awareness of the uses and benefits of assistive technology. This approach is for participant-driven training that applies adult learning principles of active trainee involvement. The recommendations presented in this chapter are appropriate for in-service staff development programs and continuing education, such as seminars, workshops, and community college sessions. The process includes conducting needs assessments, identifying training objectives, designing training programs based on participant and agency needs, and ongoing evaluation.

ADULT LEARNING PRINCIPLES

The effective educator realizes that adults learn differently than children and that they approach new learning situations with unique knowledge and experiences (Scherer, 1984). Therefore, adults cannot be viewed as recipients of knowledge but instead must be allowed to participate and bring their various skills and competencies to the educational sessions. If adults are perceived as having valuable experiences to share and are treated as partners with the educator, they are more likely to be comfortable in the learning environment and benefit from the experience. This participant-driven process includes conducting needs assessments, identifying training objectives, designing training programs based on participant and agency needs, and performing ongoing evaluations (see Table 11.1).

ASSISTIVE TECHNOLOGY IN-SERVICE PROGRAMS

How can these principles be translated into assistive technology in-service programs? First, it is important to remember that the goal of staff training in assistive technology is to assist the participant in developing skills that facilitate the independence of individuals with severe disabilities (McDaniel, Flippo, & Lowery, 1986). In fact, the goal of any training program is to

Table 11.1.   Adult learning principles

- Adults come to training sessions with previous knowledge. New ideas should be integrated with what they already know.
- Adults prefer self-directed versus trainer-directed learning. Remember that information will be used only if it is directly applicable to the person's needs. Include the trainees in all phases of the program development.
- Adults can be easily threatened in new situations. Make the learning environment as comfortable and relaxed as possible.
- Adults must have time to practice new skills in practical settings. Balance concept versus behavioral learning.
- Adults can learn much from conversations and experiences with respected peers. Provide time for practicing new skills with trusted professionals.

Adapted from Inge, Barcus, Brooke, & Everson (1991).

provide information and experiences that directly improve the ability of an individual to perform his or her job duties or life functions (Spitzer, 1985).

A participant's personal or professional experience with disabilities can transfer to different situations. For instance, a special education teacher who has worked predominantly with children who have cerebral palsy may have many skills and valuable information that will be useful for assisting individuals with other severe disabilities. This should not be overlooked as unrelated experience. Participants should be encouraged to recognize what they already know as important and to build upon this base.

Multiple opportunities for individuals to practice information delivered in lecture format should be provided. This practice session should include all aspects of assistive technology services and supports; for example, alternate lectures with practice. The first discussion topic with special education teachers may be defining assistive technology. Immediately follow up with hands-on practice using a variety of low-technology assistive devices (e.g., switch-operated appliances, toys, environmental control units). Be realistic about the amount of information covered before practice sessions are inserted. Also, use simulated training with caution, being sure that environments used during staff development closely match those available to the organizations or participants attending the training (Roth, 1987). Technology users who assist in practice sessions should have similar characteristics to the individuals that participants work with or know.

Learning a new way of performing implies that the individual must change familiar habits (Scherer, 1984; Spice & Koppel, 1984; Spitzer, 1985). Many education and rehabilitation programs have individuals with minimal or no assistive technology experience. They may believe that assistive technology only includes complex, highly technical, and difficult-to-operate devices. Funding and gaining access to information resources are unknown to them. Utilization of assistive technology services and supports implies a change in values and technical skills (Renzaglia, 1986). In this instance, it is important to remember that people change as they pursue their own goals (Zemke & Zemke, 1988). Using the adult learning principle of active involvement helps to determine what individuals want from assistive technology staff development and what their objectives are for self-improvement.

CONDUCTING NEEDS ASSESSMENTS

Assessment should focus on what is happening in an organization versus what ought to be happening (McKillip, 1987; Rossett, 1989). On an individual basis, assessment relates to new skills or procedures persons want to learn. In other words, the trainer must know how to implement a successful assistive technology service and what participants are actually doing in practice. During the analysis, questions should be asked that determine how well these individuals can do "it," how important "it" is for doing their job, and how frequently they are called on to do "it" (Rossett, 1989). The trainer's responsibility is to determine what "it" is and design a needs assessment that includes the participants' concerns. Some considerations for answering these questions in assistive technology might include the following:

- What does an assistive technology user, rehabilitation specialist, or special education teacher need to know in order to identify an individual's assistive technology needs?
- Of all the skills and knowledge related to assistive technology that a rehabilitation specialist/special education teacher could learn, which ones are critical to job performance?
- Why aren't more technology users successfully working in the community? Is this a problem that can be solved with staff development?
- How do the participants feel about the training? What do they identify as their skill deficits? Are these skill deficits critical to job performance or life functioning?

STEPS IN A NEEDS ASSESSMENT

Needs assessment cannot be conducted in just one step, such as by sending out a questionnaire or by observing staff (Rossett, 1990). Assessment is usually a combination of information-gathering strategies. For example, a program manager may begin a needs assessment by reviewing the program data collected by rehabilitation counselors in the agency. He or she might then interview the staff to determine each individual's concerns. At that point, it may be appropriate to administer a questionnaire or test to identify training objectives for staff development. Birnbrauer and Tyson (1985) suggest the following steps for conducting a needs assessment.

First, determine the short- and long-term objectives of the needs analysis. Second, identify the population to be studied. Should the needs assessment include the entire agency staff, the administrative personnel, or the front-line direct service personnel? Third, determine and design the strategies to be used for assessment, and conduct the analysis. Finally, analyze the data, identifying problem areas for developing objectives of the staff development program. For a general audience (workshop or community college course students), educators may want to send a questionnaire to those who have registered for a class or telephone them prior to the class to learn their specific needs.

TECHNIQUES FOR NEEDS ASSESSMENTS

Zemke (1985) offers five different strategies for gathering information, including a review of organizational documents, interviews, observations, questionnaires, and tests. These strategies should never be used in isolation, since no one strategy will provide the total picture needed to design a training program (McKillip, 1987; Rossett, 1989; Zemke, 1985). Each of these strategies is discussed as follows.

Organizational Documents

Zemke (1985) describes *organizational documents* as written information that the organization has collected for purposes other than staff development and training. In the case of assistive technology, this could include any of the many documents used in determining service and accommodation needs. Program managers can provide needs information based on reviews of individualized written rehabilitation programs (IWRPs), assessment reports, results, job performance evaluations, job analyses, and job training data. A review of these records could provide insight into the skill level of the staff member, completing the various components of assistive technology-related service. However, it would be important to combine this strategy with other methods such as observation, since some people's skill level may not be evident in organizational paperwork.

Interviews

Interviews can be conducted in a face-to-face format or through telephone contact (McKillip, 1987). They can be done individually or in small-group formats, and they are the most frequently used type of needs assessment (Rossett, 1989). Interviews may be tightly structured or open-ended, based on the situation (Zemke, 1985). An open-ended questionnaire allows the employees to discuss or elaborate on their answers and is particularly useful for generating ideas. Patton (1980) provides some guidelines on designing open-ended questions.

1. Design questions that do not suggest a response. For example, instead of asking, "Do you find the information gathered during adaptive driving assessment helpful?", try posing the question as follows, "What do you think about the adaptive driving analysis?"
2. Avoid using "why" questions. Instead of asking, "Why don't you suggest augmentative/alternative communication systems for the people with whom you work?" ask, "What barriers do you see in your customers using augmentative/communication devices?"
3. Try to ask one question at a time. If a question leads to several answers, probe the person's response by further inquiring "Say more about . . ." or asking "What do you mean by . . . ?"
4. Role-play questions can be helpful in conducting interviews for needs assessments. For instance, pose the following situation: "Suppose a consumer who uses an electric wheelchair wants to drive, but does not have a vehicle or a driver's license . . . what would you do?"

Interviews do require that the interviewer have a good understanding of the information required to complete the questions (McKillip, 1987). The trainer will obtain the best responses if the interview is conducted in a private, comfortable, and nonthreatening setting (Birnbrauer & Tyson, 1985).

Observations

During employee observations, the trainer may be looking for specific behaviors or for work performance in general (Zemke, 1985). For instance, when interviewed a rehabilitation counselor may identify that improving an understanding of available assistive technology financial resources is a primary concern for staff development. A trainer may arrange a time to visit this employee to assess the funding sources currently being used, or a program manager may observe the rehabilitation counselor's general skills, particularly those used during the development of IWRPs.

Questionnaires

Through questionnaires, information can be obtained directly from the individuals involved in the needs assessment. Persons are asked to indicate their perceptions about training needs in their workplace or organization (Zemke, 1985). McKillip (1987) states that a questionnaire can be designed in either a ranking or a ratings format. The ranking format calls for the employee to order his or her needs by importance. The ratings method is said to be the simplest method for the respondent, allowing for input on all of the questionnaire's options. A combination of both methods may be useful as seen in the example in Table 11.2.

Tests

Tests are designed to measure an individual's ability to perform certain tasks or functions (Zemke, 1985). In actuality, tests can measure a person's knowledge on a subject but may or may not assess on-the-job performance. Tests can also be used in pre- and posttest strategies to determine if the training designed from a needs assessment has made a difference in employee knowledge.

PERSONNEL INVOLVED IN NEEDS ASSESSMENT

A needs assessment in assistive technology services should

- Assess the needs of technology users served by the participants.
- Assess the needs of the individuals to receive training.
- Assess the desired outcomes of the decision makers.
- Summarize the needs of the participants and the desired outcomes of the decision makers.
- Define observable and measurable goals for staff development.

Bowman (1987) agrees that an effective needs assessment must coordinate the organization's needs and the employee's perceived needs. If staff are expected to use skills learned on the job and management is expected to be supportive, a broad perspective must be utilized (Bowman, 1987). Inge, Barcus, and Everson (1988) suggest that the first step in the needs assessment process is to identify the value that a participant places on assistive technology and determine whether this value reflects the organization's philosophy. Obviously, these two positions should be in agreement for successful implementation of assistive technology services. Bowman (1987) states that it is good to uncover different opinions because they may indicate the need to improve the correlation between organizational and individual goals. Assessing all individuals involved will help merge conflicting objectives for staff development (Barcus, Everson, & Hall, 1987).

Table 11.2.   Sample needs assessment questions

Rating question	Several of your rehabilitation counselor coworkers have expressed an interest in learning information on the various issues related to home modifications. Please respond to the following topics by indicating if you have no, some, or a great deal of interest in receiving training on that topic.
	A. Factors to be considered during an evaluation B. Low- and high-tech devices to aid independent living C. Role of a rehabilitation engineer D. Information on strategies for financing the purchase of assistive technology devices E. Questions to ask a consumer to determine his or her modification needs and device preference
Ranking question	Look at the list again and pick out the two issues that would be of greatest interest or need to you.

Development of Training Objectives

After the trainer has developed a good understanding of the organizations and the potential participants' needs, specific objectives for training should be established. The targeted participants' needs will determine the most appropriate objectives and, subsequently, the selection of training content, the sequence of the content, and the types of strategies used to deliver the content (Inge et al., 1988). A good training objective should be written in terms that are both understandable and measurable. Inge et al. (1988) suggest that trainers must identify objectives that focus on participants' philosophies, values, technical skills, and knowledge. A well-developed needs assessment should address all three areas to build a comprehensive training program. The objectives should be specific and indicate that the behavior or performance demonstrating the objective has been met.

Kemp (1985) states that most trainers focus on the development of cognitive objectives when designing staff development programs. These objectives are concerned with the amount of knowledge or information a participant gains from the training program. Cognitive functions can be organized into six categories of intellectual activities. These include knowledge, comprehension, application, analysis, synthesis, and evaluation. Table 11.3 lists examples of learning objectives on each of the six levels in the cognitive domain using rehabilitation technology training as the topic.

Often, trainers will focus exclusively on the knowledge level of learning and fail to include more challenging objectives (Kemp, 1985). Often without realizing it, a trainer may continue to provide information-oriented programs on a knowledge level when the participants actually need to advance to higher-level activities, such as analysis, synthesis, and evaluation. A needs assessment may be helpful in determining which cognitive level is appropriate for developing such training objectives.

Designing Staff Training Programs

Once the needs-based objectives have been identified, a method for delivering content must be determined. Strategies will depend on the number of individuals receiving training, the length of the training session, and the number and type of training objectives identified (Inge et al., 1988). In addition, the training session may emphasize values clarification, knowledge, skill development, or a combination of these areas (McDaniel et al., 1986).

Table 11.3. Rehabilitation technology training for rehabilitation counselors

Knowledge	The participant will be able to *list* assistive technology resources available to counselors and technology users in his or her localities.
Comprehension	The participant will be able to *explain* the role of assistive technology in all phases of the rehabilitation process.
Application	The participant will be able to *demonstrate* how assistive technology can be used to modify worksites and expand job opportunities for individuals.
Analysis	The participant will be able to *contrast* the differences among interface devices used to operate a computer.
Synthesis	The participant will be able to *design* a program plan for purchasing appropriate equipment based on the results of an augmentative/alternative evaluation report.
Evaluation	The participant will be able to *evaluate* computer accommodation assessment information and determine if program modifications are indicated.

Adapted from Kemp (1985).

Techniques for Small-Group Training

One important adult learning principle is participatory training. Participatory training is based on the idea that adult learners want to have an active role in determining their training needs and designing the training format and that they want to be actively engaged in the learning process. The use of small groups allows the participants to learn from each other and answer their own questions, rather than constantly relying on the trainer to lecture or provide all of the "expert" information. Typically, the small-group format allows participants to interact in a nonthreatening way and encourages the shy individual, who may otherwise remain silent, to comment (Eitington, 1989).

In assistive technology training programs, small-group training can consist of as few as two or as many as eight participants. However, small-group work should be limited to no more than three to four participants, because many persons may not participate if the group is larger. Various training techniques mentioned in this chapter can be designed for a small-group format. These include solving case study situations (such as determining funding sources for a potential assistive technology user based on information provided in the case study), performing role plays (practicing interviewing a vendor), answering questions, problem-solving scenarios (brainstorming devices and services for a fictitious user), sharing personal experiences, comparing ideas, and so on. Regardless of the number of participants in the small groups, there are several guidelines that may be useful to the staff trainer (see Table 11.4).

Field Experiences

The use of field experiences is clearly one of the most important strategies for assistive technology staff development. Participating in field experiences allows the student to practice skills that will be needed when performing his or her daily job duties. Several issues need to be considered when setting up fieldwork experiences for new participants. First, the sites, technology users, and materials selected should be similar to those served by the program or agency. For instance, designing a simulated kitchen at the agency for assessments rather than using a kitchen in a user's residence would not be advisable. Objectives for the fieldwork should be clearly identified and explained to the participants. Table 11.5 represents some of the issues that should be considered when designing and setting up a fieldwork experience.

Table 11.4.   Guidelines for using small groups

- Frequently change the membership of a small group in order to energize the participants. If the same participants interact throughout a training session, they may become too familiar with each other and fail to complete the assigned tasks.
- Arrange the room to promote small-group work. If at all possible, arrange comfortable seats in a circular fashion for eye-to-eye contact.
- Set time limits for small-group activities. Stick to the rules and expect the groups to have a final product that must be shared with the larger group.
- Determine if the small-group activity requires a team leader or recorder. The trainer may assign these roles, or let them develop naturally. In any case, inform the group that they are expected to report back to the larger group.
- Circulate among the small groups to monitor the assignment. Use this time to identify points that can be used during the larger group discussion. Many groups will not recognize important concepts that they are developing, and the trainer can highlight these for their attention. *Do not overstay your welcome.* Encourage the group and move to the next set of participants.

Adapted from Eitington (1989).

Table 11.5. Fieldwork sites

1. Has a site been identified that is appropriate to the fieldwork objective and resources of the agency?
2. Have the appropriate individuals been contacted for approval?
   a. employers
   b. parents
   c. consumers
   d. agency personnel
3. Have liability issues been considered?
4. Are the consumers being paid for their involvement? Has the paperwork for this been completed? If they are not being paid, is the reason specified in their IEP or IWRP? For instance, is the fieldwork experience serving as an assessment for a new referral to the assistive technology program?
5. Has a site contact person been identified? Does this person know the requirements for the fieldwork experience?
6. Is the trainer familiar with the identified site and comfortable with the procedures that need to be followed?
7. Have worksheets been developed specifying the fieldwork requirements?
8. Have travel arrangements been made for the participants (i.e., trainees, consumers)?

Adapted from Inge, Barcus, Brooke, & Everson (1991).
IEP, individualized education program; IWRP, individualized written rehabilitation program.

TECHNIQUES FOR DELIVERING THE TRAINING CONTENT

When providing information on various aspects of assistive technology services and devices, try to focus on concept learning. Do not just offer step-by-step instructions on the process, but provide an opportunity for participants to problem solve situations so that useful information can be obtained and used to help the participant perform his or her job. The following points may prove useful when designing training programs on assistive technology:

- Use a process of "cumulative rotation" to train staff. In other words, learning or information sessions should rotate with application in the real environment or in closely simulated sessions (Ehrenberg, 1983). For example, lead a discussion on assessment and then have a participant interview a technology user about his or her assistive technology needs at home, work, school, or in the community.
- Make sure that the participants engage in concept learning versus information learning (Ehrenberg, 1983). Individuals who develop concepts from the training can solve problems or relate their learning to the real world. Provide a discussion on the etiology of disability and then interview assistive technology users to learn how their disability affects life functions.
- Do not try to cover too much information in one session (Spitzer, 1985). If excessive information is provided, the participants may have difficulty applying what they learn. In fact, they may not even remember important facts because of information overload. Carefully observe participants during training. Fidgeting, doodling, and staring blankly are cues that the information is not being understood. Professional trainers usually prepare more information than they actually give. They are flexible to the participants' needs and abilities to retain information.
- Provide multiple opportunities for the participants to practice what they are learning (Spitzer, 1985). Make sure that they can do what they are being trained to do. Practice can involve role playing, programming augmentative communica-

tion devices, completing worksheets on funding, and fabricating switches. These exercises can be completed in the classroom under the observation of the trainer.

- Facilitate transfer of learning from the training session to day-to-day activities by developing action plans with the participants (Stroul & Schuman, 1983). Specify how the trainer will deliver follow-up support. This practice allows the trainer to assist the participant in integrating the classroom instruction into actual practice. Trainers may need to provide additional resources for this activity.

When selecting techniques based on the training objectives, the content area may emphasize values clarification, knowledge, application of a technical skill, or a combination of these areas (McDaniel et al., 1986). A lecture may be the choice if increased knowledge is the objective but inappropriate for a values clarification session. Assistive technology users who present their own technology requirements and a videotape of an assistive technology user involved in a recreational activity, such as skiing, or working in a building construction site may more appropriately stimulate a values clarification discussion. Table 11.6 describes various delivery techniques related to values clarification, knowledge, and/or application of technical skills.

The characteristics of the participants will also influence the type of training strategy that is selected. For instance, a staff development program designed for community rehabilitation program staff to explain assistive technology services may focus primarily on the value and knowledge areas of identified goals. In this example, videotapes of individuals using assistive technology devices in various competitive employment settings may be beneficial for values clarification, but fieldwork experience for actual hands-on training would be unnecessary. The trainer may also want to include various activities and/or small-group situations in which the individuals can discuss assistive technology options for the consumers currently in the program. However, sessions designed for new employment specialists in the same agency may focus on the areas of values clarification, knowledge, and application of technical skills. Technical skills may receive the primary focus for each goal and objective, resulting in an emphasis on techniques appropriate to skill application (i.e., fieldwork experience, role-play situations) (Inge et al., 1988).

The length of the staff development session will also influence delivery techniques. A 1-hour presentation on knowledge related to assistive technology may include a 20-minute lecture with a 5-minute slide/tape show, a 20-minute role play, and a 10-minute large-group discussion. Yet a day-long program might include various other techniques, such as fieldwork activity (i.e., visiting a vendor or occupational or physical therapy department in a rehabilitation hospital). The experience and comfort level of the trainer should also be considered. One presenter may prefer to illustrate a point with a role play, while another may be more comfortable with a case study example. The choice of techniques is an individual matter, and no one technique is necessarily better than another.

EVALUATION OF TRAINING EFFECTIVENESS

The effectiveness of training can be evaluated using four categories or levels, including reaction, learning, behavior, and result evaluation (Chalofsky, 1985).

Reaction Evaluation

Reaction evaluation is often referred to as participant satisfaction and seeks to determine how well the participants liked the training program. A reaction evaluation is conducted to determine how well the trainer's efforts have been perceived or accepted by the participants. If the program is seen as poor, it is unlikely that the participants will use the information on their jobsites. If the training is considered to be good, there is a possibility that new learning will

Table 11.6.   Techniques for delivering in-service content

Techniques		Values	Knowledge	Application of technical skills
Panels	Group of experienced personnel discusses assistive technology topics	X	X	
Site visits	Observation of methods being discussed during training sessions	X	X	
Videotapes	May be used for presentation of ideas and practice sessions	X	X	X
Slide shows	Presentation of actual assistive technology methods	X	X	
Small group	Two to eight people discuss/exchange ideas on a specific topic	X	X	
Working pairs	Two people discuss/practice specific information for a short period of time	X	X	X
Role play	Acting out typical situations related to assistive technology		X	X
Games	Participants play games that focus on training content	X	X	
Skits	Organized presentation/play of specific situations by the trainers	X	X	
Lectures	Recommended length not to exceed 30 minutes		X	
Case studies	Presentation of a situation for small-group analysis	X	X	X
Written products	Handouts, manuals, newsletters, etc.	X	X	
Fieldwork	Practice sessions in real-life situations		X	

Adapted from Inge, Barcus, & Everson (1988).

be applied (Eitington, 1989). The following guidelines may be useful in designing a reaction evaluation (Eitington, 1989; Flynn, 1985; Kirkpatrick, 1978).

Designing a Participant Satisfaction Evaluation

1. Determine the information that needs to be collected (i.e., critique of the instructor, learning environment, training materials, session content, time allotted).
2. Design a written evaluation form to obtain this information. Design the form to allow for quantified data as well as open-ended comments (i.e., the information provided on environmental control as a training strategy was very effective, effective, or ineffective).
3. Schedule an evaluation time at the end of each major learning component or activity. Do not wait until the end of a staff development program to obtain feedback from the participants.
4. Allow the participants to remain anonymous when completing the evaluation.
5. Encourage participants to write comments or provide evaluation feedback at any time during the training process.

6. Summarize the evaluation data and use it to modify the staff development program. Review the revisions with the participants to assure them that their feedback is being utilized for training modifications. This is an effective way of promoting participant involvement.

Learning Evaluation

Learning evaluation refers to the principles, facts, and techniques that were learned during the training session (Chalofsky, 1985). The trainer who is conducting this type of evaluation is concerned with how much knowledge the participants have acquired during the "classroom" session. Strategies for collecting this information may include written tests, observation checklists used during the training session, or critique forms of trainee performance. The following information may be helpful when evaluating learning that takes place in a training session (Eitington, 1989).

Evaluating Learned Behavior During Training Sessions

1. *Observations:* Throughout this chapter, the focus is on participant-driven staff development, including the use of activities during training sessions. If this type of strategy is used, it is possible to measure the change in participant behavior across training sessions. For example

    a. Written samples of the participants' work prior to the training session (i.e., consumer assessments, user and family interviews, funding applications, and other assistive technology reports) can be compared to the work completed after the staff development program.
    b. Participant performance during role-play activities at the beginning of a staff development program can be compared to that at the end of the session. Videotaping participants' performances may be a useful tool for this type of evaluation.
    c. Assigning case study problems after a training session can assess participant learning.
    d. Using checklists to evaluate participants during fieldwork experiences can also provide a measure to assess learning during a staff development program.

2. *Action plans:* The trainer can assess commitment to engage in a new behavior by the nature of the action plans developed by the participants.
3. *Attitude surveys:* If the training program has been designed to change attitudes of the participants, pre- and posttest attitude surveys would help determine participant learning. (Inge, Barcus, Brooke, & Everson, 1991, p. 54)

Behavior Evaluation

It is not uncommon for an in-service training participant to like what was presented during a training program and to show increased knowledge of the content, yet fail to use the information on the job. The trainer concerned with transfer of knowledge to the actual work situation would want to conduct a *behavior evaluation*. In this instance, the program manager or trainer must work closely with the participant to identify the objectives of the training, the expected behavioral change, and the resources that will be utilized to accomplish this change. The use of a learning contract, explained earlier in this chapter, would be an effective way to plan for evaluation of behavioral change in the trainee. The following guidelines from Inge et al. (1991) may be helpful.

1. Measure on-the-job performance prior to the training session or staff development program.
2. Determine when the evaluation will occur and what the source of information will include (i.e., observation, behavioral checklists).
3. Allow adequate time between the pre- and posttest evaluation for behavior to change.
4. Provide feedback to the participant. (p. 55)

Result Evaluation

Finally, training can be evaluated by the *results* or *outcomes* of the planned staff development program. Determining the final results of a program is probably the most difficult stage of evaluation. Outcome data in assistive technology programs may include increased numbers of assistive technology consumers served by an agency, increased satisfaction with an assistive technology device, an increase of assistive technology users obtaining competitive employment or independent living situations, decreased intervention hours on jobsites, reduced number of separations from employment, and increased number of assistive technology users receiving training and follow-up assistance with assistive technology devices.

CASE STUDY: ASSISTIVE TECHNOLOGY PERSONNEL PREPARATION

In the following case study, adult learning principles were followed to identify objectives and develop a community college continuing education curriculum. A major goal of the Virginia Assistive Technology System (VATS) is to build local capacity to deliver assistive technology. Although the Virginia Department of Rehabilitative Services (DRS) has one rehabilitation engineer stationed in each of its four regional offices, the demand for services far exceeds the engineers' ability to respond. Under its training and public awareness functions, VATS sponsored the development of an introduction to assistive technology course. The Rehabilitation Research and Training Center (RRTC) at Virginia Commonwealth University (VCU) received funds from VATS to develop, market, and coordinate the course. An additional task was to integrate the course within the community college system in the Commonwealth of Virginia. Because the ultimate goal was local capacity building, VATS believed that offering the course through the community college system would result in a concerted effort to equip consumers and professionals with more information and basic skills on acquiring, funding, using, and fabricating assistive technology.

Work Group

VCU/RRTC staff brought together a group of educators and professionals who either practiced or taught aspects of assistive technology. This group included occupational therapists, physical therapists, rehabilitation engineers, staff from the VATS project, VCU faculty from the Virginia Institute on Developmental Disabilities, the Medical College of Virginia's Occupational Therapy Department, the RRTC, and the director of continuing education from a state community college.

The group identified the primary objective of the course—to provide basic information and awareness of the provision and use of assistive technology, with a focus on low technology. To fit into the structure of the community college, a course section would need to consist of 16 hours of classroom instruction augmented by field practice.

Because the instructional world of assistive technology is so vast, the challenge of the work group was to determine a basic level of instruction followed by an additional series of courses, should there be a demand for such courses. Through its discussions, the work group identified a possibility of three 16-hour sessions that could ultimately result in participants gaining a certificate from the community college. The RRTC and the community college developed the first session.

Audience

Before the work group met, residential and vocational service professionals were identified as the intended audience. During the meeting, the work group expanded the potential audience to assistive technology users, their families, vendors, and other persons who wanted knowledge or skills on assistive technology devices and services. In practice, the number of persons who use or could benefit from assistive technology is limitless, and therefore the course curriculum would need to address this type of heterogeneous audience. To serve these individuals, the course would have to include observational and experiential components if these individuals were to understand how to use, buy, learn about, and build assistive technology devices.

Marketing

Approximately 100 organizations received marketing information about the course. These organizations included rehabilitation hospitals, nursing and convalescent homes, community rehabilitation programs, assistive technology vendors, centers for independent living, personnel services for nurses and home aides, state institutions, group homes, and state agencies that had responsibility for providing assistive technology devices and services.

To hold a course, the community college requires that 10 individuals register. As an incentive, VATS provides stipends to assistive technology users and their families to attend the course.

Curriculum

Table 11.7 lists the sequence of topics for the 8-week session. The primary purpose of the introduction to assistive technology course is to give the participants a basic level of knowledge about gaining access to, using, and maintaining assistive technology devices and services. The primary course objectives are the following:

1. Learn about the evolution of federal assistive technology policy.
2. Understand the definition of assistive technology devices and services.
3. Gain awareness of the consumer's role in finding, using, and maintaining assistive technology devices and services.
4. Learn about the roles and functions of service providers in the assistive technology process.
5. Understand the difference between low- and high-technology devices.
6. Understand the etiology of several physical, sensory, and mental disabilities.
7. Learn about assistive technology for persons with speech, hearing, visual, and mobility impairments.
8. Understand the importance of functional assessment.
9. Know how to gain access to local resources.
10. Learn about funding sources and their requirements.
11. Construct a low-technology device.

Course instructors are individuals who are currently involved in using or providing assistive technology, which ensures that the training is practical and relevant. These instructors are assistive technology users, staff of VATS, occupational and physical therapists, rehabilitation engineers, and assistive technology vendors.

Table 11.7. Community college assistive technology curriculum

Week 1 *Introduction to assistive technology—consumer-driven values and state and federal policy and regulations*
- Conduct student needs assessment.
- Have students answer questions on assistive technology use (in groups or pairs).
- Discuss consumer involvement in the technology process.
- Lecture on Technology-Related Assistance for Individuals with Disabilities Act of 1988 (PL 100-407), Rehabilitation Act Amendments of 1992 (PL 102-569), Technology-Related Assistance for Individuals with Disabilities Amendments of 1994 (PL 103-218), and related policy.

Week 2 *Assistive technology user perspective*
- Invite assistive technology user as guest lecturer to provide personal perspective of benefits and challenges of assistive technology.
- Have user lead a discussion of stigma and stereotypes of capabilities of individuals with disabilities.
- Demonstrate use of personal low- and high-technology devices.

Week 3 *Etiology of disability and roles of professionals in the assistive technology team*
- Provide information on some of the major disability groups, such as persons with cerebral palsy, spinal cord injury, muscular dystrophy, arthritis, spina bifida, mental retardation, head trauma, speech impairments, and hearing and visual disabilities.
- Discuss primary functions of major assistive technology service providers, such as occupational, physical, and speech therapists; rehabilitation counselors and engineers; and employment specialists.

Week 4 *Factors in assessing assistive technology needs*
- Problem solve for consumer current and future needs.
- Assess needs across domains (i.e., domestic, leisure, vocational, community).
- Analyze environments.
- Evaluate the concept of partial participation.
- Assess for changing needs.

Week 5 *Low-technology devices*
- Lecture on potential uses.
- Discuss uses.
- Purchase materials and explore local resources.
- Demonstrate low-technology devices.
- Fabricate a switch.

Week 6 *Assistive technology for individuals with dual sensory impairments and augmentative communication needs*
- Discuss functional aspects of disabilities.
- Invite provider or vendor guest lecturer to discuss services and demonstrate low- and high-technology devices.
- Explain role and responsibility of user, provider, and vendor.
- Discuss funding and other resources.

Week 7 *Resource finding, sharing, and troubleshooting*
- Explain goals and services related to the Tech Act of 1994 (PL 103-218) and state systems change grant activities.
- Demonstrate and explain assistive technology information and referral services.

(continued)

Table 11.7.   (*continued*)

	• Explain funding sources, such as Social Security incentives, Medicaid, consumer and revolving loan funds, and private foundations.
Week 8	*Seating, positioning, and mobility devices* • Discuss assessment criteria. • Review responsibilities of user, provider, and vendor. • Discuss training, funding, and evaluation concerns. • Invite equipment vendor for guest lecture. • Review and discuss all class assignments.

Because field practice is an essential element of adult learning, participants have field assignments that correspond to each session. For example, one assignment is to interview a vendor to gather information about assistive technology devices and services. (These field assignments are listed in Table 11.8.) These assignments inform the participant about local resources and further his or her understanding of the challenges of gaining access to and using assistive technology devices and services.

RRTC staff function as mentors and reviewers of the field projects. This component of instruction allows the participants to have ongoing technical assistance and resources during and after their classroom experience. The mentor aspect and field practicum offer individualized instruction and help to the participant, fulfilling another important part of adult education. Participants learn best when instruction can benefit them immediately. Engaging in field projects that either address personal needs or assist in providing services helps transfer instruction from the classroom to real-life experiences.

Rehabilitation Counselor and Evaluator Training

VCU/RRTC also developed and conducted assistive technology training for rehabilitation counselors and evaluators with the DRS. DRS believed that it was essential for its staff to understand how to apply rehabilitation engineering throughout the vocational rehabilitation process, especially with the increased emphasis on rehabilitation engineering mentioned in the Rehabilitation Act Amendments of 1992 (PL 102-569).

Various staff at DRS received assistance from VCU/RRTC to develop and deliver their instruction through train-the-trainer sessions. As with the community college training, all instructors had current experience either using or providing assistive technology. These included staff from the DRS Computer Accommodation Lab, rehabilitation engineers, physi-

Table 11.8.   Introduction to assistive technology class assignments

Week	Assignment
1	Analyze a day in your life, and identify your own use of assistive technology devices and services.
2	Interview a consumer and discuss his or her assistive technology needs (use ADA handout as a guide).
3	Complete PASS plan worksheet or obtain materials from Social Security (such as Red Book), and write two paragraphs to demonstrate your understanding of how this concept can be used to fund assistive devices.
4	Write a one- to two-page report on a specific disability.
5	Use checklist in augmentative communication chapter. Call three vendors and list their services.
6	Build on your fourth report and list a variety of assistive technology devices that may be used to enhance daily living functions.

ADA, Americans with Disabilities Act of 1990; PASS, Plan for Achieving Self-Support.

cal and occupational therapists, assistant commissioners from DRS, and rehabilitation counselors.

Table 11.9 provides the agenda for this 2-day course. Much of the course instruction included demonstrations of assistive technology devices and services. Participants had the opportunity to try several of the devices and learn about the resources located within their own agencies. The evaluation results from a pilot session indicated that the trainees were extremely satisfied with the course. They gained a greater appreciation of the value of using assistive technology to increase the independence and quality of life of individuals served in the vocational rehabilitation system.

Table 11.9. Agenda of the Virginia Department of Rehabilitative Services—Rehabilitation Counselor Assistive Technology Training

First Day

8:30 A.M.–9:00 A.M.	*Assistive technology and the agency's vision* • Introduction activity • Welcome • Values—ADA, Rehabilitation Act of 1973 • Virginia Department of Rehabilitation Services vision • Goals and objectives of training • Counselors at the center of the hub in the assistive technology process
9:00 A.M.–10:30 A.M.	*Making it possible with assistive technology: An overview* • The assistive technology team—The professionals involved in the process • Assistive technology services framework *Strategies for identifying the need for technology* • Involving the consumer and family • Functional approach • Team process activity
10:30 A.M.–11:00 A.M.	*Break*—Allow 15 minutes for travel to the next session and 15 minutes for break and refreshments.
11:00 A.M.–12:30 P.M.	
Group A	*Seating, positioning, and mobility* • Suggested referral questions • Information across all disabilities • Identification of an interdisciplinary team • Factors to be considered during evaluation • Functional checklist • Successful use in the workplace • Maintenance and repair • Resources • Apply assistive technology to the role of the rehabilitation counselor • 25 minutes of this time block will be devoted to participants engaging in a hands-on application activity.
Group B	*Augmentative communication* • Suggested referral questions • Types and cost of equipment and services available • Identification of an interdisciplinary team • Purpose of seating systems in relevance to rehabilitation • Factors to be considered during evaluation

(continued)

Table 11.9. (*continued*)

	• Functional checklist
	• Successful use in the workplace
	• Maintenance and repair
	• Resources
	• Apply assistive technology to the role of the rehabilitation counselor
	• 25 minutes of this time block will be devoted to participants engaging in a hands-on application activity.
12:30 P.M.–1:30 P.M.	*Lunch*
1:30 P.M.–3:00 P.M.	
Group A	*Augmentative communication*
	• Suggested referral questions
	• Types and cost of equipment and services available
	• Identification of an interdisciplinary team
	• Purpose of seating systems in relevance to rehabilitation
	• Factors to be considered during evaluation
	• Functional checklist
	• Successful use in the workplace
	• Maintenance and repair
	• Resources
	• Apply assistive technology to the role of the rehabilitation counselor
	• 25 minutes of this time block will be devoted to participants engaging in a hands-on application activity.
Group B	*Seating, positioning, and mobility*
	• Suggested referral questions
	• Information across all disabilities
	• Identification of an interdisciplinary team
	• Factors to be considered during evaluation
	• Functional checklist
	• Successful use in the workplace
	• Maintenance and repair
	• Resources
	• Apply assistive technology to the role of the rehabilitation counselor
	• 25 minutes of this time block will be devoted to participants engaging in a hands-on application activity.
3:00 P.M.–3:30 P.M.	*Break*—Allow 15 minutes for travel to next session and 15 minutes for break and refreshments.
3:30 P.M.–5:00 P.M.	
Group A	*Computer accommodations*
	• Suggested referral questions
	• Types and cost of equipment and services available
	• Identification of an interdisciplinary team
	• Purpose of seating systems in relevance to rehabilitation
	• Factors to be considered during evaluation
	• Functional checklist
	• Successful use in the workplace
	• Maintenance and repair
	• Resources

(continued)

Table 11.9. (*continued*)

	• Apply assistive technology to the role of the rehabilitation counselor • 25 minutes of this time block will be devoted to participants engaging in a hands-on application activity.
Group B	*Home-site modifications and daily living* • Suggested referral questions • Types and cost of equipment and services available • Identification of an interdisciplinary team • Purpose of seating systems in relevance to rehabilitation • Factors to be considered during evaluation • Functional checklist • Maintenance and repair • Resources • Apply assistive technology to the role of the rehabilitation counselor • 25 minutes of this time block will be devoted to participants engaging in a hands-on application activity.
5:00 P.M.–5:30 P.M.	*Evaluation* • Open session evaluation
Second Day 8:30 A.M.–10:00 A.M.	
Group A	*Home-site modifications and daily living* • Suggested referral questions • Types and cost of equipment and services available • Identification of an interdisciplinary team • Purpose of seating systems in relevance to rehabilitation • Factors to be considered during evaluation • Functional checklist • Maintenance and repair • Resources • Apply assistive technology to the role of the rehabilitation counselor • 25 minutes of this time block will be devoted to participants engaging in a hands-on application activity.
Group B	*Computer accommodations* • Suggested referral questions • Types and cost of equipment and services available • Identification of an interdisciplinary team • Purpose of seating systems in relevance to rehabilitation • Factors to be considered during evaluation • Functional checklist • Successful use in the workplace • Maintenance and repair • Resources • Apply assistive technology to the role of the rehabilitation counselor • 25 minutes of this time block will be devoted to participants engaging in a hands-on application activity.
10:00 A.M.–10:30 A.M.	*Break*—Allow 15 minutes for travel to next session and 15 minutes for break and refreshments.

(continued)

Table 11.9. (*continued*)

10:30 A.M.–12:00 P.M.	
Group A	*Adaptive driving*

- Suggested referral questions
- Types and cost of equipment and services available
- Identification of an interdisciplinary team
- Purpose of seating systems in relevance to rehabilitation
- Factors to be considered during evaluation
- Functional checklist
- Successful use in the workplace
- Maintenance and repair
- Resources
- Apply assistive technology to the role of the rehabilitation counselor
- 25 minutes of this time block will be devoted to participants engaging in a hands-on application activity.

Group B	*Worksite accommodations*

- Suggested referral questions
- Types and cost of equipment and services available
- Identification of an interdisciplinary team
- Purpose of seating systems in relevance to rehabilitation
- Factors to be considered during evaluation in the rehabilitation process
- Functional checklist
- Maintenance and repair
- Resources
- Apply assistive technology to the role of the rehabilitation counselor
- 25 minutes of this time block will be devoted to participants engaging in a hands-on application activity.

12:00 P.M.–1:00 P.M.	*Lunch*
1:00 P.M.–2:30 P.M.	
Group A	*Worksite accommodations*

- Suggested referral questions
- Types and cost of equipment and services available
- Identification of an interdisciplinary team
- Purpose of seating systems in relevance to rehabilitation
- Factors to be considered during evaluation in the rehabilitation process
- Functional checklist
- Maintenance and repair
- Resources
- Apply assistive technology to the role of the rehabilitation counselor
- 25 minutes of this time block will be devoted to participants engaging in a hands-on application activity.

Group B	*Adaptive driving*

- Suggested referral questions
- Types and cost of equipment and services available
- Identification of an interdisciplinary team
- Purpose of seating systems in relevance to rehabilitation

(continued)

Table 11.9. (*continued*)

	• Factors to be considered during evaluation • Functional checklist • Successful use in the workplace • Maintenance and repair • Resources • Apply assistive technology to the role of the rehabilitation counselor • 25 minutes of this time block will be devoted to participants engaging in a hands-on application activity.
2:30 P.M.–3:00 P.M.	*Evaluation* • Open evaluation with all participants identifying the strengths and weaknesses of the training • Written evaluation

ADA, Americans with Disabilities Act of 1990.

CONCLUSION

As assistive technology becomes an ever-increasing part of everyday life and school and work environments, there will be a continuing need for training and technical assistance. Adult learning requires that the instructor utilize a variety of approaches that build on the participants' experiences and facilitate their participation in instruction. This chapter provides a variety of recommendations on how to design and deliver quality training or technical assistance. The steps described here include designing and administering needs assessments; planning and delivering curriculum; presenting content through lecture, small groups, and field experiences; and evaluation.

Finally, this chapter provides specific information on designing an introductory course on assistive technology for two audiences—a heterogeneous audience consisting of assistive technology users, family members, and service providers and another of individuals employed by vocational rehabilitation agencies. The current emphasis on assistive technology for persons with disabilities as defined in recent legislation and the rapid development of new and improved assistive technology devices make it imperative that individuals and organizations understand assistive technology, how to find it, how to pay for it, and how to use it to its fullest capacity. Training and technical assistance are the vehicles that provide this information.

REFERENCES

Americans with Disabilities Act of 1990 (ADA), PL 101–336. (July 26, 1990). Title 42, U.S.C. 12101 et seq: *U.S. Statutes at Large, 104,* 327–378.

Barcus, M., Everson, J.M., & Hall, S. (1987). Inservice training in human services agencies and organizations. In J.M. Everson, M. Barcus, M.S. Moon, & M.V. Morton (Eds.), *Achieving outcomes: A guide to interagency training in transition and supported employment* (pp. 1–58). Richmond: Virginia Commonwealth University, Rehabilitation Research and Training Center.

Birnbrauer, H., & Tyson, L.A. (1985). Steps of a needs analysis. In H. Birnbrauer (Ed.), *The ASTD handbook for technical and skills training* (pp. 27–32). Alexandria, VA: American Society for Training and Development.

Bowman, B. (1987, January). Assessing your needs assessment. *Training,* pp. 30–34.

Chalofsky, N.E. (1985). External evaluation. In W.R. Tracey (Ed.), *Human resources management and development handbook* (pp. 1467–1485). New York: American Management Associations.

Ehrenberg, L.M. (1983). How to ensure better transfer of learning. *Training and Development Journal, 37*(2), 81–83.

Eitington, J.E. (1989). *The winning trainer* (2nd ed.). Houston: Gulf Publishing.

Flynn, E.B. (1985). Internal evaluation. In W.R. Tracey (Ed.), *Human resources management and development handbook* (pp. 1447–1466). New York: American Management Associations.

Inge, K.J., Barcus, M., Brooke, V., & Everson, J. (1991). *Supported employment staff training manual.* Richmond: Virginia Commonwealth University, Rehabilitation Research and Training Center.

Inge, K.J., Barcus, M., & Everson, J.M. (1988). Developing inservice training programs for supported employment personnel. In P. Wehman & M.S. Moon (Eds.), *Vocational rehabilitation and supported employment* (pp. 145–162). Baltimore: Paul H. Brookes Publishing Co.

Kemp, J.E. (1985). *The instructional design process.* New York: Harper & Row.

Kirkpatrick, D.L. (1978, April/September). How to plan and implement a supervisory training program: Parts 1–5. *Training and Development Journal.*

McDaniel, R.H., Flippo, L., & Lowery, L. (1986). *Telesis: Supported employment resource manual.* San Francisco: University of San Francisco.

McKillip, J. (1987). *Needs analysis: Tools for the human services and education.* Newbury Park, CA: Sage Publications.

Patton, M.Q. (1980). *Qualitative evaluation methods.* Newbury Park, CA: Sage Publications.

Rehabilitation Act Amendments of 1992, PL 102-569. (October 29, 1992). Title 29, U.S.C. 701 et seq: *U.S. Statutes at Large, 100,* 4344–4488.

Rehabilitation Act of 1973, PL 93-112. (September 26, 1973). Title 29, U.S.C. 701 et seq: *U.S. Statutes at Large, 87,* 355–394.

Renzaglia, A. (1986). Preparing personnel to support and guide emerging contemporary service alternatives. In F.R. Rusch (Ed.), *Competitive employment issues and strategies* (pp. 303–316). Baltimore: Paul H. Brookes Publishing Co.

Rossett, A. (1989). Assess for success. *Training and Development Journal, 43*(5), 55–59.

Rossett, A. (1990). Overcoming obstacles to needs assessment. *Training, 27*(3), 36–41.

Roth, G.L. (1987). Developing a personal philosophy for technical training. *Training and Development Journal, 41*(5), 59–61.

Scherer, J.J. (1984). How people learn: Assumption for design. *Training and Development Journal, 38*(1), 64–66.

Spice, M.B., & Koppel, L.S. (1984). Are your trainees willing? *Training and Development Journal, 38*(5), 30–32.

Spitzer, D. (1985). 20 ways to energize your training. *Training, 22*(8), 37–40.

Stroul, N.A., & Schuman, G. (1983). Action planning for workshops. *Training and Development Journal, 37*(7), 41–42.

Technology-Related Assistance for Individuals with Disabilities Act of 1988, PL 100-407. (August 19, 1988). Title 29, U.S.C. 2201 et seq: *U.S. Statutes at Large, 102,* 1044–1065.

Technology-Related Assistance for Individuals with Disabilities Amendments of 1994, PL 103-218. (March 9, 1994). Title 29, U.S.C. 2201 et seq: *U.S. Statutes at Large, 108,* 50–97.

Zemke, R. (1985). An overview of needs analysis. In H. Birnbrauer (Ed.), *The ASTD handbook for technical and skills training* (pp. 13–26). Alexandria, VA: American Society for Training and Development.

Zemke, R., & Zemke, S. (1988, July). Thirty things we know for sure about adult learning. *Training,* 57–61.

12

Creative Financing of Assistive Technology

Joseph F. Wallace

The Americans with Disabilities Act (ADA) of 1990 (PL 101-336) estimates that more than 43 million individuals of all ages with disabilities live in the United States. The presence of a disability may result in a health-related condition that frequently causes the inability to fully participate in society (Laplante, 1991). The number of individuals with disabilities continues to increase due to advances in medical technology and improved acute care networks across the country. These individuals are potential beneficiaries of assistive technology, either on a temporary or extended basis.

The costs related to the acquisition of assistive technology deter many individuals with disabilities from taking advantage of this important resource (Hemp, Youngwerth, Haason, & Braddock, 1991). This is frequently due to the low income levels of these individuals (U.S. Bureau of the Census, 1991), the cost of equipment (Hoffman, 1988), the restrictive or vague eligibility criteria imposed by potential public and private sources of funding (McGuiness, 1982; Ward, 1989), or the unwillingness of financial institutions to provide credit for this type of purchase (Reeb, 1987).

Laplante, Hendershot, and Moss (1992) note that more than 2.5 million Americans are estimated to be in need of assistive technology devices that they do not have, mostly because they cannot afford them. Between 1980 and 1990, the number of persons using anatomical or mobility assistive technology devices increased at a more rapid rate than the general population (Laplante et al., 1992).

Many persons with disabilities are denied access to certain types of assistive technology due to the high costs of purchase. An eye-gaze computer system (Figure 12.1) developed by L.C. Technologies (Fairfax, Virginia) provides persons, whose only body control may be through their eyes, a way to communicate using infrared light and computers. It has a base cost of $17,500. Augmentative communication devices, such as a Touch Talker from Prentke Romich Company (Figure 12.2), which output synthesized speech permitting persons with little or no speech to communicate and participate more fully in society, cost up to $5,170. An IBM voice-activated Dragondictate computer system, which through software provides voice input onto a computer screen for persons unable to operate a keyboard, costs $1,000.

The impact that these technological devices have on the lives of those with severe disabilities equates to the cost of freedom. Without reasonable financial alternatives to help obtain these technology solutions, individuals with disabilities will be denied the ability to learn, play, compete, work, and interact with family and friends (Enders, 1990).

Figure 12.1.   An eye-gaze computer system by L.C. Technologies.
(Photograph courtesy of L.C. Technologies; reprinted by permission.)

Inconsistent patterns of service availability for individuals with disabilities to gain access to assistive technology exist across the United States (Morris & Golinker, 1991). Many state agencies that provide funding for assistive technology have individual interpretations and policy guidelines that differ drastically from state to state (U.S. Congress, Office of Technology Assessment, 1982). This has been demonstrated through multiple needs assessment surveys conducted by individual state Tech Act projects (mandated by the Technology-Related Assistance for Individuals with Disabilities Act of 1988 [PL 100-407]) (Kentucky Assistive Technology System, 1990; Virginia Assistive Technology System [VATS], 1991). These studies consistently cite funding of assistive technology to be the single largest barrier to acquiring needed devices and services. The need to develop a taxonomy of public policies relating to loan financing of assistive technology clearly exists.

A national needs assessment of assistive technology users taken from Tech Act projects (RESNA Technical Assistance Project, 1992) reveals a population very much in need of funding options beyond current practices. Many persons surveyed are individuals on low or fixed incomes for whom the ability to gain access successfully to traditional loan avenues is unlikely. These individuals stated their willingness to contribute to the purchase of the needed equipment.

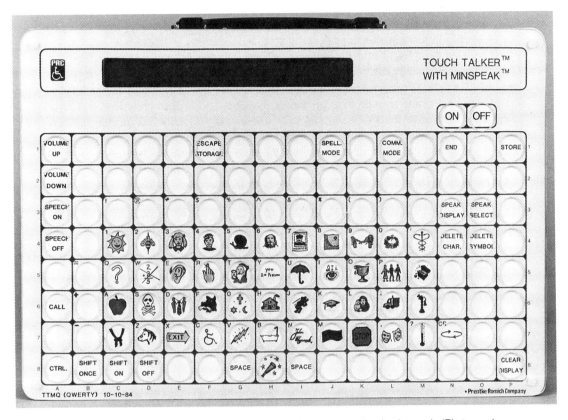

Figure 12.2.   A Touch Talker from Prentke Romich, which outputs synthesized speech. (Photograph courtesy of Prentke Romich; reprinted by permission.)

ASSISTIVE TECHNOLOGY FUNDING SOURCES

Federal, State, and Private Insurance Programs

Medicaid

The largest federal and state insurance programs are Medicaid and Medicare. Medicaid is a federally sponsored state implemented medical insurance program for welfare or Supplemental Security Income (SSI) recipients. Other programs that qualify an individual to participate in the Medicaid program include Aid to Families with Dependent Children, Optional Supplement, and Refugee Assistance. Medicaid is an assistance program designed specifically for persons with low incomes who meet certain eligibility criteria that provides payment for approved medical expenses. (Some Medicare recipients may also be eligible for Medicaid benefits based on financial eligibility.)

The Medicaid program has a durable medical equipment category within which certain items of medically necessary devices may be provided. Equipment may also be available through reimbursement from the Inpatient Hospital Care program or Community-Based Waiver programs. Typical areas of assistive technology equipment funded within these programs include aids for daily living, prostheses and orthoses, aids for vision and hearing impairments, wheelchairs and mobility aids, and, in some states, augmentative communication devices. Assistive technology services (e.g., occupational, physical, and speech therapy services and equipment fabrication) are also reimbursable. Each state develops its own regulations for program participation in response to specified federal guidelines.

The Medicaid Early and Periodic Screening, Diagnosis, and Treatment program (EPSDT) is a primary health benefits program for children that has an emphasis on preventive care. The EPSDT program requires that states cover regular and periodic exams for eligible children. They must then provide any medically necessary services prescribed by EPSDT even if that service is not covered in that state's Medicaid program. This includes assistive devices that may have been excluded in the past and are still excluded under the regular Medicaid program. Eligibility for this program includes all children under 21 years of age who demonstrate a medical need for the service and whose family income is less than 133% of the federal poverty level. Devices remain the property of the individual, although Medicaid may choose to rent the equipment. Primary areas of equipment funded by EPSDT include all major areas with the exception of computer applications, environmental control systems, and vehicle modifications.

Medicare

Medicare is a federal grant medical insurance program administered out of the Social Security Administration (SSA). Eligibility includes persons who are age 65 or older; persons who are (at any age) blind or totally and permanently disabled and have been receiving Social Security Disability Income payments for 24 months; or persons who have end-stage renal failure. This program provides for the purchase of assistive technology in some cases. This equipment typically includes prostheses and orthoses, seating and positioning aids, and wheelchairs and mobility aids. Areas typically not funded are bathroom and toileting aids and vehicle modifications. Medicare funding of assistive technology must be considered a "covered service" deemed medically necessary based on established federal regulations.

CHAMPUS

The Civilian Health and Medical Program of the Uniformed Services (CHAMPUS) is a medical benefits insurance program sponsored by the federal government intended for spouses and children of active duty uniformed service personnel, retired uniformed service personnel and their spouses and children, and spouses and children of deceased active duty or deceased retired personnel. Equipment provision through this federal program is similar to that of private insurance practices discussed in the following section.

Private Insurance

Individual insurance policies dictate the type and degree of assistive technology equipment covered. These policies frequently cover devices such as aids for daily living, prostheses and orthoses, seating and positioning devices, and wheelchairs and mobility aids. They typically do not fund hearing aids and corrective lenses. Policies may not cover "preexisting conditions," but do cover accidental injuries or conditions that manifested after coverage began. This is the first area to pursue when seeking sources for funding and frequently a rejection from this level is required by future funding sources. Determinations of funding are based on need, prognosis, diagnosis, and type of equipment.

Federal and State Agency Programs

Social Security Administration Services

The SSA has multiple work incentive programs for persons with disabilities who receive SSI benefits. An example is the Impairment-Related Work Expenses (IRWE) program. This program allows an individual to continue to receive Social Security benefits over a period of time after beginning work. Within IRWE, an individual can purchase assistive technology, even if it is not work related, and deduct these costs from the SSI amount or their earned income level.

The Plan for Achieving Self-Support (PASS) program is an income and resource exclusion that allows a person with a disability to set aside income and/or resources needed to achieve an occupational objective. The exclusion of certain income under a PASS plan can help to provide support for persons entering or reentering the work force so that they may be eligible for SSI or receive higher payments as they gain the capacity for self-support. Assistive technology can be included among the expenditures that can be excluded under a PASS plan. This program requires the presence of a disability and has otherwise broad eligibility criteria. Primary areas of funding include augmentative communication devices, home and worksite modifications, prostheses and orthoses, aids for persons with vision and/or hearing impairments, and vehicle modifications.

Veterans Administration Services

The Veterans Administration (VA) is a federal agency established in 1930 to administer the various veterans benefits programs. The VA is the largest single medical care system in the United States. Benefits provided to veterans include medical and domiciliary care, pensions for wartime veterans with limited incomes, disability compensation, education and training assistance, vocational rehabilitation, employment assistance, specially adapted homes, and other disability benefits. The VA is one of the largest purchasers of assistive devices for individuals with disabilities. Eligibility for veterans benefits is complex and does not include all veterans. Typical types of equipment provided include all major areas of assistive technology devices.

State Vocational Rehabilitation Services

Vocational rehabilitation (VR) agencies have long been a primary funding source for adults with disabilities needing adaptive devices for employment enhancement purposes (Rubin & Roessler, 1987). The VR program has multiple service categories that can be defined to include equipment provision when appropriate. There are also financial eligibility requirements related to the access of equipment such as economic means tests, but these requirements do not affect job placement assistance. VR services may include home and worksite modifications, job modifications, and assistive technology assessment. Primary areas of equipment funding include aids for daily living, prostheses and orthoses, seating and positioning devices, aids for hearing impairment, wheelchairs and mobility aids, computer equipment, and vehicle modifications.

State Vocational Rehabilitation/Independent Living Program

Independent living rehabilitation services are any appropriate VR services (as defined under Title I of the Rehabilitation Act of 1973 [PL 93-112]) and any other service that will enhance the ability of an individual with severe disabilities to live independently and function within the family or community and, if appropriate, secure and maintain appropriate employment. Typically, funds available for this program are limited, but they do allow for the purchase of assistive technology devices. Eligibility is based on 1) the presence of a severe physical or mental disability; 2) the presence of a severe limitation in the ability to function independently in the family or community and to engage or continue in employment; and 3) a reasonable expectation that independent living rehabilitation services will significantly assist the individual to improve his or her ability to function independently in the family or community, to engage or continue in employment, and to maintain independent functioning. There are no age restrictions on services for the independent living program. Primary areas of equipment funded include all major areas with the exception of environmental control systems.

State Education Services

State education funding for children ages 3–21 with disabilities occurs at the local school district level. Assistive technology devices must be shown to be necessary to allow the child to receive an education in the least restrictive environment. In the program planning step of the individualized education program (IEP), the need for assistive technology is determined. If the IEP committee determines that such a device is needed for the child to successfully meet the goals and objectives of the IEP, the school system must actively pursue funding to obtain that device for the child.

ALTERNATIVE FINANCING OF ASSISTIVE TECHNOLOGY

Private Funding of Assistive Technology

Private funding alternatives typically become a consideration following the elimination of the primary public sources mentioned previously. If an individual does not have private insurance, or the insurance coverage the individual does have will not cover the assistive technology needed, private funding should be pursued.

These organizations have historically assisted in providing financial support to meet the needs that traditional funding sources cannot provide. These providers are diverse and frequently have restrictions on what they will provide. Eligibility requirements also vary widely, and the resources available are limited. The focus of such programs is to provide assistance to individuals. Technology-related devices are typically funded when the individual's needs coincide with his or her program mission. These organizations are extremely diverse and frequently have an area of specialty or interest. For example, the Muscular Dystrophy Association focuses on muscular dystrophy and other degenerative muscular disorders, the Dream Factory focuses on children with critical illnesses, and the Lions Club focuses on blindness and other visual impairments.

These organizations need to be contacted individually with a written request that describes the need, the individual's history, the equipment needed, and the individual's ability to contribute to at least part of the cost. Typically, funding if available will be provided for a portion of the equipment's cost and usually only after proof of unsuccessful attempts from public sources is provided. Many of these sources can be found through local chambers of commerce. Service organizations will assist in the funding of devices that might not otherwise be funded by a state or federal agency. Other examples of service clubs and organizations include: the Shriners, the Kiwanis Club, the Rotary Club, the Sertoma Club, the Elks, various churches, the Knights of Columbus, the Optimist Club, sororities and fraternities, Easter Seals, and the United Way.

Employer funding for the provision of assistive technology is included under ADA as a requirement considering "reasonable accommodation" measures unless "undue hardship" would result. The areas of reasonable accommodation include modification of equipment, use of assistive and/or auxiliary devices, and removal of architectural barriers. Tax incentives exist to provide deductions to employers for workplace accommodations. The Internal Revenue Service can provide additional information to employers in this area.

Credit Financing of Assistive Technology

Credit financing is an alternative of vast potential for individuals with disabilities that may provide creative payment opportunities using the substantial resources of the credit industry for the purchase of assistive technology. Credit financing has evolved from the barter system in which products and services were exchanged, to a cash system that allowed customers to use their earned income to purchase desired goods directly, to a credit system whereby expensive items can be purchased over time. This funding option could provide another choice for persons not eligible for other third-party insurance programs and supply them with a positive credit base. State-level loan financing practices may be applied in the development of assistive technology loan financing programs.

Historically, credit financing has been a funding alternative minimally used to fund assistive technology devices (Reeb, 1989; Reeb & McFarland, 1988). Reeb (1989) suggests that this is due in part to the significance of third-party funding, which has decreased credit financing demands. Assistive technology devices are viewed by bankers as specialty products not accepted as collateral for loans because of concern over resale value and uncertainty over the potential life of the product (Peat, Marwick, Mitchell, & Company, 1979; Trachtman, 1990). Other issues contributing to the underusage of credit financing surround the limited income and financial status of many users of assistive technology. There would appear to be mutual rewards for both vendors and users in the increased availability of credit financing opportunities in assistive technology markets.

It is becoming increasingly clear that third-party funding is becoming more restrictive and policy endeavors are promoting independence for persons with the most severe disabilities (Reeb, 1987). This situation suggests the need for creative and alternative resource development initiatives to increase funding options for individuals in need of assistive technology. The credit industry would appear to be an area of vast potential to meet the expectations set forth by the Tech Act of 1988 (PL 100-407), the Rehabilitation Act Amendments of 1986 and 1992 (PL 99-506 and PL 102-569), and ADA (Hemp et al., 1991).

Public and private partnerships in loan funding design have demonstrated creative techniques for equipment purchase (Reeb, 1989). Reeb (1989) cites several examples of corporate involvement with nonprofit organizations that have opened doors for the purchase of some exclusive and high-cost devices. Other assistive technology loan funds exist that include consumer and business participation in device and accommodation loan financing. Many alternatives contributing to this consumer-responsive approach involve the use of loan guarantees to provide an incentive to potential lenders. By guaranteeing a loan to a lending organization, a bank is likely to reduce various loan criteria and may also provide credit at a lower rate. This is becoming an attractive alternative to student loan and disaster relief loan programs in which the federal government provides the loan guarantee to banks (Reeb, 1989; U.S. Congressional Budget Office, 1979). Some of the benefits of such a guarantee include longer payment terms and/or reduced interest rates on an individual loan (Reeb, 1987).

The use of credit to finance assistive technology is a concept receiving much attention by Tech Act projects across the United States. A variety of loan financing programs functioning in various states are providing assistive technology users with another alternative to gain access to the needed devices. Of the 52 operating Tech Act projects, 5 have some form of loan financing program in which they are involved.

Several of these various loan programs are discussed in this chapter to provide examples of contrasting credit financing models that are currently functioning. Table 12.1 provides a summary of these loan programs by title, specific type, and individual features of each program.

Table 12.1. Assistive technology loan programs

Title	Type of loan program	Loan program features
New York State Equipment Loan Fund	Revolving loan fund	$400 to $5,000 range loaned at 8% paid over a 2- to 8-year period; state funds program annually
Maine Adaptive Equipment Loan Program	Revolving loan fund	$150 to $50,000 range loaned at varying interest (0%–10.5%); funded by $5 million bond
Vermont Equipment for Independence Loan Fund	Revolving loan fund and minigrant program	$1,000 to $10,000 range loaned at varying interest (3%–9%); $500 minigrants available
Illinois Ready Access Loan Program	Multibank partnership with state treasurer's office	$1 million loaned to individuals and businesses for up to 4 years at 3% above treasurer's deposit rate
Nevada Assistive Technology Loan Fund	Single bank and nonprofit partnership using revolving loan and loan guarantee	$150,000 to guarantee loans provided by grant with the bank securing each loan; 4-year terms
Bank of Boston Kurzweil Personal Reader Loan Program	Corporate backed loan guarantee and interest buy-down program (30% discount) for specific high-cost equipment	$2 million fund for loans at 5% below prime interest rate over maximum 4-year term

New York State Equipment Loan Fund

The New York State Equipment Loan Fund has been in existence since 1986 and operates on an annual appropriation from the state legislature of $50,000. It is a revolving loan fund administered by the New York State Department of Social Services. A revolving loan fund allows monies loaned to be returned to the fund directly as payments are made, which gradually replenishes the fund. This fund is intended exclusively for persons certified as having a disability defined in very broad terms. The purpose of the loan fund is to purchase any essential equipment that will overcome barriers associated with a disability that exist in daily living or vocational environments.

Loan amounts may range from $400 to $4,000 and are charged 8% interest repaid over a 2- to 8-year period. Loans are reviewed by a five-member panel that meets three times yearly, with each member serving up to two terms. Two major concerns related to this loan fund are its low appropriation given the size of New York and its high default rate of 20%. This is attributable in part to the absence of credit checks or required prescriptions from physicians for the desired equipment. Motor vehicles are the only equipment not funded by this program. Through 1991, 222 loans have been approved totaling $537,026. The average loan amount is $1,953 and the predominant age range is older than 60 years. Items most frequently funded include powered wheelchairs, scooters, ramps, and lifts.

Maine Adaptive Equipment Loan Program

In 1988, the voters of Maine approved a bond referendum of $5 million to provide for a revolving loan fund for assistive technology. This program involves a partnership between the State Finance Authority of Maine, a quasipublic financial authority, and Alpha One, a nonprofit organization promoting independent living services for persons with disabilities across the state. This fund is intended for use by citizens of Maine with disabilities or for small businesses desiring to improve their accessibility either for their patrons or their employees. As of December 1992, the adaptive equipment loan program had 264 closed loans totaling $2,325,241. The average loan amount is $8,808, with actual loans ranging from $150 to $50,000. The average interest rate is 5.2%, with actual interest rates ranging from 0% to 10.5%. By statute, the interest rate cannot exceed the prime interest rate at the time the loan is approved. Average repayment term is 3.26 years, with actual repayment terms ranging from 6 months to 20 years, depending on the financial condition of the borrower and the nature of the assets purchased. The default rate for the adaptive equipment loan program has remained stable at 3%, which is much lower than traditional levels experienced by commercial banks.

The most frequently purchased items by borrowers are adapted vans and hearing aids. Other uses of the loan fund include home accessibility modifications, computers, wheelchairs, and scooters. The program defines adaptive equipment in very broad terms to permit the purchase of such things as assistive animals or yet-to-be-developed genetic or biological devices.

Vermont Equipment for Independence Loan Fund

In 1991, the Vermont legislature and the Vermont Assistive Technology Project combined to operationalize and fund the Vermont Equipment for Independence Loan Fund. The fund operates from a base of $100,000 and involves a revolving loan and a no-interest loan/minigrant component.

The no-interest loan/minigrant program approves loans up to $1,000 and grants not to exceed $500 and is funded at the same $50,000 level as the revolving loan program. The no-interest loan program has been in operation since November 1991, and no repayment delinquencies have yet to be reported. Ten percent of the total fund balance can be charged in a given year for the administrative costs of the loan fund.

The low-interest loan component also operates from a $50,000 base, which is allocated on an annual basis from Tech Act dollars to provide revolving low-interest loans for equipment costing more than $1,000. This fund will consider requests for up to $10,000 if a specific device costs more than $30,000. Since its inception, more than 15 loans have been approved with one paid in full. A total of $59,794 has been loaned out at annual percentage rates ranging from 3% to 9%. As of December 30, 1991, $8,751 has been repaid to the fund and $786 in interest earned on the principal. An additional $1,043 has been earned in interest on uncommitted monies. Interest earned on loans and uncommitted monies, together with repayments on account of principal, are added to the fund principal to ensure continuation of the fund.

Illinois Ready Access Loan Program

In July 1992, the Illinois State Treasurer's Office established a low-interest loan program that provides loans for three general purposes. These include funding for 1) businesses seeking compliance with ADA; 2) consumer equipment to promote self-sufficiency (i.e., home modifications or specially designed vehicles); and 3) consumer continuing education or self-employment purposes. Loan terms are set each week at three percentage points more than the treasurer's current deposit rate and borrowers may obtain loans for as long as 48 months. The initial low-interest loans were financed by Amalgamated Bank of Chicago, which serves as a partner in the program; presently, 10 banks are participating statewide.

The Illinois Ready Access Loan Program's average loan is $4,000, with no defined parameters for minimum or maximum amounts. As of mid-1993, the program has provided 50 loans to individuals and businesses and has loaned more than $1 million. Customers in the loan program may become permanent members of the bank and may be referred to participating lenders by local realtors, homebuilders, and community organizations.

Nevada Assistive Technology Loan Fund

Nevada initiated an assistive technology loan fund for persons with disabilities in 1992 through a partnership between Valley Bank of Nevada and United Cerebral Palsy of Southern Nevada. Valley Bank of Nevada provides loans to qualified borrowers who have been referred through United Cerebral Palsy of Southern Nevada or their designee. The bank secures each loan and shares a loan guarantee with United Cerebral Palsy thereby jointly securing the loan. This program was established by a grant of $150,000 to be loaned at the established prime interest rate (currently 6.5%).

Loan terms may extend from 12 to 36 months, and amounts range from less than $1,000 to $5,000. The average loan amount is $2,900. As of mid-1993, 28 loans had been approved for a total of more than $80,000 outstanding. Loans are made for equipment only, and personal income must be deemed adequate to repay the loan. Financial counseling is provided at no cost to the customer.

Bank of Boston Kurzweil Personal Reader Loan Program

This loan guarantee and subsidy service provides a loan alternative for individuals wishing to purchase a Kurzweil reader for their personal use or for employment purposes. The American Foundation for the Blind and Xerox Corporation established this program in 1991 with a $2 million fund. In 1993, this loan program was transferred to the Bank of Boston for overall program administration. This unique loan operation provides Kurzweil readers to persons who are blind or visually impaired at a 30% discount with a balance of the cost financed at 5% below the prevailing interest rate for a period of time not to exceed 48 months. This program is targeted for individuals who cannot otherwise secure bank loans due to their low incomes.

National Research on Loan Programs

In a 1993 National Institute on Disability and Rehabilitation Research (NIDRR)–funded study of long-term, low-interest loan programs administered by VATS, several important elements were determined to be crucial in the development of a successful loan program. Apogee Research, Inc., identified multiple approaches to loan program development that provide various levels of program control and oversight by the sponsoring organization (see the appendix at end of this chapter). A sponsoring organization generally refers to a public agency or authority or a private nonprofit organization that provides full or partial program administration. This research also developed a flow chart to assist sponsoring organizations in proceeding with loan program development and implementation (Figure 12.3).

Following loan program design considerations, a sponsoring organization can pursue a program that is appropriate to its individual circumstances. The primary implementation steps can be divided into three stages: 1) preliminary program design, 2) interim implementation steps, and 3) final implementation steps. These stages follow Figure 12.3 closely. It is important to note the feedback loops in the flow diagram, which indicate where issues may need to be addressed at multiple stages of the process and, at times, redefined throughout the process.

Preliminary Program Design

This stage consists of identifying the population to be served, formulating an assessment of the needs of that target group, and identifying the financial barriers that preclude traditional financing mechanisms. Only by following this design can the overall program mission and fundamental program components be developed. Each of these steps is presented in Figure 12.3 and as follows:

1. *Identify target population.* Careful specification of the target population to receive financial assistance is critical to successful implementation of the loan program. Examples of potential target populations include persons with any assistive technology needs, persons with specified assistive technology needs, persons with assistive technology needs and specified income or financial resources, or employers needing loans for workplace accommodations. This group may be redefined as the program develops. It is important to limit the mismatch among the number of individuals and level of financing needs of the target population and the funds available for lending. Therefore, as financial resources are defined, the target population may need to be redefined.

2. *Formulate needs assessment.* Following the identification of the target population, a needs assessment should be developed. The assessment should include the number of persons in the target population, the equipment needs of persons in the target population, and the dollar value of funding needs associated with such equipment. This process will assist in developing an understanding of the level of financial resources necessary for the program and may narrow the target population.

3. *Identify barriers to obtaining traditional funding.* Before a sponsoring organization can select the most appropriate model approach or form of financial assistance, careful consideration must be given to the specific barriers encountered by members of the target population. Possible barriers may include a lack of credit history or poor credit, banks' unwillingness to finance needed equipment, individuals' inability to afford market interest rates, or individuals' inability to meet conventional payment terms. Resolution of each of these barriers calls for a different approach. It may be the case that multiple barriers are operating simultaneously, and thus care should be taken to identify the most important barriers.

4. *Develop mission and general program elements.* Once a clear understanding of the financing needs of the target population is defined, the sponsoring organization should develop a mission and establish general program elements. Included are guiding principles and objectives, an administrative structure and planned partnerships, a general financial strategy, and basic oversight mechanisms.

Interim Implementation Steps

The interim steps to implementation of a loan program relate to the establishment of funding and contractual arrangements. Included in this interim stage are the following activities: 1) soliciting funding; 2) soliciting outside partners, if chosen as an approach; 3) seeking leg-

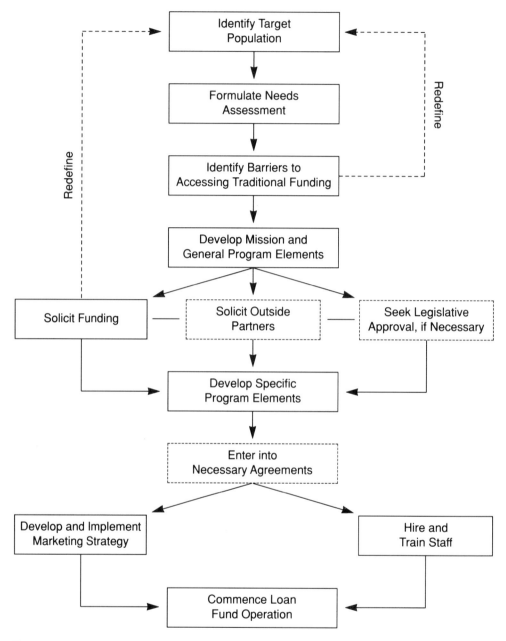

Figure 12.3. Flow chart of loan program development and implementation to assist sponsoring organization.

islative approval, if necessary; 4) developing specific program elements; and 5) entering into any necessary agreements. Some of these activities can be undertaken concurrently.

Final Implementation Steps

Once the sponsoring organization has passed through the interim implementation steps, it is ready to actively implement the loan program. This stage includes: 1) developing and implementing a marketing strategy, 2) hiring and training necessary staff, and 3) commencing operation of the loan fund. The need to market a loan program is often overlooked by program administrators. As a result, loan funds may be established and funded, but are underutilized and unable to loan all available funds. Depending on the selected approach, staffing needs may be limited, especially in the case where most of the administration is carried out by outside parties.

CONSIDERATIONS AND RECOMMENDATIONS FOR THE FUTURE

Policy Considerations Relating to the Financing of Assistive Technology

The most comprehensive policy study on the financing of assistive technology, titled *Study on the Financing of Assistive Technology Devices and Services for Individuals with Disabilities,* was conducted by the National Council on Disability in 1993. The research that led to the completion of this study included three regional public forums, which provided hundreds of suggestions on improving assistive technology funding from consumers, service providers, and agency representatives. These suggestions resulted in the identification of 16 specific recommendations, which were refined according to the following criteria:

- Magnitude of the problem
- Potential scope of impact of the proposed solution on identified barriers
- Potential for implementation
- Consistency with the principles of ADA to promote full citizenship for persons with disabilities and
- Potential to achieve cost–benefit results in quality of life for persons with disabilities and their families (National Council on Disability, 1993, p. 10)

The policy recommendations are listed in the following paragraphs.

Recommendation 1

Mandate by statute the development of a national classification system for assistive technology devices and services, and establish and collect uniform data sets across public programs.

Recommendation 2

Authorize the NIDRR to publish, by the end of each calendar year, an Annual Report to Congress on the status of funding of assistive technology devices and services for Americans with disabilities.

Recommendation 3

Establish the statutory authority for a federal Assistive Technology Coordination Council to meet quarterly and be responsible for improved coordination of services and funding for assistive technology for Americans with disabilities.

Recommendation 4

Amend the state plan requirements in multiple statutes to require assurances and a planning process with time lines for expanding funding access to assistive technology for both children and adults with disabilities.

Recommendation 5

Amend the individual program planning requirements in multiple statutes to provide notice to individuals with disabilities and their families of the right to assistive technology devices and services in response to individualized needs in a timely manner.

Recommendation 6

Add the complete definition of assistive technology devices and services adopted in the Tech Act to the following programs of the Social Security Act of 1935 (PL 74-271): Title II, Social Security Disability Insurance (SSDI); Title V, Maternal and Child Health Block Grant; Title XVI, Supplemental Security Income (SSI); Title XVIII, Medicare; and Title XIX, Medicaid.

Recommendation 7

Reauthorize the Tech Act for an additional 3 years and strengthen opportunities for inter-agency coordination, systems change, and consumer choice and control.

Recommendation 8

Establish assistive technology demonstration and recycling centers nationwide in an appro-priate city of each state and in the top 50 Standard Metropolitan Statistical Areas to be oper-ated by existing Centers for Independent Living or other community-based organizations that are consumer controlled and directed. This will enhance consumer choice in and control of assistive technology services and funding.

Recommendation 9

Authorize the use of Social Security Trust Fund as a financing source for purchasing assistive technology that enhances the capacity to work through an individualized employment account.

Recommendation 10

Establish a Technology Watch program patterned after the National Council on Disability's current ADA Watch activities to monitor compliance with enforcement of federal rights or re-quirements for expanding technology access for both children and adults with disabilities.

Recommendation 11

Authorize by statute the establishment of a National Center on Assistive Technology Legal Advocacy to specialize in funding issues.

Recommendation 12

Develop statutory authority that requires private health insurers to apply medical necessity standards to durable medical equipment, prostheses, and orthotics that enhance function in activities related to health, safety, and daily living.

Recommendation 13

Create a comprehensive set of fiscal incentives encouraging private industry to invest in the production, marketing, and distribution of assistive technology to benefit Americans with disabilities.

Recommendation 14

Amend Section 162 of the Internal Revenue Code to allow taxpayers with disabilities who do not itemize the option of claiming assistive technology expenses as above-the-line adjustments to income. Request the Department of the Treasury to develop a cohesive set of tax policies on assistive technology for persons with disabilities that clarifies national values and goals as articulated in the ADA and the Tech Act.

Recommendation 15

Authorize by statute universal product design guidelines for application in the manufacture of electronic equipment and other products to enhance accessibility by individuals with disabilities.

Recommendation 16

Amend the Communications Act of 1934 (PL 416) to establish and implement a national policy of available, affordable, and accessible telecommunication services to Americans with disabilities.

CONCLUSION

The preceding policy recommendations provide a clear and realistic agenda for legislators, consumers, advocates, service providers, and others to pursue in improving the financing for assistive technology. The importance of building on interagency cooperation at federal, state, and local levels in the provision of policy development and application has the potential to remove many existing barriers. The effort to leverage funds among agencies and resolve primary and last-payer policy issues will extend the funding resources to more individuals and expedite equipment provision to persons in need. To every extent possible, consumer involvement in assistive technology policy development, development of funding systems, and the approval and appeal processes will enhance responsiveness and create systems that are sensitive to those persons who will benefit most.

REFERENCES

Americans with Disabilities Act of 1990 (ADA), PL 101-336. (July 26, 1990). Title 42, U.S.C. 12101 et seq: *U.S. Statutes at Large, 104*, 327–378.

Communication Act of 1934, PL 416. (June 19, 1934). Title 15, U.S.C. 21 et seq: *U.S. Statutes at Large, 652*, 1064–1091.

Enders, A. (1990). Ensuring technology reaches those who can benefit by it. In A. Enders & M. Hall (Eds.), *Assistive technology sourcebook*. Washington, DC: RESNA Press.

Hemp, R., Youngwerth, C., Haason, K., & Braddock, D. (1991). *Financing assistive technology: An annotated bibliography*. Chicago: University of Illinois at Chicago, Assistive Technology Financing Project.

Hoffman, A. (1988). Funding: How you can make it work. In C.A. Costor (Ed.), *Planning and implementing augmentative communication services delivery* (pp. 80–93). Washington, DC: RESNA Press.

Kentucky Assistive Technology System. (1990). *Statewide consumer needs survey on assistive technology*. Frankfort: Author.

Laplante, M. (1991). Disability risks of chronic illness and impairments. *Disability Statistics Reports, 2*(3), 231–244. Washington, DC: National Institute on Disability and Rehabilitation Research.

Laplante, M., Hendershot, G., & Moss, A. (1992). *Assistive technology devices and home accessibility features: Prevalence, payment, need, and trends*. Washington, DC: National Center for Health Statistics.

McGuiness, K. (1982). *Stalking the elusive buck*. Boston: Environments Center, Massachusetts College of Art.

Morris, M., & Golinker, L. (1991). *Assistive technology: A funding workbook*. Washington, DC: RESNA Press.

National Council on Disability. (1993). *Study on the financing of assistive technology devices and services for individuals with disabilities.* Washington, DC: Author.

Peat, Marwick, Mitchell, & Company. (1979). Loan insurance and guarantee programs: A comparison of current practices and procedures. In R.T. Olsen (Ed.), *Loan guarantees: Current concerns and alternatives for control* (pp. 57–72). Washington, DC: U.S. Congressional Budget Office.

Reeb, K. (1987). *Revolving loan funds: Expanding equipment credit financing opportunities for persons with disabilities.* Washington, DC: Electronics Industries Foundation.

Reeb, K.G. Jr. (1989). *Assistive financing for assistive devices: Loan guarantees for purchase of products by persons with disabilities.* Washington, DC: Electronics Industries Foundation.

Reeb, K., & McFarland, S. (1988). Funding sources and strategies. In L.E. Perlman & A. Enders (Eds.), *Rehabilitation technology service delivery: A practical guide* (pp. 107–123). Washington, DC: RESNA Press.

Rehabilitation Act of 1973, PL 93-112. (September 26, 1973). Title 29, U.S.C. 701 et seq: *U.S. Statutes at Large, 87,* 355–394.

Rehabilitation Act Amendments of 1986, PL 99-506. (October 21, 1986). Title 29, U.S.C. 701 et seq: *U.S. Statutes at Large, 100,* 1807–1846.

Rehabilitation Act Amendments of 1992, PL 102-569. (October 29, 1992). Title 29, U.S.C. 701 et seq: *U.S. Statutes at Large, 106,* 4397–4433.

RESNA Technical Assistance Project. (1992). *Overarching themes of the Tech Act: Consumer-responsiveness and systems change.* Washington, DC: Author.

Rubin, S., & Roessler, R. (1987). *Foundations of the vocational rehabilitation process.* Austin, TX: PRO-ED Inc.

Social Security Act of 1935, PL 74-271. (August 14, 1935). Title 42, U.S.C. 301 et seq: *U.S. Statutes at Large, 15,* 687–1774.

Technology-Related Assistance for Individuals with Disabilities Act of 1988, PL 100-407. (August 19, 1988). Title 29, U.S.C. 2201 et seq: *U.S. Statutes at Large, 102,* 1044–1065.

Trachtman, L. (1990). *Innovative and alternative programs for funding assistive technology: Special section on service delivery.* RESNA 13th Annual Meeting, Washington, DC: RESNA Press.

U.S. Bureau of the Census. (1991). *Poverty in the U.S.: 1988 and 1989.* Current Population Reports, Series P-60, No. 171. Washington, DC: U.S. Government Printing Office.

U.S. Congress, Office of Technology Assessment (OTA). (1982). *Technology and handicapped people.* Washington, DC: U.S. Government Printing Office.

U.S. Congressional Budget Office. (1979). *Loan guarantees: Current concerns and alternatives for control.* A compilation of staff working papers. Washington, DC: Author.

Virginia Assistive Technology System (VATS). (1991). *Consumer needs assessment survey.* Richmond: Author.

Virginia Assistive Technology System (VATS). (1993). *National research of loan-financing practice.* Richmond: Author.

Ward, C. (1989). *Subsidy programs for assistive devices.* Washington, DC: Electronics Industries Foundation.

Appendix: Program Design Options and Associated Decision Factors____

This appendix provides additional detail on the selection of design elements associated with loan program model approaches. For each program element, this section provides a limited set of options and associated decision factors that shape the choice among the presented options. In addition, each subsection provides a brief discussion of the choice among program design options. Administrative, financial, and oversight components are discussed in turn, as follows. The source for this appendix is VATS (1993).

ADMINISTRATIVE ELEMENTS

Alternative Forms of Financial Assistance

Options

1. Traditional loan
2. Interest or principal buy-down
3. Loan guarantee
4. Revolving fund loan

Decision factors

- Specific financing needs of target population (e.g., simple access to capital, low interest, extended loan term)
- Administrative capacity of sponsor organization
- Financial resources of sponsor organization

The choice among alternative forms of financial assistance should be made through careful consideration of the specific financing needs of the population intended to be served by the program. In addition, the administrative capacity of the sponsoring organization, as well as its financial resources, must be considered as possible constraints on the ability to implement certain options. These trade-offs are discussed further later in this section.

Administrative Parties/Partnerships

Options

1. Public entity(ies) only
2. Public–private partnership
   - Public agency and private bank(s)
   - Public agency and private not-for-profit agencies
   - Public agency, private bank(s), and private not-for-profit agencies

3. Private not-for-profit agencies only
4. Private not-for-profit agencies and private bank(s)

Decision factors

- Administrative capacity of sponsor organization
- Administrative capacity of not-for-profit agencies and private banks
- Financial resources of sponsoring organization
- Access of potential borrowers to sponsoring organization's facility(ies)
- Reputation of potential administrating entities

Whether to involve outside parties in the establishment of a loan program is a central consideration. The options for administrative partnerships presented here represent the spectrum of alternatives. The choice among them should be based on careful consideration of the administrative capacity of each of the potential players, as well as the financial resources of each party. In addition, the reputation of the potential administrating entities and the readiness of access to their facilities should be weighed.

Eligibility Criteria

Options

1. Member of target group (e.g., with disability)
2. Intended use of funding (e.g., buy assistive technology)
3. Financial need (proof of funding of last resort)
4. Ability to repay (assets/liabilities, net worth, income, debt-to-income ratio)

Decision factors

- Available funds relative to identified needs
- Goals of loan program (e.g., meet unmet needs, meet all needs of target population regardless of alternative funding options)
- Determined importance of rolling over loan funds

The options for setting eligibility criteria presented here are only examples of the range of options in this category. As noted, eligibility criteria can be based on a combination of several factors, including membership in a particular target group, the intended use of funding, financial need, and ability to repay the loan. There are a number of trade-offs implicit in the definition of eligibility criteria, but the central decision factors are the overall goals of the program and the availability of funds relative to identified needs. For example, if more funds were available, the eligibility criteria would need to be less selective.

Credit Check Requirement

Options

1. Always require
2. Never require
3. Require in certain cases

Decision factors

- Importance of minimizing default risk
- Desire to screen out credit risks versus desire to provide funds to all applicants

While the decision to include a credit check as part of the design of a loan program may seem to be a secondary consideration, it has an important impact on the ability of loan programs to meet the needs of their intended beneficiaries. In many cases, loan applicants are unable to get traditional financing because of poor credit or a lack of credit history. Therefore, if a loan program relies on a credit check to screen applicants, it may screen out those applicants intended to be served. However, without a credit check, the security of the loan program may be jeopardized because of the risk of encountering high rates of loan default. This trade-off should be considered in light of the specific needs of the target population.

Provision of Nonfinancial Services

Options

1. Provide credit, personal finance counseling
2. Provide advocacy, assistance with other funding (e.g., medicare, medicaid)
3. Provide technical training (e.g., use of assistive technology devices)

Decision factors

- Determined importance of meeting nonfinancial needs of borrowers with this program
- Determined importance of screening out applicants that are better served with other funding sources
- Administrative capacity of loan program to fulfill multiple roles
- Availability of nonfinancial services elsewhere
- Expected bearing on credit risk/default rate

Many loan programs provide additional services to their clientele, such as personal finance counseling, advocacy, or technical training. Provision of these services may be central to the success of a loan program in meeting the needs of program beneficiaries, but comes at a cost. Some nonfinancial services actually improve the health of the loan program by acting to reduce the rate of loan default. Therefore, careful consideration should be given to the need for and ability to provide services other than direct loan assistance.

FINANCIAL ELEMENTS

Sources of Funding

Options

1. Federal grants
2. State appropriations
3. State bond issue
4. State dedicated taxes, fees, or fines

5. Foundation grants and individual donations
6. Corporate donations
7. Corporate/private loans
8. Private bank/credit union funds
9. Other

Decision factors

- Trade-offs with respect to control of loan program
- Importance of maximizing loan fund capital
- Availability of funding from various sources relative to identified need

The sources of funding for a loan program is often not so much a function of choice as practicality. Programs often seek and receive funding from the sources available at the time of program implementation. There are, however, some trade-offs worth considering. Certain funding sources carry with them the requirement to relinquish some amount of program control to the funding source. This requirement must be weighed against the determined level of need and availability of alternative sources of funds.

Funding/Capitalization

Options

1. One-time capitalization
2. Annual/renewable capitalization

Decision factors

- Measure of relative security of loan program
- Availability of one-time funding
- Likelihood of maintaining renewable funding

The choice between relying on a one-time capitalization or ongoing renewable funding is central to the security of a proposed loan program. This issue also relates to the central choice among loan program types. For example, the advantage of the revolving loan fund model is that, once funded, the loan fund should be able to continue into perpetuity, without requiring additional funding. Alternatively, traditional loan assistance programs rely on ongoing funding. To the extent that one-time capitalization funds are available, they are generally preferable to relying on continued support.

Loan Amounts

Options

1. Establish minimum loan amount
2. Establish maximum loan amount

Decision factors

- Administrative costs relative to size of loan
- Loan funding availability—potential trade-off with maximizing number of loans

A fairly specific financial element is the establishment of minimum and maximum loan amounts. The reason to establish minimum amounts is to limit the administrative costs relative to the size of each loan. Small loans may cost more to administer than they are worth. Alternatively, programs may establish grants for relatively small needs. The purpose of maximum loan amounts is two-fold. First, loan maximums limit the program's exposure to the risk of nonpayment by an individual borrower. Second, by establishing maximum loan amounts the program can spread loan funds to a greater number of recipients, thus maximizing the number of individuals served. Minimum and maximum loan amounts should be set in light of the expected cost ranges of the items to be funded.

Interest Rates

Options

1. Provide subsidized/below market rates
2. Provide loans at market rates
3. Provide loans at above market rates

Decision factors

- Specific financing needs of target population (and ability to repay loan at varying rates)
- Availability of additional funding (depending on specific program structure, subsidy can deplete loan capital)

The setting of interest rates is central to the design of individual loan programs and often shapes the success of such programs. The choice among interest rates depends on the specific financing needs of the population to be served and their ability to repay loans at varying rates. To the extent that applicants do not require reduced rates, programs may provide rates that are similar to market rates for other related items. Alternatively, in cases where beneficiaries cannot afford market rates but could afford slightly reduced rates, the provision of subsidized rates is central to the success of the program. In cases where the riskiness of the loan precludes traditional financing, above market rates can be charged and still meet the needs of some recipients. Unsuccessful programs are often those that have a mismatch between the needs of the target population and the financial assistance offered by the program.

Loan Term Lengths

Options

1. Keep terms short
2. Allow for repayment over longer periods

Decision factors

- Specific financing needs of target population
- Determined importance of providing enough time for borrower to be able to repay
- Useful life of equipment
- Determined need to recycle funds quickly to meet other borrowers' needs

The lengths of loans are often set in relation to the expected life of the equipment to be financed. This, however, is not always the only consideration to be made. In addition, consideration should be given to the ability of the target population to meet short repayment periods, which at times runs counter to the need to recycle funds quickly to meet other borrowers' needs.

Flexibility in Payment Terms

Options

1. Standard level payment stream, with first payment within 30 days of loan
2. Standard payment stream, with deferral of first payment
3. Incorporate balloon payment or deferred principal

Decision factors

- Income-generating potential of funded item (e.g., improving employment potential)
- Ability of borrowers to plan for and meet later payments
- Determined importance of recycling loan funds quickly

Similar to other financial terms, the establishment of payment terms, while relatively simple, can have a significant impact on the success of a loan program. Standard options are listed previously, with associated decision factors.

Treatment of Default Risks

Options

1. Allow for loan payment deferrals
2. Allow for loan extensions
3. Allow for loan forgiveness
4. Enforce payment schedules strictly

Decision factors

- Determined importance of recycling loans quickly
- Likelihood deferrals will result in collected payments
- Risk that providing forgiveness will increase incidence of nonpayment
- Administrative cost of enforcing payment terms

Because the mission of many loan programs is to reach populations not served by traditional financial markets, the risk of default can sometimes be higher than that experienced in the traditional market. Therefore, choices must be made about the treatment of default risks. Options include the allowance of payment deferrals, loan extensions, or loan forgiveness. The same variety of factors are associated with this choice as with many of the financial design options and are highlighted here.

Processing Fees

Options

1. Charge processing fees to cover administrative costs
2. Do not charge fees

Decision factors

- Determined need to cover administrative costs
- Possibility that fees will discourage applications

Processing fees can be used to offset the costs of administering a loan program, without cutting into loan fund capital. However, administrative fees can act to discourage potential borrowers. Therefore, as decisions are made about loan program design, the inclusion or exclusion of such fees should be considered.

Loan Security

Options

1. Use funded equipment as collateral
2. Require other collateral
3. Allow or require cosigner for loans of questionable credit quality

Decision factors

- Willingness to repossess equipment/ability to liquidate/administrative cost
- Weight of threat of repossession in borrower's prioritization of loan repayment
- Ability of borrowers to find cosigner

Traditional loan funding often relies on the potential repossession of funded items or other collateral. In the case of assistive technology, banks are often not willing to make such loans because they are unwilling to repossess this equipment or unable to liquidate it if they did. Therefore, the applicability of equipment as collateral for a loan program to fund assistive technology is limited, although has been done by some programs. Alternatives include requiring other collateral or allowing cosigners for loans of questionable credit quality.

OVERSIGHT ELEMENTS

The third category of design elements are those that relate to the oversight of the loan program. Three central elements are addressed here: loan decision/appeal authority, policy-making authority, and consumer involvement.

Loan Decision/Appeal Authority

Options

1. Bank loan review board
2. Revolving fund administrators
3. Appointed independent loan committee/board

Decision factors

- Primarily dictated by administrative parties, but important to have financial and, where possible, nonfinancial consumer-oriented expertise

Common approaches to the establishment of loan review authority are bank loan review boards, revolving fund administrators, and independent loan committees that are appointed to serve the function of reviewing loan applications. This element is primarily dictated by the administrative parties and sometimes by the funding sources.

Policy-Making Authority

Options

1. Program administrators
2. Policy review committee
3. Independent advisory board

Decision factors

- Primarily dictated by administrative parties; maximizing diversity important

Policy-making authority should be considered separately from loan decision authority, but again is largely dictated by the administrative parties involved.

Consumer Involvement

Options

1. Allow for consumer involvement in loan review
2. Allow for consumer involvement in policy
3. Allow for consumer involvement in general program management and administration

Decision factors

- Willingness to cede some control of program
- Willingness of funding source to fund program with varying levels of consumer involvement
- Importance of soliciting ongoing input on operations from representatives of target population
- Time/cost of supporting expansive boards

Some loan program administrators credit the success of their programs to the inclusion of consumers in various aspects of loan program administration. In order to do so, however, program administrators must be willing to cede some control of the program and pay the administrative costs associated with supporting such activities. For the most part, these approaches have proven to be helpful in ensuring that loan programs are designed and run with the consumers' needs as central determinants of program implementation.

13

Community Services_____

Sarah Oliver
Cindy L. Richardson

In *Discovering Community*, O'Brien (1986) wrote, "We can promote a sense of community if we develop the competence to overcome our habits of segregation, professionalization, and bureaucratization on even the smallest scale. Discovering community means testing the everyday assumptions of the service world through action and reflection" (p. 15).

No discussion of the development of community services could effectively proceed without a committed underpinning of consumer responsiveness. By *consumer*, the Virginia Assistive Technology System (VATS) means every existing and potential constituent of its overall services: users, providers, analysts, advocates, and everyone connected to those envisioned as contributing to or benefiting from the endeavor. Because of the diversity of resources available through VATS, every person in Virginia is potentially a consumer of the information and services VATS provides. Concomitantly, VATS regards all Virginians as potential partners in the identification of assistive technology needs and in the bridging of service delivery gaps. This means that in both its daily operations and its longer-range planning, VATS defines community in the most inclusive terms possible.

At the same time, VATS also recognizes that, to effectively reach this large target market, it must make its services accessible to diverse groups of persons throughout the state. VATS director Ken Knorr (personal communication, April 1982) once explained to staff, "Your job is to draw the circle larger and larger, to invite more people to the party." Although informal, this metaphor is logical. Unless VATS creates resources that are psychologically, physically, financially, and functionally accessible, it will have, in effect, thrown a party to which no one will come. Expanding the circle is an activity shared by everyone at VATS. In identifying the many forms of accessibility needed, VATS recognizes and appreciates the diverse components of its community and seeks ways to effectively meet the needs of each, while continuing to operate in an inclusive, cohesive manner.

Poet Theodore Roethke (1975) wrote of a friend, "She moved in circles, and those circles moved" (p. 122). Drop the pronoun and his language becomes an apt metaphor for the working model of community on which VATS has based the development of its outreach efforts.

VATS's statewide community is a circle constructed of many smaller overlapping and interlocking circles. While VATS regards all Virginians as its constituent and collaborative community, it attempts to identify and address the more specific needs of the subgroups that comprise the total population. This means devising information-sharing systems that are user friendly, interactive, and accessible through a toll-free number by voice, telecommunications devices for the deaf (TDD and text telephone [TTP]), modem, in person, and by mail. VATS' circles-within-circles view of community compels ongoing outreach in all directions at all levels—rural and urban, statewide and local—through traditional and nontraditional networks of users and providers of assistive technology. VATS continuously refines strategies for reaching people who could benefit from assistive technology, but who do not view themselves as having disabilities. Above all, VATS' view of community fuels a commitment to seek out and bring to the table representatives of the community who have an interest in assistive technology. VATS believes that such proactive outreach to everwidening circles of Virginians will enable many to discover that they have a real interest in what assistive technology can mean for them, a family member, student, client, coworker, employee, customer, or neighbor.

Consumer responsiveness has necessitated moving simultaneously on several fronts, sequencing and balancing VATS' programmatic and policy efforts, so that before demand is created resources are in place to meet expectations. It has meant living in a continuous loop of evaluation and revision, based on both formal and informal feedback. VATS' efforts at consumer responsiveness entail juggling conflicting views of respectful language, wrestling with issues related to the provision of equal access through facilitative rather than paternalistic/maternalistic processes, attempting to balance proactive and on-demand accommodations, and dovetailing VATS' own systems advocacy with the activities of self-empowered individuals with disabilities.

Given finite resources and burgeoning needs, VATS has an acute desire to share resources and remove turf and ego issues. VATS solicits and evaluates constructive criticism. Both VATS staff and the Virginia Council on Assistive Technology (VCAT), which guides VATS' activities, recognize that all VATS' activities are fluid and subject to constant refinement. In an attempt to develop responsive and relevant community services, every VATS endeavor is constructed on the framework of consumer responsiveness. This is a founding and guiding value of the project, and it translates into consumer involvement in virtually every level of activity—from interviewing prospective staff members and selecting grant proposals for funding to policy development and program evaluation. Experience reinforces the belief that this partnership helps make VATS' activities reflective of the real concerns and strengths of the individual and collective communities VATS was established to serve.

This chapter describes in some detail VATS' approach to community services. Aspects of other states' assistive technology projects are also discussed, and some of the common strands shared by successful community service initiatives are identified. This is not intended to be an exhaustive overview of every relevant community service paradigm in operation. It is instead a thoughtful consideration of how several programs have been conceived, launched, and tailored to fit the communities they are designed to serve.

"We have it made in Virginia" is one of the state's marketing slogans. Virginians, like most people, want to know that public dollars are being responsibly and efficiently directed to address real needs. This is a challenge in a state that includes urban centers interspersed with large areas of rural and mountainous terrain. Assistive technology and other service providers tend to be concentrated in the metropolitan areas, while many Virginians live in relative isolation from what their more urban counterparts might consider to be basic services.

Virginia's varied geography is reflected in the cultural diversity of its residents. In the rugged, expansive terrain of the Blue Ridge Mountains, many southwest Virginians live a considerable distance from their closest neighbor, much less the nearest assistive technology service provider. Along the Atlantic Ocean, residents of Virginia's Eastern Shore are separated from the land mass by the Chesapeake Bay. People here might more easily obtain services in the contiguous peninsular portions of Maryland than they could by crossing the bay.

In contrast to the largely rural expanses of the state, some of Virginia's metropolitan areas are bustling, ethnically diverse, and cosmopolitan. In northern Virginia, there are counties whose school students represent approximately 100 different countries and speak nearly 150 different languages.

Although the urban centers of Virginia are not very different from their counterparts in other states, there are parts of the state where travel from one county to the next is considered to be a major departure from routine. Much of Virginia's population shares a fondness for tradition, as well as rather conservative values. Yet side by side with these citizens are many other persons who relish change and the new possibilities provided by technology, travel, and innovation. VATS' challenge is to facilitate the development of a system that will offer all Virginians access to the assistive technology information, services, devices, and funding that they may need.

Given the nature of Virginia, VATS recognized the obvious—that a handful of people sitting in a small office in Richmond could not begin to reach all of the state's residents. Because VATS envisioned its target market as both collaborators and consumers of the system it hoped to help create, VATS staff had to get closer to where all Virginians live, study, work, and recreate. It is part of VATS' systems change mission to integrate assistive technology resources into other service delivery systems. This can only be accomplished through the broad awareness of assistive technology needs and solutions. Such awareness, along with the sense of ownership needed to propel the massive systems change that is envisioned, can come only from the grass roots involvement of thousands of Virginians across the commonwealth.

ASSISTIVE TECHNOLOGY RESOURCE CONSORTIA

VATS devoted the single largest line item of its budget for the establishment of four regional assistive technology resource centers, a term subsequently revised to assistive technology resource consortia (ATRC) to more accurately reflect their collaborative nature. In planning these regional entities, the staff realized that no narrowly defined community service model could stretch far enough to embrace all the demographic, geographic, and culturally diverse groups of Virginia's four main regions. When VATS listed the initial functions that it wanted the ATRC to perform, these functions included not only information and referral, public awareness, training, and demonstration opportunities, but also response to region-specific needs. The first four functions parallel some of the activities carried out at the state level, while the response to region-specific needs is exclusive to the ATRC. Each ATRC has fulfilled this component in its own way.

The request for proposals for prospective ATRCs required that each applicant operate a consortium of organizations interested in issues related to disability and assistive technology. As a result, even the activity of preparing the proposal required some level of networking. VATS received seven responses to its request for proposals. Assistive technology users, agency representatives, and other advocates helped review these proposals. After negotiations, four ATRCs were selected.

In the first 15 months, each ATRC learned a great deal about its own region. They began to better understand where the people in each region actually went for services and revised the borders of the ATRC regions accordingly. ATRCs began to identify that training–demonstration combination activities seemed to be the most effective means of generating assistive technology awareness, and they developed second-year plans with this in mind. They learned that, to reach people in certain communities with information about assistive technology-related events, staff needed to put up posters where people spent time (e.g., at the grocery store). The ATRCs are recognizing that there will always be a demand for basic public awareness presentations and trainings about assistive technology and about what VATS and ATRCs offer. After operating for 2 years, ATRCs are beginning to experience "repeat business" from groups desiring more in-depth presentations on a variety of specific topics. The VATS and ATRC networks are growing and deepening, providing the system with access to a variety of expertise and perspectives.

Assistive Technology Resource Consortium of Southeastern Virginia: Connecting to Communities' Needs

The Assistive Technology Resource Consortium of Southeastern Virginia (SEATRC) began establishing support within the community by first determining if there was, in fact, a need for such a program. This was done by inviting representatives from identified consumer groups, disability organizations, and community service programs in general to a meeting. This event was held prior to the sponsoring organization, Old Dominion University, making application to be the local site for VATS. At this gathering, approximately 25 consumers and professionals were asked to provide information on what they saw as gaps in service delivery regarding assistive technology and how the proposed ATRC could implement a program to address these needs accordingly. Not only were these groups asked to identify current gaps in service, they were also asked if they would be willing to support and provide assistance with the actual implementation process.

It was at this initial stage that the idea of establishing and working as a consortium first came about. Not only was it the intent of the funding agent (VATS) that the local sites work collaboratively within the community, but, based on the needs and resources within the region, it was believed that this was the only way the project could possibly accomplish this task. During the meeting, those in attendance pledged their support in many forms. Some volunteered their expertise, serving as speakers for workshops, offering guidance as board members, or working as members of a task group. Some offered resources, such as facilities or conference rooms where meetings or workshops could be held, or made available pieces of assistive equipment for demonstrations. Most important was their willingness to support and make consumers and other professionals aware of the proposed ATRC's services through their newsletters or through community contacts.

The process of involving the community in the program did not start and stop with one activity. Once SEATRC was awarded the contract to serve as the local site for VATS, an open house and press conference was held. Invited guests included those involved in the initial meeting, as well as individuals who had previously neither participated nor been identified as potential users or program supporters. The objective was to expand knowledge in the community about emerging ATRC services. As before, those in attendance were provided with the opportunity to share with staff their views on existing gaps in services and also inform staff of available resources of which they might not be aware.

In its desire to stay connected with the resources and needs of the area, SEATRC established an executive advisory board. The functions of the board include monitoring program effectiveness; identifying the needs of the community and how SEATRC could best meet those needs; and encouraging participation and support from the consumer, educational, service provider, and business committees. Individuals asked to serve on the board not only represented a cross section of these groups, but possessed abilities and interests that complemented the program's mission. They have been instrumental in helping staff identify gaps in service and in encouraging community participation, and also they have actively supported efforts at meeting certain needs by lending their expertise and assistance at various events and activities.

Even with the support staff received from organizations and individuals, creating an awareness of the program and how to gain access to its services remains the greatest challenge. Knowing that many factors often contribute to such a potential lack of awareness, as well as to the failure to take advantage of known services, SEATRC set out to establish connections with persons who could possibly benefit from its programs.

SEATRC faced an even greater challenge in this regard because the southeastern Virginia area consists of both metropolitan and rural communities, separated not only by miles of land but also, in some instances, by miles of water. A concept that served quite well in allowing staff to provide equal access to services was the establishment of satellite offices. In establishing these offices, SEATRC staff first identified organizations already serving persons with disabilities in the remote areas of the region. Members on the advisory board were instrumental in recommending agencies that might be receptive and that provided a diverse group of services in their respective communities. After the members met with the directors of these programs to introduce them to services and to communicate the desire to establish through them a link with the residents of their respective communities, contracts were signed to formalize the relationships.

These relationships have worked extremely well. The program was able to provide residents of these communities with a local point of access, as well as have trusted advocates in these areas who can identify needs, work with staff in coordinating programs and services, and serve as a link to these communities. An example of the success of these partnerships can be found in the Petersburg, Virginia, area.

Petersburg Satellite Activities

Working with the satellite office, the Crater Area Agency on Aging, the Petersburg Chamber of Commerce, and a local convention center, staff were able to sponsor a day-long workshop for 200 older adults and service providers on products and services that would enable older adults to live independently. Participants had the opportunity to hear about these products, to see them demonstrated, and, in some instances, to try them. Vendors representing mobility, low vision, and hearing products and devices, as well as an assortment of other products and devices, were on hand. In addition, speakers told participants about community resources that would assist them in purchasing assistive technology devices.

SEATRC planned the function, taking into account barriers that sometimes impede other organizations trying to offer a similar opportunity. Staff identified any obstacles, such as lack of resources on the part of the sponsors or participants, that might have interfered with the event's success. They then developed plans to overcome these potential barriers. Working together, staff and sponsors were able to offer participants a cost-free workshop that included lunch, transportation to the program, and a wealth of information and products. This opportunity was made possible only through the combined efforts of federal, state, and local agencies in tandem with area businesses.

Other activities that have allowed SEATRC to connect with those who could benefit from its services have involved similar interactive, collaborative approaches. From the outset, SEATRC staff sought to speak before as many diverse groups as possible. At times, this involved participating in events conducted by other disability organizations and programs serving older adults, or just community events in general, such as a local fair. On other occasions, SEATRC created and promoted its own events, such as workshops for employers on successfully accommodating employees with disabilities or workshops for families on how to obtain funding for assistive technology.

Whatever the occasion, staff took the time to provide information on gaining access to the ATRC program and passed out brochures and other promotional materials, encouraging persons who received them to distribute the information through their own networks. Staff intended for this material to be shared with colleagues, consumers, or other persons who could benefit from services. To this end, SEATRC was able to speak to more than 34 different audiences of users or potential users, service providers, educators, and employers during the first year of operation. Due to increased demand for presentations regarding SEATRC resources or assistive technology issues and products, the project has established a speaker's bureau to assist in handling these requests. Once again, by asking for community support from both the users of resources and other professionals in the area, SEATRC has been able to provide a broader area of expertise and keep up with the demand for this information.

Many individuals who could benefit from the services are often not connected with an agency through which they could hear about SEATRC. Many would not necessarily know how to seek out this information unless they had prior experience in doing so. With this in mind, the staff has tried as often as possible to take technology or information about SEATRC to public places of activity, such as area shopping malls.

Technology Fair

One of the most successful activities has been the annual assistive technology fair. The original intent of the fair was to create an awareness of the various types of products that are available and to afford potential assistive technology users the opportunity to gain access to a variety of devices. The results of the fair were more eventful than the staff had imagined.

To publicize the event, particularly among the users and potential users of assistive technology, SEATRC promoted the fair through a direct mailing to all individuals and organizations associated with the program, through speaking engagements before various community and consumer groups, by advertising in other disability organizations' newsletters, and via the shopping mall's public awareness announcements. Although these activities were extremely successful in drawing persons with disabilities and their families to the technology fair, there was a previously unidentified population present at the mall as well who availed themselves of the opportunities the fair presented. This group included older adults as well as spouses or family members of individuals who had recently been affected by disability.

A majority of individuals in both groups would not have been reached through the initial promotional efforts. Older adults whose lives could be enhanced by assistive technology often do not consider themselves to have a disability. Instead, they believe they are simply growing older and would not have identified with the intent of the technology fair. For the same reason, they were unlikely to have been affiliated with any disability-related organizations that were promoting the fair.

Spouses and other family members of persons who were recently disabled are often unaware of the resources in the community, at least initially. They have not previously had to seek out such services and may have no idea where to begin. The exciting aspect of holding the ATRC technology fair at the mall was that both older adults and family members of individuals who had recently been disabled were out shopping and casually happened upon the assistive technology information. Older adults marveled at the technology that had the potential of assisting them to maintain their independence. Stairlifts, scooters, and a variety of home adaptations enabled many to see how they could resume activities recently given up as a result of diminishing abilities. Family members were able to see that technology could make substantial changes in the quality of life of people with disabilities.

Several children, who prior to this event had not been directly affected by disability, stopped by the booths to learn how assistive devices could enable anyone with a disability to enjoy and participate in the same activities they themselves enjoyed. SEATRC staff could have never achieved the level of community involvement and education had this event been held at a conference hall or even at the university.

Establishing community involvement and support is not always easy. Often, ideas that seem workable in concept fail in execution. SEATRC has found it imperative to capitalize on the resources already available in the community. Because SEATRC joins with other organizations that share concerns regarding service provision and seeks opportunities that will meet both organizations' goals, the community eventually reaps the benefits of this collaboration.

A final recommendation in coordinating community services is not only to involve the people engaged in services, but also to support their self-empowerment. This is accomplished by valuing their expertise and insight and creating opportunities for them to play a vital role in identifying gaps in service and assisting the organization in addressing these needs. By promoting ownership, the organization is able to deliver a service that is truly extraordinary and that could not have been achieved through a single source of service.

Networking for Information

An important aspect of community service delivery is reaching people with information when they need it. People with newly acquired or changing disabilities suddenly begin to look for information that might have held little meaning for them just 2 weeks earlier. Employers want to understand how assistive technology supports their job accommodation efforts. Service providers want to know what technology is available for the persons with whom they work. Also, many want to know how to fund assistive technology.

One ATRC is developing a consumer consultative network to facilitate communications among experienced assistive technology users and persons who are seeking to learn more about particular devices and services. This will provide a real-world view for persons who are discovering new arenas in their lives in which assistive technology might make a difference. Another ATRC facilitates informal groups, arranging assistive technology demonstrations and related presentations on devices and topics selected by the group members.

One big question in community service delivery is always how to get information about available resources to people who are not currently connected to traditional or obvious networks. Placement of assistive technology fairs in shopping malls; informational placemats given to regional restaurants; fliers disseminated through pharmacies; and information printed on grocery bags or distributed via state paychecks, utility company bills, insurance companies, and the Motor Vehicles Division are strategies that VATS has identified to more widely disseminate information about the resources available through the system. Such activities are anticipated to reach a broader cross-section of Virginians, helping VATS get information into the hands of people who are not involved in the existing disability-related service network.

Training and Public Awareness

In addition to public awareness, training and demonstration opportunities that specifically target users and potential users of assistive technology and their family members have been delivered by both VATS and ATRC. The state and local programs have also provided corollary opportunities for service providers and members of the business community. One ATRC designed a particularly effective presentation for employers. After the informational sessions, participants are given details about a specific individual and a particular job and asked to think of ways to accommodate the job to the person using assistive technology. Usually, most employers suggest relatively expensive, high-tech solutions. After participants share their proposed solutions with the group, the session ends when the individual described in the case history comes forward from the audience to explain and demonstrate the low-cost technology he or she uses every day to accomplish the job. This simple reality check makes a deep impression on business people whose assumptions about the cost of job accommodations can be pivotal in limiting, or expanding, job opportunities within the community.

ATRCs have also recognized the importance of reaching children with information about assistive technology. By helping children think of assistive technology as part of everyday life, it is hoped that they will be less resistant and less apt to be intimidated or wary of technology than many adults. One ATRC collaborated with a local children's museum to create an interactive exhibit on assistive technology. Another ATRC sponsored poster contests in its region's schools. After in-school presentations about assistive technology, students have the opportunity to create posters about what they have learned. Artwork from the winning posters is incorporated into ATRC brochures and placemats.

Creating environments in which people can not only gain information but also connect with a number of service providers at one time has proven to be an effective and practical format. In response to the great concern over how to fund assistive technology, several ATRCs have held funding workshops. These have been tremendously well received by hundreds of Virginians. One of the most successful models began with a keynote address, followed by concurrent tracks on funding issues related to children and adults. Following these, all participants were invited to talk with the representatives of assistive technology funding sources who were at tables spaced throughout a large room where people could move comfortably between them. By the time participants left, they had an opportunity to get their specific questions answered, begin any paperwork relevant to gaining access to desired services, and meet contact persons with whom they could continue to work long after the 1-day workshop.

STATE/LOCAL SYSTEM COLLABORATION

Synergy is the modus operandi of VATS' approach to community services. The collective effort of VATS and ATRC staffs is truly greater than the sum of the individual accomplishments. By sharing experiences and resources, the system's capacity is magnified. Everyone learns from each other's mistakes and successful programs, and strategies are shared freely, preventing the need for each region to reinvent solutions to the same problems. The same holds true for ATRCs' association with the satellites throughout their regions, which help take services another step closer to the homes of more Virginians. The establishment of satellite locations has enabled VATS to gain access to networks so that the system can more quickly reach many individuals who might have an interest in the assistive technology resources it offers. By carefully selecting well-regarded programs as satellites, VATS has been able to accelerate the establishment of VATS/ATRC credibility by associating the state and local system with trusted local programs. The relationships have been symbiotic, as the host agencies have gained the capacity to provide on-site access to a number of assistive technology resources not formerly available to their constituents.

The teamwork between VATS and ATRC did not evolve without struggle. The different perspectives engendered by region, consortium composition/organization, and divergent approaches to similar missions eventually led to frustration. Questions of which tasks were best accomplished centrally and which required collaborative effort continue to be examined as new programs and products are proposed. The search for standardized operational definitions continues as staff seek to make VATS' systemwide reporting and evaluation more meaningful for analysis and decision making. Both VATS and ATRC staff are perennially stretched by multiple demands; sometimes, what is a critical need from one perspective must temporarily take a back seat on the other party's agenda.

Working with external evaluators in ATRCs' first year helped uncover the need for team-building work. This approach has been helpful, although the predictable turnovers in staff necessitate occasional reestablishment of relationships. Now VATS and ATRC have, for the most part, arrived at comfortable terms—all parties are consulted in the development of future plans. ATRC representatives sit on VCAT. Even more ATRC staff serve on the council's specific task groups (e.g., Public Awareness and Community Integration, Resource Development, Information and Referral), which provide guidance to all aspects of VATS' activities. Every year, ATRCs devote a substantial portion of their winter quarterly meeting to help shape the vision for VATS' next continuation or extension proposal. ATRCs contribute to VATS' annual assistive technology conference, frequently serving as panelists and as sources of suggestions for presenters and exhibitors.

Some ATRCs have extensive consortia membership, with each representative having equal voice. Others consist of smaller consortia, but have additional community representation through broad-based advisory committees. As long as an ATRC fulfills its mission and shows substantial involvement by individuals with disabilities and other community stakeholders, VATS remains flexible about letting each ATRC evolve in the pattern that it believes best serves its particular region.

MULTICULTURAL INCLUSION

Just as VATS staff has turned to the disability community for advice on making VATS' resources relevant and accessible, the staff also continues to seek expertise in other areas. To create and improve VATS' ability to provide equal access to VATS' resources for Virginians of all ethnic, racial, and cultural backgrounds, it has convened a focus group of individuals with expertise in an array of endeavors related to inclusion, minority outreach, and multiculturalism. Their suggestions will be incorporated into current and future VATS operations. It will always be important for VATS to ask, "How are we doing?" and "How can we improve?" at every opportunity and to take seriously the answers received from the community when refining programs and policies.

CREATIVE INITIATIVE AWARDS

A number of VATS projects other than ATRC have important community services aspects. The Creative Initiative Award represents VATS' commitment to assistive technology initiatives at the local, regional, institutional, and statewide levels. In its first three rounds, the purpose of these grants has been to support diverse explorations of innovative assistive technology initiatives, which if successful have the potential to be replicated throughout Virginia (Table 13.1). Subsequent rounds are anticipated to focus increasingly on assistive technology-related systems change initiatives. VATS has historically funded approximately 10 awards per year. The program is intensely competitive. Last year the total funds sought by Creative Initiative Award applicants far exceeded VATS' annual budget.

Proposals are reviewed by evaluation panels that include users of assistive technology, advocates, service providers, agency representatives, and family members of technology users. Both inexperienced and seasoned grant writers have submitted successful proposals. Although some Creative Initiative Awards have funded statewide activities, most of these awards support local responses to local needs. One recipient's inclusionary technology program won the Virginia Excellence in Education Award. Another award supported the first stage of the development of a navigational system that has potentially global implications for individuals who are blind. A statewide initiative funded last year helped make Virginia's emergency services more responsive and accessible to the needs of individuals with disabilities.

Table 13.1. Selected creative initiative award-funded projects

Virginia Remote Sensing Center/The College of William & Mary This project's goal is to initiate the development of a reliable advanced technology system that will enable persons who are visually disabled to independently travel in both familiar and unfamiliar areas.

Norfolk Public Schools, Department of Special Education Support Services This project was developed to establish a centrally located workstation of technological equipment that is accessible to students (ages 0–22) with disabilities, their parents, and regular and special educators, as well as technological support services. This project uses technology to enhance the independence and support the inclusion of students with disabilities into regular classroom environments.

Virginia Department for the Deaf and Hard of Hearing This organization formally surveyed public safety answering points, hospital emergency rooms, and poison control centers throughout Virginia, as well as persons who are deaf, hard of hearing, or deaf-blind. Results were used to develop a "best practices" guide and pocket handbook for public safety answering points and to develop a consumer education/awareness plan on these issues.

Richmond Cerebral Palsy Center This project funded a consumer-created conference on assistive technology.

Similarly, the Arkansas Assistive Technology Project, Increasing Capabilities Access Network (ICAN), offers subgrants for persons to develop, enhance, or expand assistive technology services in rural areas of the state. This program helps to build services locally in outlying areas. Before these subgrants are even awarded, the applicant must develop continuation plans for the program. Bob Sterling is in charge of ICAN's community programs and explains: "We are building sunsets into everything because ICAN is only here temporarily" (B. Sterling, personal communication, May 1994).

ECONOMIC FACTORS

Many VATS initiatives are driven by economic realities. It is important that VATS' annual statewide assistive technology conference have the benefit of the participation of a broadly representative range of assistive technology users. VATS is sensitive to the financial constraints that might prevent some interested individuals from attending the conference. To help circumvent economic barriers to conference participation, VATS solicits sponsorship for approximately 50 consumer scholarships each year.

In response to national and state research depicting funding as the major barrier to the acquisition of assistive technology, VATS has recently completed national research into loan models (see Chapter 12). This research will guide VATS as it designs a long-term, low-interest assistive technology loan fund for Virginia. These and other VATS projects benefit directly from the guidance and experience of individuals with disabilities who have helped staff plan meaningful responses to the needs of their community.

SYSTEMS CHANGE PROJECTS AND COMMUNITY SERVICE

Each assistive technology systems change project has designed its systems and procedures according to state needs. There are striking parallels between the Virginia and Delaware approaches. Both states turned to stakeholders for guidance in creating a system relevant to their populations' assistive technology needs. Both considered the cultural and political climate and the diversity of their communities; both considered how and where their state's citizens obtained services; and both remain flexible and function in a collegial fashion with the input of regional and state office perspectives. Delaware and Virginia each set up both central and regional/local service delivery components. Both programs have been mindful of the time-limited nature of their initial federal funding and have developed in ways that have encouraged local "ownership." Although the approaches discussed have unquestionably contributed to the evolution, ongoing progress, and evaluation of community services in Virginia and Delaware, they are by no means the only elements of successful programs (B. Mineo, personal communication, December 1993).

The entire point of developing community services is to design services that fit the community. Alexandra Enders of the Rural Institute on Disabilities in Montana has said, "There are rural places where when you need assistive technology, you start by going to the blacksmith" (1992). It is essential to understand such realities before attempting to design community services.

The Illinois Assistive Technology Project is currently focusing on building local capacity for systems change from the ground up to complement the top-down systems change work at the state office. This approach includes the use of advocates who serve as a linking agent between resources and people in need.

The Illinois Assistive Technology Project's regional advisory councils include both primary and secondary consumers and identify specific assistive technology issues and barriers in each region. As these barriers and issues are recognized, they are referred to the project's policy analyst who then develops strategies to overcome them. This strategy-building component enables systems change to occur on multiple levels with different groups at the same time. Wilhelmina Gunther, executive director of the Illinois Assistive Technology Project, says, "It is not knocking one card down at a time, but spreading tentacles in one hundred different directions. . . . Involvement of people at the regional level in issues pertaining to the legislative process builds capacity to knock down barriers" (W. Gunther, personal communication, May 1994).

Some state technology projects allocate large portions of their budgets for the provision of mobile services because they best meet the needs of their state; others work through existing regional programs. Some create demonstration centers, while others identify existing demonstration resources. These variables are necessary to tailor the service models to the community's preferences and needs.

For example, ICAN, the Arkansas Assistive Technology Project, has developed a mentoring program for service providers throughout that state. When physical, occupational, and speech therapists go to a locality to provide assistive technology assessments, they invite local therapists to join them to learn more about the process. This creates a network of provider-to-provider assistive technology mentoring.

Maine's Assistive Technology Project, Maine Consumer Information and Technology Training Exchange (CITE), has developed an outreach telecommunications program using interactive television and an electronic mail (e-mail) system developed in partnership with two consumer groups (a parents' group and a Center for Independent Living). The e-mail system has provided low-cost terminals to persons living in rural areas.

The interactive television system is connected to all seven Maine university campuses and also to 80 high school sites throughout the state. Maine CITE has developed an informational program on assistive technology that is broadcast via the television system. People at the university sites can see and hear each other over the system; those at the high schools have two-way audio, but can see only one site (K. Powers, personal communication, May 1994).

South Dakota's population of approximately 700,000 people is scattered over 77,000 square miles. The populations of its three largest cities range from 35,000 to 100,000 people.

After that, city sizes drop to the 15,000–20,000 range. In fact, there are many towns comprising only 200–300 people each. For many South Dakotans, it may be literally hundreds of miles to the nearest community, which may not have medical services.

To address these geographic and demographic realities, DakotaLink, South Dakota's Assistive Technology Project, has developed two 32-foot mobile units pulled by truck across the state. These units are accessible to persons with a variety of disabilities, and they can go to any location. The trailers are completely self-contained, have their own air conditioning and heating systems, and travel with their own generators so that the entire unit can run in locations that do not have electricity.

DakotaLink works with consumer groups, agencies, and school districts, which invite it to bring the trailers to their communities. The trailers are designed to meet ADA standards and include a hydraulic wheelchair lift, two main computer stations, and four workstations where people can try out a number of other assistive technology devices. Input from an advisory committee and consumers helped structure exhibits that include a broad cross-disability focus.

Everything in these mobile units is designed to be both functional and visible. Low-tech devices are included, as well as a rolltop desk on the counter so that persons who are blind or who have low vision can feel the types of devices that might be useful to them. There are two telephones that enable visitors to try out the amplified phones and ringers. There is a work modification unit in the back of the trailer.

When the trailers were first developed, public service announcements (PSAs) helped get word of their availability to the public. PSAs are still developed for use in each community the mobile units visit and to encourage local participation. DakotaLink has a toll-free phone number that South Dakotans may call to get information about the trailers or to schedule a visit by one.

The mobile units are now booked months in advance. Rural communities have begun to request that the units come to their areas so that the equipment in them can be used by local teams of occupational and physical therapists, psychologists, and so on for assistive technology evaluations and assessments (R. Reed & P. Czerny, personal communication, May 1994).

It is helpful to look at a number of existing models before deciding how to structure community services. There is a wealth of experience and ongoing experimentation in this area by the assistive technology systems change projects, as well as by other projects that have fostered community activities. These are not exclusively related to services for persons with disabilities. By sampling broadly, VATS gained insight into the relative merits of models that it might otherwise have missed had it focused only on technology-related programs. While VATS looked to Virginians to help identify the state's needs and resources, staff looked to the entire United States to better understand what approaches might work best at home.

CONCLUSION

The identification of resources and needs, the participation of a broad array of stakeholders, and the willingness to continue refining services so that they fit the community's changing needs are among the common characteristics of successful programs (Table 13.2). Another characteristic is the tenacious belief that all persons deserve to be heard, not only as consumers of services but also as contributors whose experiences can inform and shape the development of relevant community services. Community-oriented services definitely will take advantage of this expertise.

One of the members of VCAT is an ardent and effective community organizer and advocate. She credits her childhood physical therapist for fostering the attitude that has enabled

Table 13.2. Some common components of successful community services

- Is driven by a broad array of consumers and other stakeholders
- Engages in ongoing dialogue with constituent and collaborative communities
- Identifies and responds to community-specific needs
- Promotes local autonomy and supports self-empowerment of constituents and collaborative partners
- Builds public awareness to inform community of resources offered
- Fosters coalition building at all levels, both inside and outside of the organization
- Creates ways to reach beyond traditional audiences to involve other persons who might be interested in the program, but who may not identify their connection without some targeted information or outreach
- Makes collaboration a way of business
- Promotes a coordinated multilevel approach: grass roots efforts in concert with larger (e.g., statewide) top-down efforts
- Fosters visionary approaches to organizational goals
- Proactively involves culturally diverse communities
- Identifies community resources and needs
- Continually refines services to fit community's changing and emerging needs

her to fight numerous uphill battles during her lifetime. As a young child, she would sometimes become discouraged when every apparent approach to a task still failed to produce results. Whenever she would say, "I can't do this," the therapist would harness the child's creativity and determination and encourage her by saying, simply, "Let's think how we *can*."

Those words apply as much to persons who seek to design effective community services as to a small girl learning to walk. Community services are effective when a community's needs and resources are identified and articulated by the community, when stakeholders work collaboratively to achieve common goals, and when new partners are continually brought in as the scope of services expands. Quality community assistive technology services require becoming comfortable with the continuous loop of evaluating and refining programs. Above all, those involved know that they *can* make a difference.

REFERENCES

Enders, A. (1992, May). Left to your own devices. Presented at the Virginia Assistive Technology System's annual conference on Assistive Technology, Norfolk, VA.

O'Brien, J. (1986). *Discovering community*. Atlanta: Responsive Systems Associates.

Roethke, T. (1975). I knew a woman. In Roethke, T. (Ed.), *The collected poems of Theodore Roethke* (p. 122). Garden City, NY: Doubleday Anchor.

14

The User's Perspective of Assistive Technology

Ed Turner
Chris Barrett
Ann Cutshall
Bryan K. Lacy
Jean Keiningham
Mary Kay Webster

The Americans with Disabilities Act (ADA) of 1990 (PL 101-336) was designed *by* persons with disabilities *for* persons with disabilities. This highly celebrated piece of legislation established a new process and framework that has permeated other disability legislation. The 1992 reauthorization of the Rehabilitation Act (PL 102-569), the Individuals with Disabilities Education Act (IDEA) of 1990 (PL 101-476), the Individuals with Disabilities Education Act Amendments of 1991 (PL 102-119), and the 1994 reauthorization of the Technology-Related Assistance for Individuals with Disabilities Act (Tech Act) (PL 103-218) are all distinguished examples of new legislation that share ADA's language and framework. Members of the disability community have begun to play an active role in shaping legislation.

Slowly, individuals with disabilities are also beginning to realize that they too must play a role in government at both the state and local levels if these new public laws are going to change services and ultimately have a positive impact on local communities. Never has the issue of advocacy been more crucial than with assistive technology. Long-term satisfaction with assistive devices can be achieved only when individuals with disabilities advocate for themselves by speaking out and expressing their wants, desires, and goals. Assistive technology users must pave the way, demonstrating how assistive technology services and devices can be major liberating forces.

Technology users can begin by taking a leadership role in their communities and defining assistive technology to other persons in these communities. Communities must gain a broader perspective of assistive technology; that is, they must view assistive technology as being any process, device, or means that an individual with a disability personally chooses to perform a critical function or achieve a desired goal (Williams, 1991). Once communities ac-

The authors wish to acknowledge the support of Valerie Brooke, Virginia Commonwealth University Rehabilitation Research and Training Center on Supported Employment, for her support in the preparation of this chapter.

cept this definition, persons with disabilities can put assistive technology to work in their homes, on jobs, and at play. Using assistive technology to obtain employment and to live independently will enable persons with disabilities to be economically independent. However, individuals with disabilities cannot do this alone; they will need the assistance of both technology experts and the community. Each party must be committed to finding the best way for technology to work for the individual.

Currently, there is much being written about the changing field of rehabilitation services, the value of assistive technology, and the availability of assistive devices (Brooke, Barcus, & Inge, 1992; Mann, 1991; Sowers, 1991). Rehabilitation-related articles, conference notifications, pamphlets, and advertisements that make claims of "consumer choice" or "consumer empowerment" are not hard to find. Such information often describes the value of assistive technology and the miraculous impact that it has on the lives of persons with disabilities. This chapter does not dispute the literature, yet there is still much work to be done. Many individuals with disabilities have not gained access to assistive technology devices and services, remaining unserved (Mann, 1991). Furthermore, the vast majority of persons with multiple disabilities and severe physical disabilities have not yet entered community employment (Revell, Wehman, Kregel, West, & Rayfield, 1994). There are literally hundreds of thousands of persons who could live independently with the proper application of assistive technology, but who remain in state-run institutions or nursing homes.

Many individuals with disabilities who have been able to gain access to assistive technology devices and services are involved in a national crisis of technology abandonment (Phillips, 1993). Simply, technology abandonment is when an individual acquires an assistive device or piece of equipment and subsequently puts the item in storage because it does not meet the user's needs. There are numerous theories on why technology abandonment is occurring, ranging from users outgrowing a particular assistive device to professionals ordering what they think is appropriate as opposed to listening to the assistive technology user. The authors of this chapter view this dilemma as a service issue. In other words, as long as professionals do not listen to their clients and continue to assume the responsibility for determining their clients' needs and choices, this crisis will not only persist but will reach epidemic proportions.

This chapter presents the authors' personal experiences with obtaining and using assistive technology devices and services. In addition, the authors share specific strategies for improving service delivery for individuals with disabilities, professionals, and community members. These strategies focus on the coordination of technology services among service providers, developers, retailers, and third-party payors. Finally, the authors share their vision for the future.

The authors wrote this chapter from a user's perspective on assistive technology devices and services as a result of their participation in a focus group. Each author has a disability and uses assistive technology devices and services on a daily basis. For the purpose of clarity, the authors use *individual* and/or *person with a disability*, *assistive technology user*, *technology user*, *client*, and *customers* when referring to individuals who use assistive technology services.

USERS OF ASSISTIVE TECHNOLOGY DEVICES AND SERVICES

The chapter authors represent a variety of ages, backgrounds, disabilities, and experiences with assistive technology; yet it is interesting to note that the authors had amazingly similar experiences when attempting to obtain and use assistive technology devices and services. Those authors with extensive exposure to assistive technology have personally witnessed strange and creative solutions to various complex physical challenges.

One dated but memorable example is of a particularly creative therapist who used skis and an overhead garage door opener to create a harness to assist several students in learning how to walk. Although present-day liability laws would probably prevent any therapist from continuing such a practice, it was a creative and useful answer for the individuals who benefited from its use. Other individuals remembered using early assistive technology devices, such as leg-long braces, portable typewriters, and keyguards. Unquestionably, motorized wheelchairs and computers are the two biggest technological breakthroughs for persons with physical and sensory disabilities according to the focus group. Velcro received the largest vote for being *the* best invention of all time.

As a result of the focus group, the authors realized that all of them had met both barriers and challenges as they attempted to gain access to assistive technology services in their communities. In the past, systems barriers were so great that several authors agreed that they would rather sit on a street corner with a tin cup than repeat some of the degrading experiences they had when attempting to obtain their first electric wheelchair. However, for most communities, rehabilitation services have changed during the last 10 years. Technology users have gained experience with the system and are now able to offer some strategies to overcome barriers. The strategies offered in the following section hinge on assistive technology users becoming familiar with key pieces of disability legislation and on becoming self-advocates.

Know the Law

Many individuals with disabilities celebrated their newly won civil rights with the passage of ADA. ADA seeks to end discriminatory practices against persons with disabilities and states that every effort should be made to provide reasonable accommodations. Employers can no longer screen persons with disabilities based on ambiguous job descriptions or medical requirements that are unrelated to the actual functions of the position. Yet ADA does not specify what accommodations are considered to be "reasonable" or how to pay for the assistive devices and services that might be necessary to fulfill individual job accommodations. Such specification and detail is beyond the scope of the law and, in the long run, would not serve individuals with disabilities. Rather, it is the responsibility of persons with disabilities and their advocates to work with employers, rehabilitation counselors, and vendors to find creative solutions to individual circumstances.

The Tech Act of 1988, which is an extremely thorough piece of legislation with a broad definition of assistive technology, is another important mandate. Store-bought items that are adapted; services that help individuals select, acquire, and use assistive technology devices; and the devices themselves are all examples of assistive technology (Morris & Simpson, 1993). The Tech Act specifically recognizes that technology should be used in assisting individuals to gain greater control over their lives, to contribute in their homes, to participate in employment, and to take part in community life. In general, this act states that individuals with disabilities should use assistive technology to benefit from the same opportunities that temporally able-bodied persons take for granted as part of their daily lives. Understanding the design and purpose of the Tech Act can prove to be powerful knowledge when confronted with individuals who wish to take a narrow view of assistive technology.

It is important to remember that with these new civil rights comes responsibility. Few persons are experts in disability policy; however, all individuals with disabilities should become familiar with the disability legislation cited at the beginning of this chapter. At the very minimum, persons with disabilities should know the titles of the public laws and understand the basic intent of each law. There are disability policy experts in most communities; establishing a relationship with such experts will be an important part of self-advocacy.

Self-Advocacy

Typically, individuals with disabilities who are in need of assistive technology make three major mistakes as they attempt to acquire the devices and services necessary to make life easier and/or to obtain employment. First, all too often, persons with disabilities do not go to the agencies or organizations that could actually help them because they frequently end up feeling like a number. Their telephone messages are unanswered and they are asked to sit in waiting areas for long periods only to be shuffled from one intake worker to another. Second, they expect one agency to answer all of their assistive technology needs for home, work, and recreation. When agency professionals refer clients to other organizations, many individuals become frustrated with the entire system and end up not receiving any services at all. Eventually, this restricts their opportunities for gaining access to work and recreation opportunities. Third, many persons with disabilities have given up on the system rather than adopt self-advocacy skills. Consciously or unconsciously, potential technology users decide that the funding options for assistive technology (e.g., Social Security, Medicaid) are too complicated, and they do not learn their rights associated with these federal programs. The end result is that persons with disabilities are not living independently, are not entering the work force, and are underemployed. If the disability community wants to see a change in the status quo, individuals with disabilities will need to become active and speak out when they are not satisfied with service providers. Table 14.1 presents strategies for assistive technology users as they attempt to reduce some of the barriers they confront.

Implementing the strategies outlined in Table 14.1 provides users of assistive technology with some strategies that will enable them to see themselves as customers. Yet one of the biggest barriers can be attitudinal. If persons with disabilities wait for someone (generally the professional) to tell them what they want, when they want it, and how to get it, they will be disappointed in the device and/or service. This dependency cycle must stop. Individuals who need assistive technology must remember that they are the customers and the organization is there to serve them.

REHABILITATION PROFESSIONALS

One way for professionals to begin to understand the views of technology users and the issues that they face as they gain access to specialized service systems is to look toward the recent consumer rights movement in the United States. This movement has been so successful that most secondary education programs across the country now include consumer education classes as a part of the general curriculum. Specifically, this movement has taught persons to question the role of the professional in their community. Persons should no longer accept their physician's diagnosis as gospel, rather they should question their physician and get a second opinion, if necessary. Many rehabilitation professionals provide a high-quality, needed service to persons with disabilities; however, in their quest to obtain the assistive devices and services that their clients seek, many professionals view the persons with disabilities as their clients whom they need to "help." This professional attitude has a tendency to place the rehabilitation professional in the dominant role (Gazda, Asbury, Balzer, Childers, & Walters, 1984). The professional becomes the ruler and governor of agency policies, funding

Table 14.1. Strategies for assistive technology users

Assistive technology user action	Definition of action	Strategies for obtaining assistive technology
Be proactive.	Make your needs known from the beginning.	• Set time lines with the agency professional to obtain outcome. • Keep a log and document agency contacts.
Expect to be treated as a customer.	Request literature on assistive technology devices and ask questions.	• Agency professionals should offer you options for your selection. • Report delays, unprofessional behavior, and/or comments to supervisors.
Try out assistive technology devices before you agree to purchase an item.	Before purchasing an assistive technology device, use it for several days prior to making a final purchase decision.	• Review agency or vendor policies. • Agency personnel should be using a team approach to include such professionals as occupational therapists, physical therapists, rehabilitation engineers, and/or rehabilitation technologists.
Be assertive.	Do not accept substitutes.	• Ask for a copy of the design specifications. • Compare design "specs" with final product.
Keep it simple.	Remember that simple technology answers are often the most effective.	• Agency must explain the need for complex technology and why it is the best alternative. • Obtain information on the reliability of a product and the cost of repair.
Look toward the future.	When selecting an assistive technology device, take into account how your disability may change in the future.	• Get information about the longevity of the device and how it can be adapted or exchanged in the future. • Get data on the quantity of sales of a particular product, as well as customer satisfaction and response.
Get training.	Determine if you will need short-term or long-term training to use the assistive training device.	• Get commitment from agency or vendor on its provisions for training. • Get information on how the agency is preventing technology abandonment.

streams, and technical information related to assistive technology. For many years, persons with disabilities have accepted the less dominant position and have not questioned agency professionals. This should not be the case today. State and local rehabilitation agencies, for example, are viewed by many individuals with disabilities as places to obtain a broad array of technical rehabilitation information and/or services. The disability community expects rehabilitation professionals to be knowledgeable and curious, and to serve as equal partners in the rehabilitation process.

Business Community

Rehabilitation professionals who assist individuals with disabilities to obtain employment can play a vital role that will have long-term benefits to clients as well as to employers. Often, professionals with knowledge of specific employment demands, combined with information about a potential employee's strengths, are in a unique position to offer assistive technology accommodations. Thereby, professionals can expand a person's vision of employment possibilities and circumvent potential problems that may arise in the future. As rehabilitation professionals and individuals with disabilities work together to find community employment, they must consider how assistive technology can be utilized to meet a potential employee's needs. All too often, persons with disabilities search for the perfect job when simple technology considerations could and should have been employed to create a larger pool of possible job opportunities.

Rehabilitation professionals need to include the individual with the disability and the employer in the assessment, selection, and evaluation of an assistive technology device to be used at a jobsite. Ultimately, individuals with disabilities want employers to view job-related assistive technology devices as work-related equipment, not as rehabilitation equipment. Getting employers involved in the process will ensure that assistive technology devices have long-term benefits to both the individual and the employer. At the same time, rehabilitation professionals can provide an important educational component to the business community. Employers need to understand that, while an individual is attempting to learn how to use an assistive device, his or her production level will probably be low. However, once the employee is proficient with the device, his or her production rate will increase. This type of education can have a powerful effect on long-term job satisfaction and on the employer-employee relationship.

Technology Abandonment

Assistive technology users and their family members have taken the blame for the national phenomenon of technology abandonment. At first glance, technology abandonment seems somewhat understandable because persons with disabilities are the ones stacking technology in their closets, attics, and basements. Yet the responsibility for this phenomenon does not rest solely with the disability community (Phillips, 1993).

There are several strategies that professionals could employ to prevent technology abandonment. The key to success in implementing any of these strategies requires a major shift in thinking for the rehabilitation professional. Professionals must begin viewing users of technology as customers. Using a customer-focused approach, the professional listens to the individual who is seeking services and together they determine what the service will look like and the best possible method for delivery. Table 14.2 contrasts the traditional service delivery model with a customer-focused model.

For many persons with disabilities, technology represents the difference between dependence and independence. They recognize that rehabilitation professionals, for example, must work harder and longer with them because the assistive technology field is highly specialized, with many complex evaluation, equipment, and funding issues. Activism on the part of the customer and the resulting landmark legislation that was mentioned in the beginning of this chapter are indicators that change has started to occur between professionals and the individuals whom they serve. If rehabilitation professionals apply the six steps in the customer-focused model, everyone will achieve better outcomes.

Table 14.2. Customer-focused model for assistive technology services

Traditional model	Customer-focused model
• Professional does an evaluation of the client in a clinical environment.	• Customer leads the evaluation team process that includes home, work, and leisure environments.
• Professional assesses client and determines needs for the future.	• Customer gives specific information about his or her wants, needs, and aspirations for the future.
• Professional selects the device.	• Customer receives an array of options to make a final decision.
• Professional orders device from the vendor and gives device to the client.	• Customer deals directly with the vendor in the selection and purchase of the device.
• Professional determines if the device is satisfactory for the client.	• Customer stays in contact with the professional, vendor, and third-party payor with regard to level of satisfaction.
• Professional orients client to device and sometimes trains client to use device in a clinical environment.	• Customer receives training in the environment in which he or she will be using the device.

COMMUNITY

Local neighborhoods are changing. Persons with disabilities are no longer hidden away in large institutions. Today, more than ever before, individuals with disabilities can be seen at the mall, the corner store, and the park. Yet, whether the community presence of persons with disabilities has resulted in increased understanding and tolerance for individual differences is still in question. Furthermore, has an effort been made to include persons with disabilities into their communities? Have persons with disabilities made an effort to become community members? Too often, the answer to these questions is "no." Segregation, prejudice, and discrimination against persons with disabilities continue. The passage of ADA proves that legislators recognize the bigotry that exists in the United States. This legislation clearly states that the continued practice of discrimination against persons with disabilities is unlawful; however, the disability community cannot take the backseat now that ADA has been passed. Rather, individuals with disabilities need to foster new visions for local communities that include diversity, tolerance, and acceptance. Individuals with disabilities need to meet this challenge with their family members, friends, employers, and coworkers at their side. As community members live, work, and recreate together, persons with disabilities must assist other persons in confronting the stereotypes they hold.

True understanding of persons with disabilities will evolve in what Condeluci (1991) refers to as informal dimensions and systems. These dimensions and systems are the community diners, corner bars, and laundry facilities where persons gather and where relationships are developed. It will be in these types of community settings that persons with and without disabilities will find that they have more in common than they thought. However, persons with disabilities cannot wait for other persons to approach them. They must be willing to share their vision for community.

The United States has an aging population, and many of the barrier-free accommodations and assistive technology devices used by persons with disabilities will be suitable for many community members in the future. Proof of this can be found in communities across the country in which persons of all ages are using such common community accommodations as curb cuts, door pulls, and ramps. Parents with infants and young children in baby strollers are becoming outspoken in favor of curb cuts and ramps instead of steps at entrances of buildings.

CONCLUSION

Circumstances are changing for persons with disabilities. However, it is possible that professional and/or disability service delivery organizations have just learned a "new walk" and a "new talk" that makes them appear to be concerned about the wants, desires, and choices of persons with disabilities. No one really knows how much change has actually occurred, but the authors suspect that change differs among communities and individuals. Therefore, it is imperative that technology users, advocates, professionals, family members, employers, and coworkers question policies and attitudes on a regular basis as all persons work together to improve access in their communities.

The authors would like to see the separation of persons with disabilities, along with all discussions of special accommodations for persons with disabilities to end. It is our vision that society should hold onto and work toward a community in which all members are valued and respected. This community would not discuss assistive technology issues in isolation of other community members. Rather, the community would be eager for *all* members to participate and contribute and would therefore seek opportunities to create a barrier-free, accessible community.

REFERENCES

Americans with Disabilities Act of 1990 (ADA), PL 101-336. (July 26, 1990). Title 42, U.S.C. 12101 et seq: *U.S. Statutes at Large, 104,* 327–378.

Brooke, V., Inge, K., & Barcus, M. (1992). *Consumer advocacy and supported employment: A vision for the future.* (Monograph). Richmond, VA: Virginia Commonwealth University, Rehabilitation Research and Training Center on Supported Employment.

Condeluci, A. (1991). *Interdependence: The route to community.* Orlando, FL: Paul M. Deutsch Press.

Gazda, G., Asbury, F., Balzer, F., Childers, W., & Walters, R. (1984). *Human relations development: A manual for educators.* Boston: Allyn and Bacon.

Individuals with Disabilities Education Act of 1990 (IDEA), PL 101-476. (October 30, 1990). Title 20, U.S.C. 1400 et seq: *U.S. Statutes at Large, 104,* 1103–1151.

Individuals with Disabilities Education Act Amendments of 1991, PL 102-119. (October 7, 1991). Title 20, U.S.C. 1400 et seq: *U.S. Statutes at Large, 105,* 587–608.

Mann, W. (1991). State-wide planning for access to technology applications for individuals with disabilities. *Journal of Rehabilitation, 57*(1), 17–20.

Morris, M., & Simpson, J. (1993, June/July). Tech Act reauthorization. *Word from Washington.*

Phillips, B. (1993). Technology abandonment from the consumer point of view. *NARIC Quarterly, 3*(2, 3), 4–91.

Rehabilitation Act Amendments of 1992, PL 102-569. (October 29, 1992). Title 29, U.S.C. 701 Section 101[c]. et seq: *U.S. Statutes at Large, 100,* 4344–4488.

Revell, G., Wehman, P., Kregel, J., West, M., & Rayfield, R. (1994). Supported employment for persons with severe disabilities: Positive trends in wages, models and funding. *Education and Training in Mental Retardation and Development Disabilities, 29*(4), 256–264.

Sowers, J. (1991). Employment for persons with physical disabilities and related technology. *Journal of Vocational Rehabilitation, 1*(2), 55–64.

Technology-Related Assistance for Individuals with Disabilities Act of 1994, PL 103-218. (March 9, 1994). Title 29, U.S.C. 2201 et seq: *U.S. Statutes at Large,* 108, 50–97.

Williams, R. (1991). Assistive technology in the eye of the beholder. *Journal of Vocational Rehabilitation, 1*(2), 9–12.

Index

Page numbers followed by "t" or "f" indicate tables or figures, respectively